Biologist Philosopher

Life of Science Library 43

Biologist Philosopher

A STUDY OF THE LIFE AND WRITINGS
OF
Alfred Russel Wallace

WILMA GEORGE

Abelard-Schuman
LONDON TORONTO NEW YORK

Library of Congress Catalogue Card Number 64.12738
First published 1964

LONDON
Abelard-Schuman
Limited
8 King Street WC2

NEW YORK
Abelard-Schuman
Limited
8 West 57 Street

TORONTO
Abelard-Schuman
Canada Limited
896 Queen St. West

TO
NORA GEORGE
AND
GEORGE CROWTHER

Contents

Introduction

"In retrospect of British biology during the 'wonderful century' there stand out four men whose names will endure—Lyell, Darwin, Wallace and Galton" (Osborn 1912).

Fifty years after this was written it is doubtful whether the name of Wallace stands out in the public mind to anything like the same extent as that of Darwin or Lyell. Admittedly, the 1958 celebrations of the first formulation of the theory of natural selection have honoured Wallace equally with Darwin, but few, other than biologists, would be prepared to name any other contributions made to nineteenth century thought by Alfred Russel Wallace. For this, Wallace himself was partially responsible, for it was he who gave the word Darwinism to all aspects of the theory of evolution by natural selection, when in 1889 he published his views on the evolution of colour, speciation and human evolution in a book entitled *Darwinism*.

Yet in another field of biology Wallace is pre-eminent: the modern study of zoogeography stems from his major contribution *Geographical Distribution of Animals* published in 1876. It was he who first attempted the synthesis of all available evidence on the geographical distribution of animals, not confining himself as others had done to one particular class of animals or part of the world. He drew for the first time on fossil evidence, glacial theories and, of course, the theory of evolution by natural selection. Before this, however, Wallace's Line had been drawn and it is probably for his line that he is best known amongst biologists. From his personal knowledge of the fauna of the islands of the Malay Archipelago he had traced a line of demarcation between a predominantly Oriental fauna and a predominantly Australian one, and this boundary line between the two regions, in spite of disputes over its validity, is still known as Wallace's Line. From this specific study grew the general principles which he was to formulate to account for zoogeographical regions all over the world and which remain the foundations of the modern science of zoogeography.

More than a hundred years have passed since Wallace made his first important contribution to biological thought. During that time progress in biology has been rapid and many ideas and interpretations of the nineteenth century have passed into oblivion. But much of Wallace's work has survived. Some of his theories have persisted almost unchanged; others survive but have been modified in the light of later knowledge; some have disappeared from serious consideration, whilst others might seem due for re-assessment. Almost all have at least important historical interest and they are worthy of consideration in the light of increased knowledge and the ideas of the mid-twentieth century.

It is the purpose of this study to assess the position of his ideas in the evolution of biological thought, to discuss them therefore both in their context and in the light of recent developments; to inquire into the influences that led up to his major contributions and their subsequent effects. No attempt has been made to study Alfred Russel Wallace the man, nor to investigate the psychological reasons for his being both spiritualist and founder of zoogeography, nor to uncover hitherto unknown aspects of his personal life. The events of his life have necessarily been sketched in as a background to the development of his ideas, but this is above all a study of his writings with the emphasis on his scientific contributions.

Should Wallace's name be prominent amongst the nineteenth century scientists? Do the years increase or decrease respect for his ideas? Do we still agree with his friends who, two years after his death, dedicated a medallion to him in Westminster Abbey? There he is commemorated with Joule, Stokes, Adams, Lister and Hooker near to the tombs of Herschel, Kelvin and Lyell, and next to Darwin.

Acknowledgements

In the course of writing a book the author receives help and encouragement from numerous friends and acquaintances and to all these unnamed helpers may this acknowledgement and the publication of the book be thanks.

In particular the author wishes to thank Dr S. A. Barnett for reading the typescript and offering helpful criticism, the Officers of the Linnean Society of London for making the manuscript of *Palm Trees of the Amazon* and unpublished notebooks available and permitting the publication of quotations from them, the librarian of the British Museum (Natural History) for help in finding further unpublished notebooks and drawings and the Trustees of the British Museum for consenting to the use of a previously unpublished letter.

It was as philosophers rather than as research scientists that Darwin and Wallace gave an impetus to the study of biology that has lasted a full century, and will continue to stimulate it in the future to an extent that cannot be foreseen.

L. Harrison Matthews, 1958.

I am a firm believer that without speculation there is no good original observation.

Charles Darwin to A. R. Wallace, 1857.

Early Years

Alfred Russel Wallace was born in 1823, a near contemporary of Galton, Pasteur, Mendel, Herbert Spencer and Huxley. His life falls into roughly four phases. During the first of these, 1823-48, he had no formal scientific training nor aspirations, but an independent, outdoor life awakened in him a keen interest in wild flowers and animals, and his work as a surveyor taught him something of geology.

The second phase, 1848-62, laid the foundations for all his major contributions to natural science. During this time, he was a field naturalist, collecting and observing, and writing from the Amazon and later from the Malay Archipelago.

The main period of scientific writing constitutes the third phase, from his return to London in 1862 to the publishing of *Darwinism* in 1889.

The final phase, until his death in 1913, was a period of continual activity, of lecturing and writing. By then, however, comparatively little of his attention was focused on scientific subjects. Problems of trade, war, vaccination, spiritualism, and human rights occupied his attention. And at this time, when his scientific work was at an end, honours poured in on him from universities.

Wallace wrote a detailed story of his life and work which was published in 1905. From it and from those of his other written works which take the form of a narrative of travels, the facts of his long life can be learnt. He himself attempted to trace the development of many of his most important ideas in this autobiography, and these can be supplemented from his other published books, from a large number of published papers, from a collection of his letters published by Marchant in 1916 and from a few unpublished journals and letters in the keeping mainly of the Linnean Society of London and the British Museum.

Nearly a third of *My Life: a record of events and opinions* describes his childhood and early years, leading up to the decision at the age of twenty-four to become a naturalist. The rest is concerned with a brief outline of his expeditions to the tropics, followed by personal reminiscences and assessments of his work during the main period of scientific writing, and it ends with a considerable amount of space devoted to problems relating to human rights and spiritualism.

He attempted to trace the influences which were important in determining the direction of his career and in the development of his ideas, picking out particular events and particular friendships, so that *My Life* is a very personal narrative; personal primarily on the intellectual level. At the same time as his scientific ideas were given prominence, a distinct impression of the man behind them shines through, a man who was modest and candid even to the point of naïvety, a man full of humour and charm, a man who wrote with clarity and vigour.

By his own account Wallace was born at Usk in Monmouthshire on 8th January 1823, the eighth child of an unremarkable family. There was no money for luxuries and Mr Wallace himself taught his children at this time. As the surviving children grew up they were thrown on their own resources to make their own ways in life. According to Alfred Wallace this was an entirely beneficial circumstance since the whole family appeared to inherit from the father a tendency to laziness and inactivity.

In 1828, when Wallace was five, the family moved to Dulwich for a brief period and thence to Hertford, Mrs Wallace's native town. Alfred Wallace and his brother John were sent to Hertford Grammar School, and there Alfred stayed until he was fourteen. School was not an important influence in his life. Far more important to him was learning from John how to make his own toys and listening to his father reading aloud Defoe's *History of the Great Plague* and Mungo Park's *Travels* which he liked particularly. His father had a continual supply of books, and soon after they came to live in Hertford he became librarian of a small library. From the mass of reading which this permitted, Wallace picks out particularly, Smollett, Fielding, *Paradise Lost, The Iliad* and the *Inferno,* the occasional bit of *Pickwick* that was appearing in serial form and "almost any book that I heard spoken of as celebrated or interesting".

While he was at school, a book was published which was to

have a great influence on him later in life. This was the first edition of Lyell's *Principles of Geology*. It put an end, in this country at least, to Cuvier's theory of catastrophes. Catastrophes were sporadic, sudden and violent changes in the earth's surface, eliminating life and changing the contours of the land. Catastrophes were interspersed by long static periods. In contrast, Lyell argued that continual small movements and changes in the earth, similar to those that he himself could observe, were sufficient to account for the events that had taken place in past ages. Natural forces could account for the changing face of the earth from the earliest times to the present day. The earth evolved gradually.

There is no record of when Wallace first read Lyell's *Principles*. It may not have been until he went to Leicester at the age of twenty-one, but it was to have as great an effect on the development of his scientific theories as anything else he ever read.

After leaving school at fourteen, Wallace lived for a few months with John, who was apprenticed to a master builder in London. Having nothing to do, Wallace spent most of his time in the builder's yard, talking to the men and watching them work. He seems to have gained a thorough and fairly accurate idea of working conditions, and it made a deep impression on him, for he remembered the details many years afterwards.

In the evenings, he and his brother used to go to the Hall of Science off Tottenham Court Road where the followers of Robert Owen would meet, sometimes for lectures, sometimes just to talk, to read books or to play draughts. Here they met working men and discussed books such as Paine's *Age of Reason*. Once they heard Robert Owen give a short address. Wallace was impressed by his "lofty head and highly benevolent countenance". This was Wallace's first acquaintance with doctrines which, according to himself, were to have a profound effect on his later thinking, and he described Owen's work in considerable detail.

From the writings of Owen, Wallace first became aware of a determinist theory of human behaviour. Contrary to established religious beliefs, Owen taught that a man's character was formed by both heredity and environment from earliest infancy. "And that, *as are the natural qualities of each one at birth, and as are the surroundings in which he is placed, so will the individual be*" (Owen 1857). This theory Owen attempted to put into practice in the New Lanark experiment. This was contrary to the generally held view which maintained that a man could be good if he tried and that if he were not good it was by his own wilful transgression. Wilful sinning therefore deserved punishment. As Wallace's father was a conventional churchman, Wallace had been brought up in that tradition, and it was not until this contact with the Owenites that the beliefs of his childhood were shaken. He worried over the problem of why if God were good and omnipotent he could not prevent evil. The question troubled him so much that he eventually put it to his father who, however, brushed him off with a conventional and entirely unsatisfactory answer. Not unnaturally, this only made him consider the problem even more closely, and there seems little doubt that it was as a result of this short stay in London that Wallace first became conscious of the religious and political conflicts of the nineteenth century. In the Hall of Science and the builder's yard the seeds of socialism and religious scepticism were sown. ". . . Although later in life," he was to admit, "my very scanty knowledge of his work was not sufficient to prevent my adopting the individualist views of Herbert Spencer and of the political economists, I have always looked upon Owen as my first teacher in the philosophy of human nature and my first guide through the labyrinth of social science" (I 104).

In the early summer of 1837 Wallace was sent to his eldest brother William to learn to be a surveyor, and there seemed no reason to suppose that he would ever be anything else. He found the independent, open-air life pleasing and healthy, and he was fascinated by the theoretical principles of surveying. For the first time he became aware of the applications of mathematics to practical purposes; he was soon immersed in the problems of mechanics and optics and delighting in the art of map-making. He describes as the most astonishing experience his observations of the structure of the land. Before this he had always thought that land was chalk, but near Luton, where they were working, he discovered that land could also be made of gravel. This, and the discovery that the *thunderbolts* of his childhood were the fossil remains of molluscan belemnites were his first lessons in geology.

In general, however, survey work was neither lucrative nor had good prospects. Wallace had no overriding ambitions, so for a time he was apprenticed to a clock-maker and, as he himself says, he might well have become a clock-maker if his employer had not moved to London. He preferred country life to life in

London, and so returned to surveying, this time mainly in Wales and the Marches. He took a particular delight in the Welsh countryside, and his interest in geology increased. He had come from the comparatively recently made chalk of Hertfordshire, through the ancient silurian shales of Radnor to the old red sandstone of Brecon.

The surveying they undertook in mid-Wales was sometimes for purposes of enclosure. This was Wallace's first encounter with the enclosure of common lands. Although he thought it a pity to be fencing off picturesque moorland, he was not moved then by the same sense of injustice that he was to feel many years later, a feeling that made him devote many pages of *My Life* to discussing "This all-embracing system of land-robbery".

In Neath the brothers were asked to design and superintend the building of some warehouses. They had neither training for this work nor experience, but they set to work to understand something of the theory and technique of architecture by reading Bartholomew's *Specifications for Practical Architecture.*

But by now Wallace's interests were turning mainly to a study of natural phenomena. He came to regard these peaceful three years as crucial, and wrote: "Now, I have some reason to believe that this was the turning-point of my life, the tide that carried me on, not to fortune but to whatever reputation I have acquired, and which has certainly been to me a never-failing source of much health of body and supreme mental enjoyment" (I 196). He made instruments to observe the sun and the stars, and he bought a few books about wild flowers. Very soon, collecting flowers became a passionate interest and supplanted every other pursuit. He had never known the names of the flowers around him, but now he added new specimens and new names to his herbarium every day. He began to write down his thoughts in the form of hypothetical lectures. One of the first of these was a short discourse on the problems of botanical classification. With this, in a chapter headed *First Literary Efforts*, he described another lecture on *The Advantages of Varied Knowledge* and gave in full a hitherto unpublished article which he wrote at the time, on *The South Wales Farmer*, describing the country, the customs and language of the Welsh.

These idyllic months of intensely fascinating pursuits did not last. In April 1843, his father died, the family home was given up and the family dispersed. Again Wallace was sent from survey work to find a way of earning a living. But there was no trade or profession that particularly interested him, no reason why he should do one thing rather than another. The end of that year and the beginning of 1844 found him in London with John, doing nothing, on a small legacy. But the legacy did not last long and he had no other money. In 1844 Wallace was twenty-one and out of work.

Looking back in 1905 to this period of his life, he attempted an assessment of his own character at the age of twenty-one. On the credit side he listed the power of correct reasoning, an appreciation of beauty and a passion for justice. On the debit side he considered that his deficiencies were no ear for music, no verbal memory, no sense of humour, no assertiveness, no physical courage and "It is, that though fond of order and systematic arrangement of all the parts of a subject, and especially of an argument, I am yet, through my want of the language-faculty, very much disinclined to use technical terms wherever they can be avoided" (I 226).

Early in 1844 he was successful in gaining a teaching post at the Collegiate School, Leicester, where, for a salary of some £30 a year, he was to teach reading, writing and arithmetic to the juniors, and surveying to the older boys.

In spite of his exceptional shyness and modesty, and an antipathy for speaking in public, he got on reasonably well. This was mainly because of the kindness of the headmaster and his wife with whom he lodged. To Wallace, the one advantage of schoolmastering was that it gave him leisure enough for reading and opportunity to extend his own knowledge of academic subjects. To this may perhaps be added one of the great advantages of teaching others which is, that it forces the teacher to put his thoughts into words and to attempt to put them into some sort of order and pattern which can be communicated to others.

With the help of the headmaster Wallace made a determined effort to master mathematics, persevering through trigonometry and the differential calculus. By the time he got to the integral calculus, however, he decided he would never be a mathematician because "here I found myself at the end of my tether" (I 231). But his other great interest, reading in Leicester town library, was more successful. There he read Humboldt's *Personal Narrative of Travels to the Equinoctial Regions of America* and Darwin's *Journal*. Both of these works fascinated him, opening up an entirely new world. Of Darwin he wrote, "His style of writing I very much admire, so free from all labour, affectation, or egotism, and yet so full of interest and original thought" (I 256). Through the writings of Humboldt and Darwin he lived in strange foreign places, saw animals and plants he had never heard of before, and made contact with ideas whose interest and originality amazed him. For the first time he felt a great desire to see the tropics for himself.

It was in Leicester library, too, that he read his first book on what he called biological philosophy, *An Essay on the Principle of Population* by Malthus. It made a deep impression, although at the time it was mainly of theoretical interest. Fourteen years later he was to have a vivid recollection of this work of Malthus.

And Leicester library was the scene of yet another and equally important event. It seems to have been there that Wallace met H. W. Bates, a meeting which might be said to have been responsible for some of the major contributions to biological thought of the nineteenth century. Bates was an enthusiastic entomologist, Wallace a less experienced botanist. It was hardly surprising, therefore, that the two men should rapidly become friends. Wallace had never collected anything but wild flowers, but in Leicester, Bates introduced him to beetle-collecting. He had no idea of the enormous numbers of animals that could be found in only an afternoon's collecting, and he was astonished to learn that there might be as many as a thousand species of beetle within ten miles of Leicester.

Wallace bought pins, a collecting bottle and a manual of British coleoptera and he spent his Wednesday and Saturday afternoons collecting in the country. Beetle collecting has been the first zoological interest of many a famous biologist. While Darwin was at Cambridge (1828-31) his enthusiasm for beetles was so great that "one day, on tearing off some old bark, I saw two rare beetles, and seized one in each hand; then I saw a third and new kind, which I could not bear to lose, so that I popped the one which I held in my right hand into my mouth. Alas! it ejected some intensely acrid fluid, which burnt my tongue so that I was forced to spit the beetle out, which was lost, as was the third one" (Darwin 1887). A story that bears some resemblance to this was told of Wallace by his children: "One day one of us brought home a beetle, to the great horror of the servant. Passing at the moment, he picked it up saying, 'Why it is quite a harmless little creature!' and to demonstrate its inoffensiveness he placed it on the tip of his nose, whereupon it immediately bit him and even drew blood, much to our amusement and his own astonishment" (M II 110).

In Leicester, Wallace first heard of phrenology and mesmerism and became fascinated by the practical possibilities of these subjects. Phrenology led to an interest in spiritualism and, although at this time he had abandoned formal religion, in later years spiritualism came to take the place of a religion. But at first it was the practical aspect that interested him, in particular the possibilities which were being much discussed at the time of surgical operations during a mesmeric trance. He did not believe in telepathy and considered that, at least in its connexion with the practice of phrenology, he had disproved its existence.

Wallace was apparently a success as a teacher, although the profession did not much appeal to him, mainly because he felt he did not know any subject well enough to teach, and because he disliked being subordinate to anyone. Throughout his life he lived as independent an existence as anyone could who had to work for a living. He never became part of an organization nor co-operated with anyone in his biological work. He was an individualist, making his own life, thinking his own thoughts, and having no particular desire to conform, though he did not object to the conformity of others.

Wallace was never faced with the prospect of being a schoolmaster for the rest of his life, because after a year in Leicester, in February 1845, William died from pneumonia caught travelling at night in a third class carriage from London to Bristol. Wallace went to Neath to put his brother's affairs in order, and, once there, decided to go back to the surveying business which seemed to suit his temperament better than any other profession. Wallace was twenty-two and still unsettled, although this time he thought that he would take up the surveyor's life for good. William had a reasonably good business in South Wales and because the speculation in railway property was at its height, survey work was well paid. The survey for a railway up the Vale of Neath to Merthyr Tydfil, which Wallace undertook almost at once, was one of the most profitable ventures of his life. For the first time, he had a small capital sum and work enough to enable him to live.

As a result of this good fortune, he brought his mother and John to Neath to share a cottage with him, and for the next two years he and John worked together on building and surveying projects. Although John was a carpenter, neither of them was a builder or architect; yet they submitted plans for a new town hall at Swansea, and in 1847 designed and supervised the building of the Mechanics' Institute in Neath. "It was, of course, very plain, but the whole was of local stone, with door and window quoins, cornice, etc, hammer-dressed; and the pediments over the door and windows, arched doorway, and base of squared blocks gave the whole a decidedly architectural appearance" (I 245).

Since the 1820's, Mechanics' Institutes had been springing up all over the country for the introduction of scientific subjects to working men. The founder of the Neath Institute was a Mr Jevons, who had been a friend of his brother William, and was an uncle of W. S. Jevons, the logician and economist. Mr Jevons was anxious to get Wallace to lecture to the Neath mechanics but it took a great deal of coaxing and persuasion before he could be prevailed on to do so. Eventually he agreed, and for two winters gave courses in elementary physics to the working men of Neath. Although he disliked lecturing, these first attempts were a considerable success; they were characterized by the simplicity and clarity that were to appear in both his written work and his more erudite lectures. Many years later, in 1895, Wallace received a letter from a member of his Neath Institute audience complimenting him on his lectures.

In the summers at Neath Wallace and his brother found time to indulge in what had now become Wallace's main interest—the study of living things. Their collections and studies had extended from wild flowers and beetles to cover almost anything that was alive. They collected insects of every kind and they spent many hours identifying birds and reptiles. They shared their experiences by letter with Bates, exchanged specimens with him, and commented to him on scientific books and ideas. Wallace had at last found someone with whom he could discuss in detail, biological problems of both practical and theoretical interest.

In 1844 the anonymous *Vestiges of Creation* had been published, and at the end of 1845 Wallace and Bates were discussing its merits in their letters. The *Vestiges* set out to show that animal species had descended from other species: that evolution or, as the author called it, "progressive development", had occurred. Although the author believed that the Almighty had initiated the process, he was firmly against the generally held view that each species had been created *in situ*. As to explaining how it had happened, he was not very successful, and he ascribed modifications to the direct effects of the environment and the Aristotelian vital impulse. In the letter he wrote to Bates on 28th December 1845 Wallace's main interest begins to define itself: "I have rather a more favourable opinion of the *Vestiges* than you appear to have. I do not consider it a hasty generalization, but rather as an ingenious hypothesis strongly supported by some striking facts and analogies. . . . It furnishes a subject for every observer of nature to attend to; every fact he observes will make either for or against it, and it thus serves both as an incitement to the collection of facts, and an object to which they can be applied when collected" (I 254).

In September 1847 Wallace's only surviving sister, Fanny, returned from America and took her brothers for a holiday to Paris. They visited the museums and the Jardin des Plantes and, on the way home through London, Wallace spent a day in the insect room at the British Museum. Afterwards he wrote to Bates discussing the immensity of the numbers of beetles and butterflies he had seen in museums, and he ended: "I should like to take some one family to study thoroughly, principally with a view to the theory of the origin of species." Later in the letter, discussing a new publication, he commented: "It contains some remarkable views on my favourite subject—the variations, arrangement, distribution, etc., of species" (I 256). The rest of this letter has not been preserved so that Wallace's general impression of Paris at the age of twenty-four is not recorded. But, talking to the Mechanics' Institute of the arrangement and building of museums, he expressed the view that they "did these things better in France".

His curiosity on the origin of species aroused, Wallace felt convinced from his readings of Humboldt and Darwin that in the tropics of America he would be able to find conditions he required for studying modifications and their origins within a group of animals. His interest had turned from animals to plants. And then in 1847 he read *A Voyage up the Amazons, including residence at Para* by W. H. Edwards, which described the life and conditions of a tourist. What was even more important, Mr Edwards wrote that the expenses of living and travelling were reasonably small. For the first time Wallace's hankering for an expedition to the tropics seemed to come within the bounds of possibility. His only passion was natural history, he had saved money from the Neath railway project, and now it seemed as though he might be able to do what he had come to want more than anything else.

He had become disgusted with surveying. It was not that he disliked the work. The days spent out of doors and the making of maps had always appealed to him, but now that he was in charge of a business, he found the duties and responsibility unpleasant. He had an intense dislike of money matters. He was disappointed when anyone cheated him, and depressed when he had to exact payment from those who were too poor to pay.

It was not altogether surprising, therefore, that in 1847 Wallace should propose to Bates a collecting expedition to South America. South America was only just beginning to be extensively explored and there was still considerable demand in England for specimens of animals from the tropical regions. It seemed likely that they would be able to finance themselves by the sale of their collections.

After twenty-four years of chopping and changing, of trying first one occupation and then another, Wallace had at last found his métier. He was interested in the origin of species, so intensely interested that he determined at once to pursue the problem and to make it his profession. The opportunity he needed had grown out of two fortunate events, his friendship with H. W. Bates and the last period of survey work which both provided him with money and persuaded him to change his profession once again. As he says himself, after describing his life in Neath "the great problem of the origin of species was already distinctly formulated in my mind; that I was not satisfied with the more or less vague solutions at that time offered; that I believed the conception of evolution through natural law so clearly formulated in the *Vestiges* to be, so far as it went, a true one; and that I firmly believed that a full and careful study of the facts of nature would ultimately lead to a solution of the mystery" (I 257).

To the Amazon and Rio Negro

When Wallace and Bates set off for equatorial South America in 1847 they were going to a continent whose flora and fauna had excited interest since the sixteenth century. The first explorers had brought back accounts of animals and plants unknown to Europe, and men such as Acosta in *Historia Natural y Moral de Las Indias* (1589) and de Bry in *America* (1590) had provided reasonably accurate accounts of many mammals and birds. It had been known for many years that long-tailed parrots, humming birds and toucans, prehensile-tailed monkeys, tapirs, llamas, armadillos and opossums existed in the continent, and zoological observations on their habits were available. But it was not until the eighteenth century that much advance had been made over the early days of discovery.

Following the Spanish occupation in the sixteenth century, the continent had been virtually closed to foreigners until the middle of the eighteenth when de la Condamine obtained permission to take a French expedition there (1735-45) to test by measurement the Newtonian theories of the shape of the earth. Towards the end of his stay in South America, he sailed down the length of the Amazon and provided the first map of the river. Further south, the Spaniard, Azara, had explored Paraguay (1781-1800) and wrote the first natural history of that country; and in the north Humboldt and Bonpland explored Venezuela and the Orinoco (1799-1804), making far-reaching observations on the geography and botany of the region.

Early in the nineteenth century there had been the professional visits of Darwin to coastal areas of the great continent (1831-35) and of d'Orbigny mainly to the Andes (1826-34) from whence he brought rich collections to France. Many less famous men had also collected in the Amazon region; the museums of Europe were well stocked with specimens of the more obvious animals and plants.

In spite of this, Mr Doubleday of the British Museum assured Wallace that all sorts of insects, as well as birds, mammals and land shells would find a ready sale to museums and to the many private collectors who were eager to stock their cabinets with rare and preferably decorative objects. Mr Samuel Stevens agreed to act as an agent in England, disposing of the collections as they were sent home, and Mr Edwards, the author of *A Voyage up the Amazons,* gave them local information and letters of introduction. By April 1848 Bates and Wallace were prepared to earn their living by collecting. Whereas earlier explorer naturalists had been men of means like Humboldt, or had official financial support like de la Condamine or were officially attached to naval surveys like Darwin or Huxley, these two were without financial support and were preparing, by paying their way entirely from the sale of their collections, to be two of the earliest professional collectors.

On 26th May 1848 the barque *Mischief* anchored off the coast of Brazil. For the next four and a half years Wallace travelled along much of the length of the Amazon and to the source of the Rio Negro, undergoing many hardships and sorrows, learning to be a biologist the hard way. The material results of four and a half years of collecting were a small sum of money, a slight collection of animals, some seven communications to learned societies and two books.

Palm Trees of the Amazon (1852) described the appearance, the distribution and uses of all the palms he had observed along the reaches of the great rivers. It was illustrated with lithographs from his own sketches. Only 250 copies of this little book were printed and published at Wallace's own expense, and their sale just covered the capital outlay. The book was slight but charming, entirely descriptive and it was not very well illustrated.

More ambitious was *Travels on the Amazon and Rio Negro* (1853) which was written up from the notes and journals he kept during his travels. It describes in detail and in chronological order his journeys, together with his own observations on the flora and fauna of the Amazon valley. He refers to it when writing in 1861 as "that absurd book". Although he does not say why he thought it absurd, there is no doubt that it is superficial from a zoological point of view compared with his later works though it is a very readable account of the Amazon and Negro. Darwin wrote to Bates in 1861: "I was a *little* disappointed in Wallace's book on the Amazon, hardly facts enough."

Like many naturalists Wallace had been led to expect brilliance and luxuriance in the plants and animals of the tropics. However, he found that the appearance of Belem (Pará in those days) was "not more foreign than that of Calais or Boulogne" (A 2). Many years later he recorded: "Previous to leaving England I had read many books of travels in hot countries, I had dwelt so much on the enthusiastic descriptions most naturalists give of the surpassing beauty of tropical vegetation, and of the strange forms and brilliant colours of the animal world, that I had wrought myself up to a fever-heat of expectation, and it is not to be wondered at that my early impressions were those of disappointment. On my first walk into the forest I looked about, expecting to see monkeys as plentiful as at the Zoological Gardens, with humming birds and parrots in profusion. But for several days I did not see a single monkey, and hardly a bird of any kind, and I began to think that these and other productions of the South American forests are much scarcer than they are represented to be by travellers. But I soon found that these creatures were plentiful enough when I knew where and how to look for them, and that the number of different kinds of all the groups of animals is wonderfully great" (I 270).

But if there was a scarcity of animals and flowers for the eyes to look at, there was grandeur in the trees and an "uproar of life" in the evening for the ears. Bates gave his impressions of: "The whirring of cicadas; the shrill stridulation of a vast number and variety of field crickets and grasshoppers, each species sounding its peculiar note; the plaintive hooting of tree frogs—all blended together in one continuous ringing sound—the audible expression of the teeming profusion of Nature" (Bates 1863).

Wallace and his fellow-explorer may not have found immediately the prodigal profusion they expected, but they quickly realized that there was immense variety amongst the insects and lizards and above all among the trees. When they were ready, therefore, to send off their first collections after only a few months' work, they found they had 1,300 different species. A year later Wallace was able to record the despatch of 284 saleable specimens of bird. And soon afterwards they were able to add to their collections some of those animals which they already knew to be typical of South America, South American monkeys, toucans and jacamars, *Galbula*.

Wallace describes in *Travels on the Amazon and Rio Negro* his progress from the amateur inexperienced collector of Belem who got up soon after dawn to spend a few hours looking for birds, who returned to breakfast at nine o'clock, spent the morning collecting the abundant insects, dined at four, had tea at seven and spent the evenings sorting out and preserving the day's collection and making notes, with every day for fourteen months much like every other day, where quantity rather than rarity of species counted, to the professional naturalist searching for a white umbrella bird, *Cephalopterus,* and the painted turtle *Chrysemys* "in a part of the country that no European traveller had ever before visited". In this unexplored country, where forty entirely new species of butterflies were a matter of satisfaction but not amazement, every hour might have been his last and on 28th December 1850, Spruce wrote from São Gabriel: "I had sad news from my friend Wallace. He is at São Joaquim, at the mouth of the Vaupes, a little above São Gabriel, and he writes me by another hand that he is almost at the point of death from a malignant fever, which has reduced him to such a state of weakness that he cannot rise from his hammock or even feed himself. The person who brought me the letter told me he had taken no nourishment for some days except the juice of oranges and cashews."

The tale of hardship and endurance is recorded in the *Travels*. There was, for instance, the desertion of his Indian crews at the source of the Orinoco. "They had been rather uneasy for some days past, asking me when I meant to go back. They did not like being among people whose language they could not speak, and had been lately using up an enormous quantity of farinha, hoping when they had finished the last basket that I should be unable to purchase any more in the village, and should therefore be obliged to return. The day before I had just bought a fresh basket, and the sight of that appears to have supplied the last stimulus necessary to decide the question, and make them fly from the strange land and still stranger white man, who spent his whole time in catching insects, and wasting good caxaca [sugar cane alcohol] by putting fish and snakes into it" (A 180-1). There was the tedium of rains which prohibited all collecting for several valuable months in Manaos at the beginning of 1850. There was the agony of small black pium (*Simulium*) flies drifting about in clouds biting his feet, ankles and hands until they were swollen and inflamed to a dark purple and "the torments I suffered skinning a bird or drawing a fish, can scarcely be imagined by the unexperienced" (A 213). And, the hardest blow of all, there was the tragic loss of his young brother Herbert from yellow fever in 1851.

Two years earlier Herbert had arrived in Belem to join his brother's expeditions, but after some experience of the Upper reaches of the Amazon he had decided to return to England. In Belem both he and Bates contracted yellow fever which was raging through the population and, in spite of Bates' care and attention, Herbert Wallace died in June 1851. But it was not until many months later that Wallace learnt of his brother's fate, although he had been informed of his illness. When he eventually heard of his brother's death, he was more than ordinarily distressed. Not only had they shared difficulties of Amazon travel, but Wallace seems to have felt himself responsible also for Herbert's death, by letting him come to the Amazon. It seemed to leave a deep mark on his emotions, for when he came to write *My Life* in 1905, a whole chapter was devoted to a memorial of Herbert. None of his other brothers or sister received such a tribute, although he lived for a time with each of the surviving members of his family and seems to have had a deep affection for them all.

Wallace persevered through all these hardships, however. He even surmounted the final tragedy of shipwreck when returning to England, a tragedy in which he nearly lost his life and lost practically all his notes and a large proportion of his important collections from the Vaupes and Negro.

In the middle of the Atlantic, 700 miles from Bermuda, the brig *Helen,* carrying a cargo of indiarubber, caught fire. Wallace put his drawings of fishes and palms, his watch and his purse into a small tin, but he had to leave everything else behind. Of the live animals he was bringing home, only one parrot was rescued when it fell into the sea from the burning ship. For ten days they were adrift in open boats and then, when their despair had become acute, a sail was sighted. A few hours later they were picked up by the ship *Jordeson,* still 200 miles from Bermuda. "It was now, when the danger appeared past, that I began to feel fully the greatness of my loss. With what pleasure had I looked upon every rare and curious insect I had added to my collection! How many times, when almost overcome by the ague, had I crawled into the forest and been rewarded by some unknown and beautiful species! How many places, which no European foot but my own had trodden, would have been recalled to my memory by the rare birds and insects they had furnished to my collection! How many weary days and weeks had I passed, upheld only by the fond hope of bringing home many new and beautiful forms from those wild regions, every one of which would be endeared to me by the recollections they would call up—which should prove that I had not wasted the advantages I had enjoyed, and would give me occupation and amusement for years to come! And now everything was gone, and I had not one specimen to illustrate the unknown lands I had trod, or to call back the recollection of the wild scenes I had beheld!" (A 277).

To some extent the *Travels* have been considered naïve and superficial. Superficial they may be in so far as they were written without the benefit of the most important notes and collections of the expedition. They can also be called naïve if the word can be considered synonymous with candid, and to imply an innocent wonder for all that can be seen if the mind is allowed to be unprejudiced, uncommitted and receptive. He could record the blank verse he wrote during the lonely evenings at Javíta—

> Their food is simple—fish and casava-bread
> With various fruits, and sometimes forest game,
> All season'd with hot, pungent, fiery peppers.
> Sauces and seasonings too, and drinks they have,
> Made from the mandioca's poisonous juice;
> And but one foreign luxury, which is salt.
> Salt here is money : daily they bring to me
> Cassava cakes, or fish, or ripe bananas,
> Or birds or insects, fowls or turtles' eggs,
> And still they ask for salt. Two teacups-full
> Buy a large basket of cassava cakes,
> A great bunch of bananas, or a fowl (A 178).

In contrast, he could question seriously the views of older and more established naturalists in passages like: "It has been assumed by some writers on Natural History, that every wild fruit is the food of some bird or animal, and that the varied forms and structure of their mouths may be necessitated by the peculiar character of the fruits they are to feed on; but there is more imagination than fact in this statement: the number of wild fruits furnishing food for birds is very limited, and birds of the most varied structure and of every size will be found visiting the same tree" (A 59).

The *Travels* combines the candid observer with the early speculations of the mentally tough biologist. In writing this book, Wallace was following the tradition of Darwin, Humboldt and the early explorers, retailing the day to day events, interspersing them with descriptions of animals and plants and the occasional thought on a wider issue of biological theory. "On one or two days of bright sunshine, a beautiful *Papilio* came about the house, settling on the ground in moist places: I succeeded in taking two specimens; it is allied to *P. thoas,* and will probably prove a new species" (A 209) or "we had nine pretty little blackheaded parrots, which every night would go of their own accord into a basket prepared for them to sleep in" (A 210). In this way he detailed the whole of his journeys up the Amazon to Santarem and Manaos, and from there up to the furthest reaches of the Negro, in the steps of Humboldt to the source of the Orinoco, along a ten-mile track from one great river system to another, through the country of the fabulous El Dorado, and up the river dos Vaupes, a tributary of the Negro unknown and unmapped by Europeans.

However, the *Travels* were not as successful as many of his later works, for he had not yet mastered the technique of weaving biological theories into personal narrative, a technique that he was to acquire with such outstanding success later. After telling his adventures, he added at the end of *Travels* a few short chapters on the geology and geography, fauna and flora of the Amazon.

During this time his interests in man and his social background were stimulated further by the way of life of the natives he visited. Whilst he records with amusement the wonder of the natives at seeing him skin a bird, and their decision that the butterflies were preserved as new patterns for printed calicos and the ugly insects for medicines, he also observes: "When I consider the excessively small amount of labour required in this country to convert the virgin forest into green meadows and fertile plantations, I almost long to come over with half-a-dozen friends disposed to work, and enjoy the country; and show the inhabitants how soon an earthly paradise might be created, which they had never even conceived capable of existing" (A 230). But perhaps it would not have been quite as easy as Wallace believed, because cleared jungle soil is very acid and not suitable for cropping without fertilisers.

The development of his scientific ideas is difficult to follow, for he did not make many contributions to scientific thought during his Amazon travels. From later writings, however, it is possible to see the influence of these early observations. He had not solved the species problem, which he had intended to do, and he had not apparently given it much thought. Problems of speciation are only considered superficially at this time in his writings which were mainly descriptive.

He describes in a paper to the Zoological Society of London in 1850 and again in the *Travels* the rare umbrella bird *Cephalopterus ornatus*. It was almost unknown to ornithologists, and he and his hunters had obtained twenty-five specimens from the small islands around Manaos. "This singular bird is about the size of a raven and is of similar colour. . . . On its head it bears a crest, different from that of any other bird. It is formed of feathers more than two inches long, very thickly set, and with hairy plumes curving over at the end. These can be laid back so as to be hardly visible, or can be erected and spread out on every side, completely covering the head, and even reaching beyond the point of the beak: the individual feathers then stand out something like the down-bearing seeds of the dandelion. Besides this, there is another ornamental appendage on the breast, formed by a fleshy tubercle, as thick as a quill and an inch and a half long, which hangs down from the neck, and is thickly covered with glossy feathers, forming a large pendant plume or tassel" (A 116).

From his training as a surveyor he was able to make maps of the Rio dos Vaupes and described the Rio Negro for the Geographical Society: "Having only a pocket surveying sextant, without any means of viewing two objects much differing in brilliancy, I endeavoured to obtain the latitude as accurately as I could, first by means of the zenith-distance at noon, obtained by a plumb-line and image of the sun, formed by a lens of about fifteen inches focus, and afterwards, by the meridian altitude of a star obtained on a calm night, by reflections in a cuya of water" (A 249). Considerable corrections to the estimates of latitude and longitude were necessary when Dr Hamilton Rice made an accurate survey of the whole river in 1907-08, but Wallace's map was found to be generally correct. "I am assured by authorities on the Rio Negro region that your father's work still holds good," wrote Dr Scott Keltie to Wallace's son on 21st May 1915 (M I 29).

These were not his only contributions to the thought of the time. He was observing the variety of structure to be found within a group of animals. Most naturalists at this time believed that a bird's beak, for instance, had been constructed especially for the type of food on which it fed and that no other explanation was either possible or needful. But Wallace had noticed that birds which eat the same food very often had differently shaped beaks. The flycatchers had broad bills and a wide gape, whilst the jacamars with the same habits had long pointed bills. He observed: "Naturalists are now beginning to look beyond this, and to see that there must be some other principle regulating the infinitely varied forms of life" (A 58). He was becoming aware of variation in wild populations and looking for its cause.

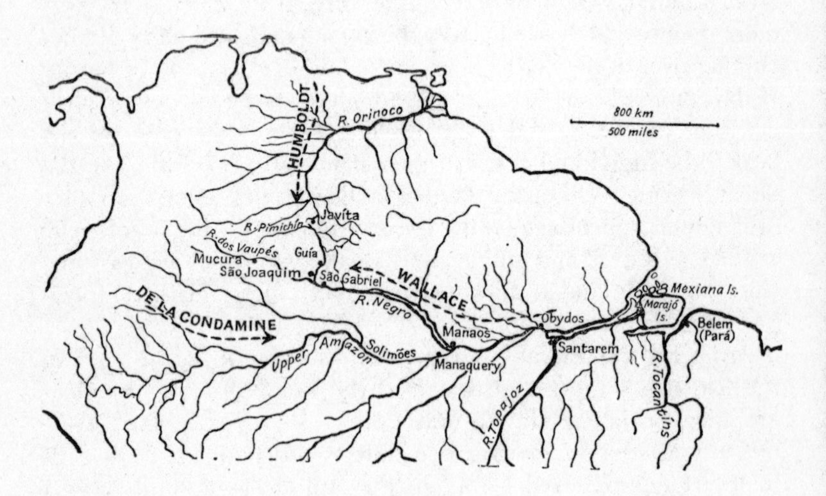

Fig. 1. The Amazon Basin showing areas explored by de la Condamine 1735-1745, Humboldt 1799-1804 and Wallace 1848-1852.

The most outstanding development of his ideas, as he progressed from one part of the Amazon system to another, was the realization of the importance of locality in biological observation. Rivers and vegetation changed from one place to another, the fauna differed from country to country, from lowland to mountain and from one side of a river to the other.

From gazing "with emotions of admiration and awe . . . upon the stream of this mighty and far-famed river," (A 93) with "its vast expanse of smooth water, generally from three to six miles wide; its pale yellowish-olive colour;" (A 94), he travelled in a month to Santarem where the river Topajoz joins the Amazon. Here blue clear waters were running into the soupy Amazon. A month later came the Rio Negro, and one morning, "we looked with surprise at the wonderful change in the water around us. We might have fancied ourselves on the river Styx, for it was black as ink in every direction, except where the white sand, seen at the depth of a few feet through its dusky wave, appeared a golden hue" (A 112).

These colour differences were due of course to the different geological formations, and hence vegetation, through which the tributaries ran. The character of forest trees changed along the lengths of the rivers, from the palms and leguminous trees of the lower reaches to the predominating myrtles and laurels of the high Negro. Even individual species of palms were sometimes localized, as he recorded in *Palm Trees of the Amazon*. But it was the correlation of animals with locality which proved the most surprising and interesting to him.

Most collections did not give clear indication of the locality from which a specimen had been brought. "The Amazon" or "Brazil" might be the extent of the detail given. It became clear to Wallace that exact and detailed records of the place of capture of all specimens was needed. One of his earliest contributions to biology was this insistence that locality should be included with all other characteristics used in describing a species. In 1852 he wrote ". . . there is scarcely an animal whose exact geographical limits we can mark on the map. . . . Are very closely allied species ever separated by a wide interval of country? What physical features determine the boundaries of species and genera?"

Before arriving in South America, he had been aware that many distinctive animals occurred there and nowhere else, even though similar habitats might be expected to exist in other parts of the world. "The tapir alone takes the place of the elephants and rhinoceroses of the Old World" (A 310). This phenomenon he accounted for by the isolation of the different continents by wide extents of sea "supposing the animal productions to have been originally distinct, they could not well have become intermixed" (A 327).

His own observations added to this an appreciation of smaller local groups, and in some cases they provided an indication of the reasons for the localization. One of these earliest observations had been made during an expedition from Belem to the large islands of Mexiana and Marajó at the mouth of the Amazon, at the end of 1848. The flat open country contrasted markedly with the forest from which he had come; the islands teemed with birds and insects of different species; there were alligators; the hunters brought in deer, armadillos, fish and jaguars for food, and Wallace was forced to the conclusion that: "The plains are always more thickly peopled than the forest; and a temperate zone, as has been pointed out by Mr Darwin, seems better adapted to the support of large land-animals than the tropics" (A 71).

Just as the Rio Negro differed in colour from the main Amazon stream, so he found that the animals he collected at different places differed in species, even though the general characteristics of the terrain might appear to be similar. Each part of the Amazon system had its own species of howler monkey, prehensile-tailed monkeys confined to the South American continent. *Alouatta* (*Mycetes*) *Beelzebub* lived along the lower Amazon in the province of Pará; the black *A. caraya* was found on the banks of the Upper Amazon; and the red *A. ursinus* belonged to the Rio Negro and Upper Amazon. What physical features determined this localization? Might it perhaps be that the river itself was the main barrier? Another and related monkey, Wallace's sloth monkey, or the saki *Pithecia,* was represented by the species *monachus* (*irrorata*) on the south bank of the Upper Amazon, and by another species *P. pithecia* on the north bank. Wallace suspected that the river might form a barrier for monkeys, because he suspected them of not being swimmers by choice. Whilst he had seen sloths and such unlikely mammals swimming the river, he had never seen monkeys swimming. Further support for his hypothesis came in 1849 during collecting expeditions from Santarem. One day he caught a large skyblue butterfly *Callithea sapphira,* one of a genus of thick winged blue butterflies found only in tropical America. Soon after, he caught another *Callithea,* not far from the place of his first catch but on the other side of the river. The new butterfly differed from the first in the deeper blue, and in the markings of its wings. It was a different species, separated from its relatives by a comparatively short distance, but a distance of water : the width of the Amazon.

"In mammals the fact was not so much to be wondered at, but few persons would credit that it would apply also to birds and winged insects. Yet I am convinced it does, and I only regret that I had not collected and studied birds there with the same assiduity as I have here [Malay Archipelago]" (to Bates 1861 I 377).

For all this lack of assiduity he was able to record that the green Jacamar of Guiana, *Galbula ruficauda* (*viridis*) *rufoviridis,* which occurred all along the north bank of the Amazon had not been reported from the south where, as he himself had observed in Belem, *G. albirostris* (*cyanocollis*) and *G. ruficauda* (*maculicauda*) *ruficauda* occur. Since then, many species and subspecies have been found to be restricted to one or other bank of the river. The ant-bird *Phlegopsis nigromaculata* occurs all along the south bank but it has never been recorded from the north, according to Mayr (1942). But although this restriction is true of several species of bird, the Amazon is probably not the main barrier for these mobile animals. The edge of the Amazonian forest to the south is probably a more effective limiting feature.

The width of the river was also not necessarily the main physical barrier dividing other species of animals besides birds. It did not account for the distribution of several of the monkey species which proved not to be confined to one bank of a river so much as to the upper or lower reaches of the river. And this type of localization Wallace found in some of the fish populations.

When conditions for collecting were poor or the weather unsuitable, or when it was simply a question of providing food for himself and his crew, Wallace would set his men to work collecting fish. This could be done by nets, or on a larger and more destructive scale by the use of timbo (a poisonous liana *Paullinia pinnata*). The roots of the timbo were reduced to fibres by beating and then mixed with water and clay and squeezed until the juice ran out. When the juice was poured into the stream, small fish jumped out of the water or lay on their backs at the surface with their gills wide open, and in a few hours there would be a basketful of small fish. The timbo contains an alkaloid, rotenone, which inhibits cell respiration in fish (Lindahl & Oberg 1960), but which is evidently not poisonous to human beings for, after the interesting fish had been selected for scientific use, the rest went into the pot for supper.

By this means Wallace made an impressive collection of fish, drawing and describing them as they came in; some 160 species had been found in the Rio Negro alone. Notebooks with the pencil drawings of 200 are in the British Museum, but little use was ever made of them either by Wallace or anyone else. Dr Tate Regan was able to identify about half from the drawings. The rest were probably new species and were certainly not identifiable from the drawings. All the actual specimens were lost at sea.

The importance of these fish to Wallace lay not so much in their newness as in their extraordinary variability from one locality to another. Each tributary had its own range of species, a few of which it shared with other tributaries but most of which were peculiar to itself. "But the Amazon has most of its fishes peculiar to itself and so have all the numerous tributaries, especially in their upper waters; so that the number of distinct kinds inhabiting the whole basin of the Amazon must be immense" (A 187). Restriction of species within an apparently continuous medium could thus occur, but at this time Wallace could offer no explanation of the phenomenon.

When yet another example of restricted habitat was brought to his notice it proved easier to account for, however. The flame-coloured cock of the rock *Rupicola rupicola* (*crocea*) was caught in open scrubby floodland westwards of the Rio Negro. A range of granite peaks and rocks runs along the centre of the Guiana mountains, across the sources of the Rio Negro and Orinoco, towards the Andes, and it coincides with the range of the cock of the rock. The birds are thus confined to a particular geological formation because they make their nests among granite rocks and nowhere else.

This constantly recurring theme of the localization of groups of animals runs throughout the account of his travels in equatorial South America. At that time he was chiefly observing the localization itself and recording with accuracy the locality of capture, seeking an explanation for it occasionally in a comparatively obvious geological feature. Later, when he had left the Amazon, this problem of localization of groups of animals interested him for the evidence it contributed to the theory of common descent. It showed that nearby species were alike and therefore could have had a common ancestor, but were also different enough to have diverged from that ancestor, each in its own way, suggesting therefore that evolution of species from pre-existing species had indeed taken place. His interest in localization developed eventually into his major scientific work: the geographical distribution of animals over the world.

Although this must be considered the main development in Wallace's scientific thought during his stay in South America and the following sixteen months in England, the germ of another scientific idea had also been implanted. A paper and a short note contributed in 1853 were concerned with the habits of some of the butterflies of the Amazon valley. He questioned why members of the Hesperiidae (skippers) should differ in the position of their wings when at rest, and suggested this behavioural difference might form a basis for their classification. Further, he noticed and recorded that some butterflies, particularly the bright coloured ones, appeared to expose themselves to trouble by resting on the upper surfaces of leaves.

The Travels may not have been in itself a profound contribution to the thought of the nineteenth century and it may have compared unfavourably with Bates's equivalent, the *Naturalist on the Amazons* (1863), but in it appear the first inklings of most of the major theoretical contributions that Wallace was to make to biology in later years.

London 1852 to 1854

Wallace arrived in England at the end of 1852, eighty days after leaving Belem, an event that caused the exclamation : "Oh glorious day ! Here we are on shore at Deal, where the ship is at anchor. Such a dinner, with our two captains ! Oh beefsteaks and damson tart, a paradise for hungry sinners" (I 308). He settled in London, taking a house in Albany Street with his sister Fanny and her husband, and began to work on those of his collections which had arrived safely in England.

His bird collections were neither extensive nor new to science, since the Amazon had already been well worked by ornithologists, and so they were sold to a private collector who presented them afterwards to the British Museum. Other specimens, duplicates of his own working collections, had been sold as they arrived from South America, and he had paid his current expenses by their sale. An entry in Bates's diary in 1850 gives an idea of their receipts and expenditure. "I find I have taken 7,553 specimens of insects, which at 4d. each will bring £125.17.8, and my expenses have been . . . 600 miliers, or £67.10.0. Stevens's commission is 20 per cent, and commission for remitting money, with freight of boxes, etc., is about 5 per cent, thus leaving the produce of my collection £94.9.0. I then gain only £26.19.0 in one year eight months" (Clodd 1892). In addition to the proceeds from sales Wallace had £150 from the insurance on the collections that were lost in the shipwreck. This was enough for his needs, for it "enabled me to live a year in London, and get a good outfit and a sufficient cash balance for my Malayan journey" (II 360).

A further collecting expedition was essential if Wallace were to make a livelihood as a naturalist. He had neither the training nor the reputation to have any chance of obtaining a post as a zoologist in England. Such a post would almost necessarily have been an academic one, and there were very few of these. As T. H. Huxley wrote to his sister in the same year: "Science in England does everything—but *pay*. You may earn praise but not pudding" (Huxley 1903). Wallace had no university degree. He does not seem to have had much desire for an academic appointment even later in life, though it was not the meagreness of the salaries that repelled him, but rather the restrictions on his freedom. The problem of a livelihood was common to all biologists. A year earlier Huxley had also written to his future wife: "There is no chance of living by science. I have been loth to believe it, but it is so. There are not more than four or five offices in London which a Zoologist or a Comparative Anatomist can hold and live by. Owen, who has a European reputation, second only to Cuvier, gets as Hunterian Professor £300 a year! which is less than the salary of many a bank clerk" (Huxley 1903).

Luckily, Wallace was still intensely interested in the species problem. Collecting in an unknown part of the world seemed the best plan for the satisfaction of this interest, even if there had been attractive alternatives at home. The life of a field naturalist also meant independence, no restrictions, no superiors. It should provide him with both money and information. The less well-known the area he visited, the more valuable would be the specimens he sent home. The richer the area, the more specimens he could collect.

During his stay of sixteen months in London he regularly attended the meetings of the Zoological and Entomological Societies, and he met and talked with members. Being shy and diffident, and thinking himself a bad speaker, he does not seem to have made much impact, but he became acquainted with many of the leading naturalists of the day. It was at a meeting of the Zoological Society in December 1852 that he first saw T. H. Huxley who was reading a paper on some liver parasites of a zebra which had recently died at Regent's Park. "I was particularly struck with his wonderful power of making a difficult and rather complex subject perfectly intelligible and extremely interesting to persons, who, like myself, were absolutely ignorant of the whole group" (I 323). In later years Wallace became very friendly with Huxley and his family.

In the autumn of 1853 he made his first visit to Switzerland, a country which was to be the scene of many of his later holidays and which was to influence his ideas on the glaciation of the northern hemisphere.

Most of his time, however, was spent in extensive studies of the insects in the British Museum. The insect room was then in Great Russell Street, and it was here that he first met Darwin. He was introduced to him sometime at the beginning of 1854, but the event left only a vague imprint on the minds of both.

His studies of the various collections revealed that some of the most striking deficiencies were in the fauna of the Malay Archipelago. It was, therefore, to these islands that Wallace decided to go. The large westerly islands were known in Marco Polo's day, even if only indistinctly, and the Moluccas and many of the smaller islands of the Archipelago had been visited regularly and described, in the sixteenth century.

Many of the earlier travellers had made observations on the fauna and flora of the region and had brought back specimens of some of the things they had seen. As early as 1497-99 Vasco da Gama had visited Malacca and reported that "there are many big parrots in this country, whose plumage is red, like fire". Half a century later a Spanish expedition from Peru to the Solomon Islands, under Alvaro de Mendana, could add to the red parrots of Malacca, white cockatoos yellow crested, quantities of pigeons, many "larger beyond comparison than ours", geese, mice, bats, turkeys (megapodes), birds of paradise and papuan dogs that do not bark, from these most easterly islands of the Archipelago (Amherst & Thomson 1901). From New Guinea in 1605 the Spaniard, Diego de Prado y Tovar, reported cassowaries, crocodiles and an unknown animal like a greyhound with a scaly tail, a kangaroo (Stevens & Barwick 1930).

The subsequent years provided more and detailed information, but apparently it was not until 1776 that the first naturalist, the Frenchman Sonnerat, visited the region, to be followed by a Dutch expedition in 1828.

Enough was recorded of this area to indicate that it was rich in species. Except for Java, however, it had not been thoroughly explored by naturalists. It had the advantages of novelty and, therefore, financial reward, but had the disadvantages of a solitary life and lack of the technical guidance usually found in the books of earlier naturalists.

Wallace used as his basic book of reference Prince Lucien Bonaparte's *Conspectus Generum Avium* which contained descriptions of all the main species of birds known up to 1850 within its 800 pages. To this he added details taken from other books on Malayan species so that he was never at a loss to identify a bird if it belonged to a known species. A book by Boisduval supplied him with detailed descriptions of two families of butterflies, the Papilionidae and the Pieridae. For the rest he had to manage with the notes and sketches he had made in the British Museum.

In March 1854 he left England in the *Euxine* after several weeks' delay in sailing because of the outbreak of the Crimean War. He took with him, as his assistant, Charles Allen, a boy of sixteen, son of a carpenter. They disembarked at Alexandria and, as neither the canal nor the railway was yet built, the journey to Suez was made overland in "small four-horse two-wheeled omnibuses, carrying six passengers each". The baggage went by camel trains. "The road is excellent. The skeletons of camels—hundreds of them—lay all along the road" (I 335). At Suez they embarked on the steamer *Bengal* which took them to Singapore, arriving there on 20th April 1854.

Malay Archipelago

The six months Wallace spent in the Malay Peninsula collecting around Singapore and Malacca, together with the journeys of the following seven and a half years, have been told by him in *The Malay Archipelago: the land of the Orang-utan, and the Bird of Paradise. A narrative of travel, with studies of man and nature,* published in 1869. It tells the story of his adventures between 1854 and 1862, not in chronological order but woven into his zoological observations and arranged to present a hypothesis : a hypothesis to explain the peculiarities of the fauna of the islands. To this end he groups the islands he visited into a zoogeographical classification. Thus, he describes Borneo with Java and Sumatra as the Indo-Malayan islands, although he visited Borneo at the start of his journeys through the Archipelago and Sumatra for the first time seven years later. The order in which he visited the islands was determined by expediency, and resulted in only brief stays.

During the eight years he spent in the Malay Archipelago he travelled approximately 14,000 miles, made some 96 moves, and visited almost every group of islands between Malaya and Australia, though not every individual island. His most easterly voyages took him as far as the Aru Islands and New Guinea but never to Australia itself.

The mainland of Malaya had already been fully explored by naturalists, but even so Wallace's first consignment of some 1,000 insects from Malacca contained at least forty that had not previously been named. Already, too, the birds and insects had made a strong contrast with those of the Amazon. Instead of humming birds, there were sunbirds; instead of toucans, there were hornbills, and "compared with the Amazon valley, the great and striking feature here is the excessive poverty of the Diurnal Lepidoptera" (I 350).

In October 1854 Wallace left Singapore and went to Sarawak. His primary intention was to study in its natural surroundings the orang utan, the large ape of Sumatra and Borneo. The natural history of the orang utan, one of only four living ape genera in the world, was not accurately known, and, furthermore, the skins and skeletons would fetch a good price in England. He was well rewarded both in his captures and in his studies of the live animals.

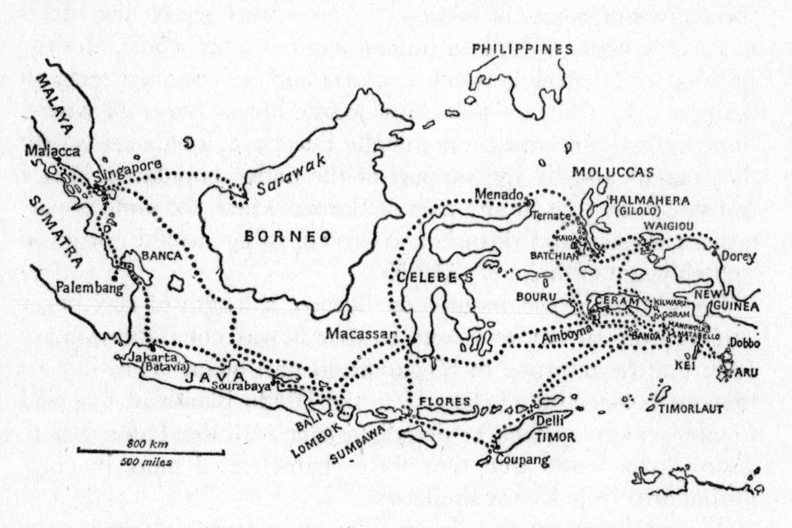

Fig. 2. Journeys in the Malay Archipelago 1856-1862.

Sarawak was a locality also rich in beetles. Many of these were new species, very strange shapes and beautifully coloured. Beetles and orang utans he had come prepared for, but he describes his amazement and delight when something quite unheard of was brought to him, the flying frog *Polypedates* (*Rhacophorus*) *nigropalmatus*. "One of the most curious and interesting reptiles which I met with in Borneo was a large tree-frog which was brought to me by one of the Chinese workmen! He assured me that he had seen it come down, in a slanting direction, from a high tree, as if it flew. . . . This is, I believe, the first instance of a 'flying frog'" (MA I 59-61). The frog (an amphibian, not a reptile) is about four inches long, a deep green with large expansible yellow and black webs on all four feet. It is still known as the flying frog, a fact that appears to depend for its veracity on this same observation of Wallace's Chinese workman—but many have doubted its flying capabilities and have preferred to account for the webs as aquatic adaptations. No one else seems to have seen the frog fly from a tree, and so the reasons for its webbed feet and any details of its life-history remain an enigma.

Malay Archipelago describes not only the interesting animals of the islands and the theory of their distribution, but also observes the countryside and the physique and ways of the inhabitants. As in South America, he was impressed by the native civilization. Of the natives of Sarawak he says: "The more I see of uncivilised people the better I think of human nature on the whole, and the essential differences between civilised and savage men seem to disappear.... We are two days' journey from Sarawak where, though the Government is nominally European, it only exists with the consent and by the support of the native population. Yet I can safely say that in any part of Europe where the same opportunities for evil and disturbance existed, things would not go so smoothly as they do here" (M I 55).

He spent fourteen months on Borneo, a length of stay never achieved on any other island, so that it was not until January 1856 that he returned to Singapore to start again. This time he found a passage on a schooner to the Hindu islands of Bali and Lombok, islands which he described later with the Timor group, although he found that they were characterized more by their dissimilarity than by any similarity.

The schooner stayed only for a few days at Bali. "I had never beheld so beautiful and well cultivated a district out of Europe" (MA I 236). It was so well cultivated with rice, cocoa nut palms and fruit trees that it was hard to find the native fauna in such a short stay. But from what he saw of it he had the general impression that it resembled closely the Malayan fauna with which he was by now familiar but "my ignorance of how important a locality this was for the elucidation of the geographical distribution of animals caused me to neglect obtaining some specimens which I never met with again" (237). There were barbets and woodpeckers, Javanese orioles, starlings and weaver birds, and a white butterfly, richly marked in black and orange, *Huphina* (*Pieris*) *tamar,* a new species.

From Bali to Lombok, twenty miles of water; from the present day to the mesozoic, according to the German Darwinian

Haeckel. But leaving aside the exaggeration, the differences between the two islands were indeed astonishing. The countryside was similar; both grew rice and coffee, but the fauna, particularly on first sight the birds, was different. "... I now saw for the first time many Australian forms that are quite absent from the islands westward. Small white cockatoos were abundant, and their loud screams, conspicuous white colour, and pretty yellow crests, rendered them a very important feature in the landscape. This is the most westerly point on the globe where any of the family are to be found" (MA I 243). Here on Lombok there were green Australian bee-eaters, long-necked honeysuckers and mound-making megapodes.

It was a surprise to find Australian forms so far west, and the contrast between the two islands astonished him so much that he tended to exaggerate it when he wrote about it later on. He was experiencing for the first time a sudden faunal break, an experience which was to have a profound effect on his theories of Archipelago faunas, and which gave him one of his first clues to the zoogeography of the area.

Up to this time he had been living only in thoroughly Europeanized islands where the native culture was sometimes difficult to discover. But Lombok was ruled by a Hindu Rajah and Europeans were discouraged from living there. His hunters were terrified of having their throats cut every time they went out, but Wallace walked alone in the forest and came to no harm at all. Lombok belonged to the story books, and Wallace told this tale of it:

The chief revenues of the Rajah were derived from a tax in the form of a contribution of rice from every man, woman and child in the island. This tax was collected annually. For some time, the Rajah had noticed that his revenues were getting smaller, but, at the same time, everyone in the land seemed well fed and prosperous and the "krisses of his chiefs and officers were getting handsomer and handsomer; and the handles that were of yellow wood were changed for ivory, and those of ivory were changed for gold, and diamonds and emeralds sparkled on many of them" (MA I 277). He resolved to find out exactly how many subjects he had. So one day after a week's assumed melancholy, he summoned his princes, chiefs and priests and told them of a dream he had had. The spirit of the great fire mountain had appeared and told him to go to the top of the mountain alone, where he would learn things of great importance. With much ceremony and procession, the Rajah was conducted to the mountain. When the great cortege was near the summit, the Rajah left his followers and went on alone. At the top he found the sun very hot. He was tired, so he sat under a rock and fell asleep. And then he descended and returned to his palace. Three days later he again summoned the princes and chiefs and the priests and told them how he had been warned by the great spirit that a plague was coming to the earth, but that it could be averted by the people of Lombok if they followed the instructions of the great spirit. Twelve sacred krisses must be made, and to make them, each village must send to the palace a bundle of needles, a needle for every head in the village. When sickness visited a village, one of the sacred krisses would be sent to it and, if everyone had contributed a needle, the disease would immediately go, but if the number of needles had not been exact, the kris would have no virtue. And so the needles were brought and the krisses were forged by the best steelmaker in Mataram and put away, carefully wrapped in silk. When the rice harvest was next gathered in and the rice tax was delivered to the Rajah, to those who were short of the full amount by only a little the Rajah said nothing, but to those were were very noticeably short he asked them why there had been so many needles from their village and yet so little rice. And the next year the amount of rice increased greatly and the Rajah grew very rich and none of the Rajahs or Sultans among the Malays were so great or so powerful as the Rajah of Lombok. When sickness visited a village, a sacred kris was taken there, and if the sickness disappeared, the village sent thanks to the Rajah, and if it did not go, the village knew that it had only itself to blame for, obviously, everyone had not contributed his needle.

But Lombok was only the first of many entrancing islands in the more easterly part of the Archipelago, and after two and a half months Wallace managed to get a passage to Celebes.

On 2nd September he arrived at Macassar. "Celebes is quite as unknown as was the Upper Amazon before your visit to it, perhaps even more so," he wrote to Bates (I 354). On a small coffee plantation about two miles from Macassar a house was lent to him, but he had no sooner moved in than he and his boy Ali developed a severe attack of intermittent fever. In spite of this bad beginning, Celebes subsequently provided them with a satisfactory number of new birds and insects. Again, there were more Australian forms mixed with the Malay than he had expected. Celebes was not like Borneo. There were woodpeckers and cuckoos, but there were also lorikeets. But the most striking thing of all was the number of new species. In fact, the fauna of Celebes proved of such individuality that he returned to the island twice afterwards, once in July 1857 to the Macassar district again and the second time two years later to the northern arm round Menado.

On his first visit to Celebes, he caught the cuckoo *Rhamphococcyx* (*Phoenicophaus*) *calorhynchus,* with its yellow, red and black beak and observed "it is one of the characteristic birds of the island of Celebes, to which it is confined". The lyre-tailed drongo shrike *Dicrurus hottentotus leucops*, little green and gold speckled weevils, a pale blue and black butterfly *Pareronia* (*Eronia*) *tritaea,* and one with an orange band on a black ground, *Appias* (*Tachyris*) *ithome*, were also entirely new.

By the second visit to Celebes he was getting a clearer idea of the distribution of animals throughout the area and he began to study certain groups in considerable detail. By then he was looking particularly for papilio butterflies on the island. Some like *P. demolion* were common also in Malaya, others like the blue *P. ulysses* were eastern forms, and yet others like the rare *P. rhesus* and the golden green *P. adamantius* (*macedon*) were peculiar to Celebes. Thus, eastern and western forms overlapped and mixed with species which were confined to the island.

But this had not exhausted the possibilities of Celebes, and when he next had a chance to visit the island in 1859 he arranged to spend several months exploring. He had already seen the tailless black macaques which, isolated on Celebes and neighbouring islands, have come to resemble the baboons. He was anxious now to see some of the other mammals which were reputedly confined to this island: the dwarf buffalo *Anoa depressicornis* and the babirussa. Here he was successful, seeing the animals alive and obtaining skulls, of which the babirussa pig was perhaps the most spectacular. The upper tusks of the male grow upwards instead of downwards, and they curl over the head and eyes and occasionally grow back into the skull again. The reason for this is not known, but it has been suggested that they are secondary sexual characters developed originally for fighting or threatening, or guards for their eyes in the thorny thickets, or even characteristics fancied by the islanders and encouraged by selective breeding. These endemic species were mixed with western civets and tarsiers and with cuscuses from the east.

Among the birds he had already observed this same slight overlap of faunas and the great concentration of peculiar species. Amongst these last were the raquet-tailed parrots *Prioniturus* and eleven distinct pigeons out of a total of eighteen that he recorded. On the coast at the far end of the island Wallace spent days watching the megapodes, birds which occur in the Moluccas and further east, with the strange exception of the species that inhabits the Nicobar islands. Megapodes, or brush turkeys, do not brood their eggs but lay them in sand or in huge mounds constructed by the male. The mounds may be as much as eight feet high and thirty feet round, built of sand and rotting vegetation. In these the females lay their eggs. Whilst the mound incubates the eggs the male looks after it, opening it up to the sun or closing it in, testing its temperature with his head. The megapodes of Celebes and *Eulipoa* (*Megapodius*) *wallacei* of the Moluccas do not build mounds. They lay their eggs in the strips of black sand on the shore. They lay an egg and then return to the forest for about a week, returning again to the shore to lay another egg, until six to eight have been laid in the same well-concealed hole. Then they leave them for ever to be kept warm by the heat of the sun. Unfortunately for the megapodes, both they and their eggs are good to eat. Wallace observed of them : "It has generally been the custom of writers on Natural History, to take the habits and instincts of animals as fixed points, and to consider their structure and organization as specially adapted to be in accordance with these. This assumption is however an arbitrary one, and has the bad effect of stifling inquiry into the nature and causes of 'instincts and habits', treating them as directly due to a 'first cause', and therefore incomprehensible to us" (MA I 419).

Where Celebes had been of special interest in its endemic species and also, surprisingly enough, in the absence from it of common species from Borneo and other neighbouring islands, his voyage eastwards was to provide him with a picture of an eastern or near Australian fauna, characterized by birds of paradise and the abundance and unusual colouring of the pigeons and parrots. Here he was to adventure by native boats and to visit areas almost unknown to naturalists.

At the end of 1856 he embarked for the first time in a prau. The prau was a cumbersome boat of 70 tons, shaped like a Chinese junk, with one huge and one small mat sail. It carried a crew of thirty and in good conditions could make 5 mph. Two weeks after leaving Macassar they called at the Kei Islands.

"Here my eyes were feasted for the first time with splendid scarlet lories on the wing, as well as by the sight of that most imperial butterfly, the 'Priamus' of collectors. . . . Of one grand new beetle, glittering with ruby and emerald tints, I got a large quantity, having first detected one of its wing-cases ornamenting the outside of a native's tobacco pouch" (MA II 187).

On 8th January 1857 Wallace landed at Dobbo on the Aru Islands, 1,000 miles from Macassar, his furthest point east. He stayed on Aru for seven months, living sometimes on one island, sometimes on another and beginning and ending his stay at the active trading centre of Dobbo. The traders of Dobbo came mainly from Celebes and from Ceram, bringing sago, knives, arrack, tobacco, textiles and elephants' tusks to exchange for bundles of smoked bêche de mer (holothurian echinoderms), dried shark fins, mother-of-pearl shells, birds of paradise and tortoiseshell brought to Dobbo from the more distant islands of the Aru group. To Wallace, the first European to live on the islands for any length of time, the Aru Islands were "almost fairy realms" filled with wonderful animals "and so I jump up and begin my day's work very happily" (MA II 226).

New animals abounded, Aru was a feast for a naturalist. There he found *Papilio aegeus ormenus* and *P. aegeus onesimus* and the cuscus *Phalanger maculatus,* a white woolly marsupial with a prehensile tail, and the pigeon *Ptilonopus wallacei*, and a black cockatoo *Probosciger aterius goliath* (Gray 1858). There were so many spiders and lizards that he was constantly reminded of the Amazon forests. But most exciting of all, one of the things he had come all this way to see, were the birds of paradise, birds of the easterly islands only.

Unfortunately, he lost at least two months of the seven because of serious ulceration of his feet. But not even this could spoil the pleasures of these islands, their inhabitants and their birds of paradise. The first of these "perfectly lovely of the many lovely productions of nature" that he saw was the King Bird of Paradise *Cicinnurus regius,* an orange crimson bird with a shoulder fan of grey and emerald green and "golden buds borne upon airy stems that spring from the tail" (1862a). And also on Aru was the Great Bird of Paradise *P. aboda* L. "The bird itself is nearly as large as a crow, and is of rich coffee brown colour. The head and neck is of pure straw yellow above, and rich metallic green beneath. The long plumey tufts of golden orange feathers spring from the sides beneath each wing, and when the bird is in repose are partly concealed by them. At the time of its excitement, however, the wings are raised vertically over the back, the head is bent down and stretched out, and the long plumes are raised up and expanded till they form two magnificent golden fans, striped with deep red at the base, and fading off into the pale brown tint of the finely divided and softly waving points. The whole bird is then overshadowed by them, the crouching body, yellow head, and emerald green throat forming but the foundation and setting to the golden glory which waves above. When seen in this attitude, the Bird of Paradise really deserves its name, and must be ranked as one of the most beautiful and most wonderful of living things" (MA II 253).

"It seems sad, that on the one hand such exquisite creatures should live out their lives and exhibit their charms only in these wild inhospitable regions . . . while on the other hand, should civilised man ever reach these distant lands . . . he will so disturb the nicely-balanced relations of organic and inorganic nature as to cause the disappearance, and finally the extinction, of these very beings whose wonderful structure and beauty he alone is fitted to appreciate and enjoy. This consideration must surely tell us that all living things were *not* made for man" (MA II 224).

These exquisite, almost legendary birds, were known almost entirely from skins brought back by the early spice traders, skins from which the feet and sometimes also the wings had been cut.

The earliest European account of birds of paradise seems to have been that of the Portuguese traveller, Tomé Pires, who was one of the first to visit the easterly islands of the Archipelago between 1512 and 1515. He recorded that these most prized of birds were sent over from Aru dead "and they say they come from heaven, and that they do not know how they are bred" (Cortesão 1944). Later, Italian descriptions called them Birds of God, and the Italian Porcacchi (1576) recounted that when the native king went into battle he took a bird of paradise with him because, knowing them to be immortal, he believed he too would not be killed.

Birds of paradise were thought to live always in the air, turning towards the sun and never alighting on the earth until they died. In 1589 Acosta described them as: "Certaine birds from

China that have no fete, and all their bodies are almost feathers. They sit not upon the ground, but hang upon boughs, by strings or feathers which they have, and so rest themselves like flies or airie things". The hen was alleged to lay her eggs in a hole on the back of her mate. The Portuguese gave them the name *Passaros de Sol* and, later, the Dutch called them *Avis paradiseus*. In 1760 Linnaeus named the Great Bird of Paradise *Paradisea apoda,* describing it from a skin which had undergone the usual mutilation, and in 1775 Buffon maintained that they had neither feet nor intestines but were filled instead with fat. He continued the legend that they live on dew and air and hang by the two long feathers above the tail.

It seems odd that these legends should have persisted so long because only a few years later Goldsmith (1776) in England was well aware of the damage such skins had undergone. ". . . their usual method is to gut them and cut off their legs; they then run a hot iron into the body, which dries up the internal moisture; and filling the cavity with salts and spices, they sell them to the Europeans for a perfect trifle." Pennant (1791) published a picture of the Great Bird of Paradise with feet clearly shown, maintaining that Pigafetta in 1525 had testified to their having feet.

The birds of paradise are all moderately sized birds and all have some remarkable developments of plumage, more especially the males, silky texture, gorgeous colours and extravagant plumes. They belong to the family Paradisiidae, related to the crows, and there are several genera. In 1850, thirteen species were known; by 1900 this had been increased to fifty; and in 1950 these had been consolidated to forty-three (Iredale 1950). The birds of paradise were so much prized in Europe and Asia that between 1870 and 1924 when their export was prohibited, more than 1,000,000 skins had been sent out from New Guinea (Mayr 1942).

A chapter of *Malay Archipelago* is devoted to the birds of paradise because "being (as far as I am aware) the only Englishman who has seen these wonderful birds in their native forests, and obtained specimens of many of them, I propose to give here, in a connected form, the result of my observations and inquiries" (MA II 387). A description of eighteen species with illustrations of six of them follows. To the two Aru species, the Great Bird of Paradise and the King Bird of Paradise, Wallace himself added only three more, but one of these was a new species. But this was later. In the first half of 1857 he was still busy with the treasures of the Aru Islands.

One of his new finds in this easterly region was what he considered to be a distinctive human type, and he gave a good deal of space to its description. In contrast with the reserved lank-haired Malays of the west, he found here exuberant, frizzly-haired Papuans, inquisitive and active. On Aru the natives were traders and could understand no other occupation. What the white man was doing there was beyond their comprehension. They brought him animals and shells and he paid for them, but they could not understand. Whenever any of them came from some other part of Aru they would be sure to visit this friendly white man "to see with their own eyes the unheard of phenomenon of a person come to stay at Dobbo who does not trade" (MA II 201). What was he doing with all those birds and insects? They could not believe it when he told them that people in his own country would come to look at the dead and stuffed specimens. They had their own ideas on that subject. " 'What becomes of them when you go on to the sea?' 'Why they are all packed up in boxes,' said I, 'what did you think became of them?' 'They all come to life again, don't they? . . . yes, they all come to life again, that's what they do—they all come to life again' " (MA II 248). He must have supernatural powers because how else could a stranger to their country know more about their animals than they did themselves? And if he knew that, he must know everything. " 'You must know,' say they; 'you know everything: you make the fine weather for your men to shoot . . . and you go alone into the forest and are not afraid,' " (264) and " 'Before you came we had rain every day—very wet indeed; now ever since you have been here, it is fine, hot weather' " (248).

But although they were obviously in some awe of this man with medicinal powers, they trusted and liked him and they were curious to learn about the place he came from. But when he told them they laughed and did not believe a word of what he said. They wanted him to stay on with them, and they pleaded: " 'Don't go away, but send for more things . . . and stay here a year or two.' " This was not only for the knives and materials he brought with him. They had a genuine regard for him. So much so that in 1874 Wallace received a letter in Arabic from a native who had piloted him up Wonumbai Creek in the Aru Islands. In spite of attempts by experts the letter was never satisfactorily translated, but it appeared to be to the effect that this native pilot had so much regard for Wallace that he thought he ought to come out to govern the islands. He was still treasuring a silver headed cane that Wallace had given him (BM).

Wallace's Aru collections were valuable, valuable for their rarity as well as their attractiveness for the cabinet. He sold the greater part of them for £1,000. One small box of shells alone fetched £50. The Aru collections, however, were exceptional. Usually a "box of insects" brought something from £15 to £45, an average of 1/- a specimen, with some rare forms like the white beetle *Choeromorpha* (*Agelasta*) *wallacei* being valued at 7/6.

But Wallace could not stay on Aru for ever. By July the trading season was over and everyone was going home. So he went back to Macassar, making the journey by prau in nine and a half days. The Macassar natives looked on the journey to Aru and back as a wild and romantic expedition, and its successful completion was the ambition of a lifetime. Wallace was inclined to agree with them. "This journey was the most successful of any that I undertook," (I 357) and it was "the portion of my travels to which I look back with the most complete satisfaction" (MA II 284). Not only were the islands, the animals and the natives some of the most delightful he ever met, but he had also enjoyed the sea voyage. "My first voyage in a prau being thus satisfactorily terminated, I must, before taking leave of it for some months, bear testimony to the merits of the queer old-world vessel. Setting aside all ideas of danger, which is probably, after all, not more than in any other craft, I must declare that I have never, either before or since, made twenty days' voyage so pleasantly, or perhaps, more correctly speaking, with so little discomfort" (194).

Unfortunately, this could not be said of other voyages he made amongst the Papuan group of islands. It was here that he had some of his most disastrous experiences, and they are recounted in detail in *Malay Archipelago*. In June 1860 he planned to sail from Ceram in the Moluccas to Waigiou in the Papuan group, off the tip of New Guinea, a distance of 200 miles. It took him seventeen days to make the journey, for he was blown away from every island where he attempted to land, even missing the forty-mile long Mysol, temporarily losing two of his crew on an uninhabited island and arrived on the coast of Waigiou without a pilot, completing "our tedious and unhappy voyage".

Physical discomforts on Waigiou were many, but Wallace spent three months there. The first house they lived in was built by themselves and the roof leaked. The second house he describes as a dwarf's house; it was nine feet square and raised on posts so that the floor was four and a half feet from the ground and only five feet below the roof. For a tall man these were cramped surroundings, but Wallace succeeded in living there for six weeks, using the open ground floor as living space and the top floor as a store room and bedroom. It was difficult to find anything to eat; there was little to buy because the natives were poor and had nothing themselves. They had to rely almost entirely on the birds they could shoot. But to compensate for Waigiou's poverty, Wallace got there twenty-four specimens of yet another bird of paradise, *Uranornis* (*Paradisea*) *ruber*, the Red Bird of Paradise, noted for its "rigid, polished, wavy ribbons", a new genus of ground pigeon, *Henicophaps albifrons,* several splendid butterflies, the light violet blue *Thysonotis* (*Lycaena*) *wallacei,* the new *Papilio wallacei* and "a superb specimen of a green *Ornithoptera* (*Trogonoptera*) absolutely fresh and perfect, and which still remains one of the glories of my cabinet" (MA II 366).

As if this journey from Ceram to Waigiou had not been bad enough, the journey from there to Ternate was even worse. Not only were the winds against them; they met fast running tides and swells, probably caused by an earthquake somewhere in the region; their anchor carried away and they were constantly battling against coastal currents through terrifying squalls. This time they were thirty-eight days on a voyage that should have taken twelve, running short of food and water, and with no oil for the compass lamp. The natives were convinced that all this bad luck was entirely due to the omission of an important ceremony. Before setting out they should have poured oil through a hole in the bottom of the boat, and then nothing like this would have happened. "That you ever returned alive is wonderful after all your risks from illness and sea voyages, especially that most interesting one to Waigiou and back. Of all the impressions which I have received from your book, the strongest is that your perseverance in the cause of science was heroic," Darwin wrote to Wallace in 1869 (M I 237).

Before this Wallace had had bitter experiences in travelling and living condiditions round New Guinea. New Guinea held a fascination for him, for it was virtually unknown, and held out vast possibilities for collecting. But sailing was difficult in those parts of the world; a voyage from New Guinea back to the Kei Islands had to be abandoned, and even his first visit by schooner in March 1858 was delayed by contrary winds.

New Guinea was strange and foreign, unused to visitors. There were savage tribes over the bay, although the natives of Dorey itself were friendly enough even if they did not understand Malay. This made building a house difficult. Gesture succeeded, however, where language failed, and in three days Wallace, his Malays and some dozen local Papuans had built a house, not on stilts over the water like most of the village, but inland. The day after the house was finished, the schooner departed, leaving Wallace the only European inhabitant in the whole of New Guinea. At first he and his men slept with loaded guns beside them, but after a few days they realized that such precautions were unnecessary. But once more Wallace had bad luck, and for a month he was kept indoors by an inflammation of the foot. His men had fever, dysentery or ague. This was disappointing in a place where no naturalist had ever lived before, in the land of the birds of paradise. Even when he was able to get about again, he was disappointed by the scarcity of colourful birds and insects: only beetles were abundant.

But it was from New Guinea that a new genus of deerflies *Phytalmia* (*Elaphomyia*) came. One of them, a dark brown and yellow fly with broad flat horns of pink, bears his name *E. wallacii.* He collected the brilliant rose chafer *Ischiopsopha* (*Lomoptera*) *wallacei* and the rat-like marsupial *Myoictis meeas wallacei.* He noticed red and black lories and a black cockatoo, differing from the more usual yellows and greys of the western parrots and, in contrast, the pale cream, crowned pigeons and the pale papilios. Birds of paradise however were not common. Most of them lived far inland and he was only able to get the Lesser Bird of Paradise *P. minor* (*papuana*) at Dorey. The Lesser Bird of Paradise resembles the Greater which Wallace had already caught on Aru, but it is smaller and generally lighter and more yellow in colour.

His disappointment in New Guinea seems to have been, to a large extent, the result of the unfortunate time he spent there, with so much illness, because when he got back to Ternate and laid out all his New Guinea birds for his Dutch friends to see "Even I myself was surprised at the beauty of the show when thus brought together and displayed on the white table, which so well set off their varied and brilliant colours" (I 364). Amongst them were the owlet nightjar *Aegotheles wallacii wallacii* and the blackish long-tailed lory *Charmosyna papou* and another fruit pigeon, *Ptilonopus iozonus*.

But apart from fever, the death of one of his men, and inflamed feet, Wallace's main recollections of New Guinea were the ants. There were ants everywhere, swarming over the table, carrying away specimens and tearing them from the cards. They drove him nearly frantic. To prevent them from running up the table legs and swarming over his specimens, he learnt to put the legs of the table in cocoa nut shells filled with water, and this ensured some immunity from attack from below. There was still the likelihood of attacks from flies, dogs, rats, cats and other vermin. The bluebottles teemed on bird skins and laid their eggs firmly glued to the feathers. What was to have been one of his most exciting visits and the most fascinating of all the islands to a naturalist had turned into a depressing nightmare. It was with great relief that he boarded the *Hester Helena* at the end of July and left New Guinea.

In December 1857 Wallace had visited the Moluccas for the first time, and it was amongst these islands that he made his headquarters for three years. He found a house on Ternate to which he returned time and time again to pack up his collections and prepare for the next expedition. His first sight of the Moluccas was the small island of Amboyna. "Passing up the harbour, in appearance like a fine river, the clearness of the water afforded me one of the most astonishing and beautiful sights I have ever beheld. The bottom was absolutely hidden by a continuous series of corals, sponges, actiniae, and other marine productions, of magnificent dimensions, varied forms, and brilliant colours. . . . In and out among them, moved numbers of blue and red and yellow fishes, spotted and banded and striped in the most striking manner, while great orange or rosy transparent medusae floated along near the surface. It was a sight to gaze at for hours, and no description can do justice to its surpassing beauty and interest. For once, the reality exceeded the most glowing accounts I had ever read of the wonders of a coral sea" (MA I 463). But on the whole, the animals of Amboyna resembled those of the more easterly Aru islands and, apart from scarlet lories and a few outstanding kingfishers, he did not add much to his collections there. After a month, he continued his journey northwards among the Moluccas, to Ternate.

Ternate is a small conical volcanic island off the coast of the then almost unknown island of Halmahera, one of the largest of the group. During this first visit he made short collecting trips to Halmahera. Here, in spite of continual illness, he made a good collection of insects, and Ali shot "one of the most beautiful birds of the East, *Pitta maxima* (*gigas*), a large ground thrush, whose plumage of velvety black above is relieved by a breast of pure white, shoulders of azure blue, and belly of vivid crimson" (MA II 16). This proved to be a species distinct from the nearby Ternate jewel thrush *P. cyanonota* and the Bouru *P. rubrinucha*. The following July, whilst exploring the Moluccan island of Batchian, he found the hitherto undescribed bird of paradise, *Semioptera wallacii* or Wallace's Standard Wing. "I saw a bird with a mass of splendid green feathers on its breast, elongated into two glittering tufts; but, what I could not understand was a pair of long white feathers, which stuck straight out from each shoulder. . . . I now saw that I had got a great prize, no less than a completely new form of the Bird of Paradise" (MA II 41). There was also the magnificent golden-capped black sunbird *Hermotimia* (*Nectarinea*) *auriceps,* and the coppery green Nicobar pigeon, a bulky ground-living bird, several marsupials and "one of the most gorgeously coloured butterflies in the world", the entirely new *Papilio* (*Ornithoptera*) *croesus,* with a wing span of more than seven inches, its velvety black wings marked with fiery orange. "On taking it out of my net and opening the glorious wings, my heart began to beat violently, the blood rushed to my head, and I felt much more like fainting than I have done when in apprehension of immediate death. I had a headache for the rest of the day, so great was the excitement produced by what will appear to most people a very inadequate cause" (MA II 51).

For Wallace the chief characteristic of the Moluccas was the predominance of pigeons, parrots and kingfishers, which formed by far the largest proportion of birds. As he had already observed on Aru, the pigeons and parrots reach their greatest diversity of anywhere in the world in the eastern part of the Malay Archipelago, varying in colour and form from island to island. The metallic green fruit pigeons *Ptilonopus,* for example, hardly extend westwards of the Moluccas and are notably split into island species. Jewel thrushes *Pitta,* and kingfishers also have their island species here.

Three times between 1857 and 1861 Wallace visited Timor, an island which he grouped in *Malay Archipelago* with Bali and Lombok. His first visit was only for a day. But on the other two he spent two weeks at the western end of the island and three months at the eastern. In Coupang he stayed with a German doctor in the town. Knowing little German, he began by talking French, but soon they passed into Malay, a language in which they conversed successfully on many scientific and philosophical subjects.

Ornithologically, Timor had already been well worked by French and Dutch expeditions, and Wallace's chief collections were concentrated, therefore, on pigeons and orioles, of which he found some new species. His most interesting Timor catches were papilio butterflies. Some of these proved to be related to those he had already caught on Celebes, some to Malayan forms and one of the endemic species to an Australian. Noting that the endemic papilio with Australian affinities differed more from its relatives than did endemics related to Malayan forms, he observed that "change of species is a slow process" (MA I 322) and concluded, therefore, that the Australian form was an earlier arrival on the island than were the Malays.

By the time of his final visit to Timor in 1861 he was becoming tired of perpetual travelling and recurring illness, and he wrote to his brother-in-law: "I assure you I now feel at times very great longings for the peace and quiet of home—very much weariness of this troublesome, wearisome, wandering life. . . . My health, too, gives way, and I cannot now put up so well with fatigue and privations as at first" (M I 179). And of the fauna he could write "with one or two exceptions, the birds of this tropical island were hardly so ornamental as those of Great Britain."

There only remained the large, comparatively highly civilized islands of Java and Sumatra and the small Banca to visit. It was amongst these islands that he spent the last six months of his stay in the Malay Archipelago.

Java was so much more civilized and cultivated than anything he had been used to for the past seven years that he found it difficult to find the native fauna. Travel was usually by carriage, not the ideal way for a naturalist, and he had to go high up into the centre of the island to find what he was looking for. In Java he was back in the region of pheasants, fine peacocks and rare green jungle fowl, *Gallus varius* (*furcatus*). There were woodpeckers and hornbills, and at the western end, among the coffee plantations, some forty species of birds proved peculiar to Java. In the dark ravines he captured the butterfly *Papilio arjuna*, "whose wings seem powdered with grains of golden green condensed into bands and moon-shaped spots" (MA I 177). A tiger was killed nearby and he hoped to be able to get its skull, but the hunters ripped it to pieces to get out the teeth to wear as decorations, and the skin was ruined by their spears.

But the charms of the naturalist's life were wearing thin indeed and he had decided to go home. "I shall no more be obliged to carry about with me that miscellaneous lot of household furniture—bed, blankets, pots, kettles and frying pan, plates, dishes and wash basin, coffee-pots and coffee, tea, sugar and butter, salt, pickles, rice, bread and wine, pepper and curry powder, and half a hundred more odds and ends, the constant looking after which, packing and repacking, calculating and contriving have been the standing plague of my life for the last seven years," he wrote to his mother from Java in July 1861 (M I 84).

Before he landed on Sumatra at the beginning of November 1861 he spent a few days on Banca, where he found yet more species of jewel thrush *Pitta*. Two species were new and confined to the island.

Sumatra is a land of monkeys, long-tailed, white, black and grey, Old World monkeys without the prehensile tails and flat noses of the South American forms. There are gibbons and the flying colugo *Cynocephalus* (*Galeopithecus*). The colugo is found only in the Malay region where it lives in trees, feeding at night on leaves. A membrane of soft fur extends round the body from the neck to the end of the tail, including the limbs. "It rests during the day clinging to the trunks of trees, where its olive or brown fur, mottled with irregular whitish spots and blotches, resembles closely the colour of mottled bark, and no doubt helps to protect it" (MA I 210). Here too were more Malayan papilios, the large *P. memnon*, "a deep black colour, dotted over with lines and groups of scales of a clear ashy blue," whose females may be like the male in shape though they vary in colour from black to nearly white, or may more nearly resemble a related species, the spoon-tailed *P. coön*, which also lives in Sumatra.

In January 1862 he was back in Singapore. He had spent eight years in the Malay Archipelago. They were years of hardship and danger, and they had been endured by a man who described himself as having no physical courage. His calm descriptions of these adventures belie this as much as the fact of the voyages themselves, but his own interpretation of this endurance was given in some notes he made for an address to the Linnean Society on his return: "Of real dangers I say nothing—for I do not believe that with proper precautions there is more danger in one part of the world than another. 'Familiarity breeds contempt' of dangers as well as of persons—and a picture might be drawn of the terrors of London Streets—with their mad bulls and mad dogs, their garrotters, runaway cabs and falling chimneys—that would make an inhabitant of tiger infested Java or run-a-muck Macassar thank his stars he was not a Londoner and wonder how people could be foolhardy enough to live there" (Linn. Soc.).

He may have made light of the physical dangers of the islands, but what was always one of the most frustrating of hazards was the constant assorted illnesses that not only lowered his general resistance to the primitive living conditions and poor food, but kept him in the house when he wanted to be out catching animals. With illness and the time spent on such domestic duties as building houses, Wallace estimated that he had lost two of the eight years he spent in the Archipelago. Six years seem to have been enough to collect so many new species that he expected it would take him the rest of his life to describe them, although, as he wrote to Bates, there was enough exploring and collecting to do in the Malay Archipelago to occupy twenty years (M I 70). Altogether, he collected a total of 125,660 different species of animals, the actual number of specimens amounting to many more, often five times as many. The greater part of the collections were made up of beetles, a group in which he was still particularly interested.

Not all of these thousands were new species. Some had already reached Europe from this part of the world, others were examples of species already well known from other places. Some were entirely new however. He found, for instance, at least 900 new species of Longicorn beetle (large beetles with long antennae whose larvae live in wood), and 200 new species of ants, as well as some new species of most of the other sorts of terrestrial animals. His interest in fish, however, seems to have waned.

Of the sixty-six species of birds which he collected in two months on the island of Bouru, seventeen were new ones. And some of his specimens were the only ones of their kind. A calliper butterfly from Java, *Eriboea dehaani* (*Charaxes kadenii*), was still the only representative of its kind in an English collection in 1869 and another, *Prothoë* (*Nymphalis*) *calydona* from Malacca was the sole specimen in England for twelve years.

Some of his more interesting finds he described on the spot, sending home his descriptions to be published in the *Proceedings* of the Entomological or the Zoological Societies. "Perhaps the most elegant butterfly in the world," the velvety black and green spotted *Trogonoptera* (*Ornithoptera*) *Brookiana* was named by him after Sir James Brooke of Sarawak. He described the drongo bird of Celebes, *Dicrurus hottentotus leucops,* and the pigeon *Ptilonopus iozonus humeralis.* But he soon gave up describing the new species he found. There were too many. He left the task of description to others, many of whom, in recognition of his work, named the species after him.

Wallace's collections were not valuable for their extent and novelty alone. During his work on the Amazon he had become aware that at least part of the value of a specimen lies in the exact description of its habitat and its exact location, and his success in supplying this information led to his collections being ranked amongst the most important of all time.

On 20th January 1862 he left Singapore for England. Besides his collections, he took with him two living Lesser Birds of Paradise and a few lories, bought from a Chinese merchant in Singapore. Such birds had rarely been seen alive in Europe and it was this that encouraged Wallace to try to get them home. They caused him considerable anxiety. The railway from Suez to Alexandria was now open and used in preference to the road. But it was only after considerable persuasion that the railway officials agreed to let live birds travel on it. In the Mediterranean even worse difficulties were encountered. There were no cockroaches on the ship. Without cockroaches it was impossible to provide his charges with an adequate diet, and so he had to break his journey at Malta. For a fortnight he stayed there in a hotel close to a bakery where an unlimited supply of cockroaches could be obtained. The rest of the journey, in spite of the cold of the Mediterranean and the frost in France, was uneventful, and the two birds of paradise were brought safely to the Zoological Gardens in London.

Wallace reached London on 1st April 1862.

Scientific Works from the Malay Archipelago

While he was in the Malay Archipelago Wallace was a regular contributor to learned journals, some forty-three papers and letters being published between 1854 and his return to London in 1862. He was, by 1854, a corresponding member of the Royal Entomological Society and a Fellow of the Geographical Society and he kept in touch with them by letters as well as by more learned papers. His agent, Mr Stevens, frequently exhibited samples of his collections to the Entomological and Zoological Societies. Many of his written contributions were descriptions of journeys or descriptions of the capture of some particularly interesting specimen. Several early ones were devoted to the orang utan of Borneo, including an account of adopting a baby orang utan that he grew very fond of during the three months he was able to keep it alive. He described a new flycatcher from Celebes *Denbrobiastes rufigula*, and the brightly coloured lustrous jewel thrush *Pitta rubrinucha* from Bouru, as well as many less outstanding birds and insects from almost every island he visited.

At the same time, others were identifying and describing the new species which he continued to send home without his own description on them. The *Proceedings* of the Zoological Society from the years 1858 to 1861 contain at least three papers in each year devoted to descriptions of new birds, insects, molluscs and mammals "captured by Mr A. R. Wallace". Many of these were given the specific names *wallacei* or *wallacii*. There was the fruit pigeon, *Ptilonopus wallacei* from Aru (Gray 1858b), a beautiful green and grey bird, a kingfisher from Sula, *Ceyx lepidus wallacii* (*C.wallacei*), the big mound-making megapode *Eulipoa wallacei*, the land snail *Truncatella wallacei* from Waigiou and the rat-like marsupial *Myoictis melas wallacei* from Aru; and to give some variation on the name there is the kingfisher from Aru *Ceyx azureus wallaceanus* (Gray 1858, 1860, Adams 1865). At the meetings of the Entomological Society, "a box of Lepidoptera taken at Sarawak by Mr Wallace," was exhibited by Mr Stevens, and with appropriate modifications in the wording, this was a common entry in the *Proceedings*. His collections were being bought by the British Museum and by private collectors.

He attempted at this time to reclassify the passerine birds. In 1856 almost all living birds were classified together as the Passeres, a group which included birds ranging from parrots and humming birds to cuckoos and sparrows. Following a modified Cuvierian system, the group Passeres was subdivided, mainly according to the nature of the beak formation. There were thus the Conirostres, cone beaks (starlings, finches), the Dentirostres, tooth beaks (tanagers, flycatchers), the Tenuirostres, slender beaks (humming birds, sunbirds), Fissirostres, split beaks (swallows, kingfishers) and the Scansores or climbers (cuckoos, parrots).

While on the Amazon Wallace had commented on beak formation in birds, although at that time he was mainly surprised at the variety of beak structure in birds with similar feeding habits. "It must strike everyone, that the numbers of birds and insects of different groups, having scarcely any resemblance to each other, which yet feed on the same food and inhabit the same localities, cannot have been so differently constructed and adorned for that purpose alone" (A 58), he had written in 1853. Further experience, of the Malay birds, had driven him to the conclusion by 1856 that a classification of birds based primarily on beak structure was not altogether satisfactory, for not only did birds with different beaks feed on the same food, but conversely other birds with very specialized feeding habits had come to resemble one another in their beak structure even though they might not be similar in other respects. Beak structure, he concluded, was not a reliable basis for classification.

Primarily, he argued that the majority of the Cuvierian subdivisions were, in fact, collections of unrelated birds, alike in beak formations, because of similar habits, but not alike in many other and equally important ways. He proposed, therefore, to abolish all but the groups Fissirostres and Scansores, both of which he felt had some justification for retention. He considered in detail the grounds for abolishing the Tenuirostres, and from this he implied similar reasoning for the break up of the other groups. Cuvier had grouped in the Tenuirostres the humming birds and the sunbirds, and now Wallace showed that this, like the other groups, was an artificial arrangement. He argued that the similarity of beak structure in the humming birds and sunbirds was an elaborate adaptation to similar feeding habits. Both the New World humming birds and the Old World sunbirds are small brilliantly coloured nectar-eating birds. Both have long slender beaks for probing the flowers on which they feed; both often resemble flowers in their colouring. Other structural features were not at all alike and, therefore, he argued that the two groups showed no natural affinity with one another. It was like classifying together two red books instead of two by the same author.

Already then in 1856 Wallace was arguing about natural affinity, evolutionary affinity. So, following Bonaparte (1850) he put the humming birds with the swifts instead of with the sunbirds, showing that humming birds and swifts had characteristics in common such as the structure of the sternum, and the arrangement of the feather tracts. He saw the importance of using apparently insignificant characters in tracing affinities, while ignoring the more easily adaptable features such as, in this case, the beak and the colouring which had led the earlier classifiers astray. He was to elaborate this problem in later years, after the general acceptance of the theory of evolution by natural selection (TN 156). The humming birds then were to be taken out of the Passeres and made into the order Micropodiiformes with the swifts. The sunbirds were to remain in the order Passeres. And today this classification stands with only minor modification (Peters 1931, Mayr & Amadon 1951).

In 1859 he made a further contribution and attempted to clarify the "chaos which had so long existed in ornithology", by sorting out the parrots. He argued that the Trichoglossinae, the brush-tongued parroquets, of the eastern part of the Malay Archipelago, are really lories and should be classified with them whilst the cockatoos should be put with the parrots proper. In 1864(c) he went further, removing the whole parrot group from the Scansores and "... I am now quite convinced that they deserve to rank as a primary division of the class Birds...."

Modern ornithologists agree in ranking the parrots as a distinct order, the Psittacidae, but there is still a good deal of dispute about the rank of the groups within this order. Some (Mayr & Amadon 1951) would group all parrots into one family, others (Peters 1931) would divide them into subfamilies, separating off the lories as Wallace did but also retaining the separation of cockatoos from parrots proper. The chaos may not be as extensive as when Wallace found it, but there is still a measure of disorder.

For the birds in general the tendency has been to continue the splitting that Wallace was advocating. All the old subdivisions have been broken up and the birds are divided into thirty-one different orders.

For the rest, Wallace's works at this time fall into two main categories, those which have a bearing on the geographical distribution of animals and those which were directly related to the problems of the origin of species. It is obvious that these two categories are interdependent in a sense but, because they lead towards two separable achievements, they can be conveniently discussed separately.

In September 1855 there appeared in the *Annals and Magazine of Natural History* a paper entitled *On the law which has regulated the introduction of new species* written by Wallace in February of that year whilst he was staying at the mouth of the Sarawak river, at the foot of the Santubong mountain. "I was quite alone, with one Malay boy as cook, and during the evenings and wet days I had nothing to do but to look over my books and ponder over the problem which has rarely been absent from my thoughts" (I 354).

This paper was the outcome of his efforts to combine the views of Sir Charles Lyell on inorganic change with his personal observations of living things over the world. Commenting on Lyell's view, expressed in the *Principles of Geology* (1830-33), that the present state of the inorganic world was the result of a series of changes that had been going on since the earliest periods and were still going on, he wrote in his notebook (Linn. Soc.), ". . . it would be most unphilosophical to conclude without the strongest evidence that the organic world so intimately connected with it [the inorganic world], had been subject to other laws which have now ceased to act, and that the extinction and production of species and genera had at some later period suddenly ceased."

The 1855 paper put forward his convictions that evolution had, in fact, taken place. But, instead of supporting this contribution with the broad generalizations usually cited, that one large class of animals had probably been derived from another in direct succession, Wallace treated of evolution at the species level, feeling his way towards the reasons for the origin of species.

He visualized evolutionary history as the branching of a tree, the branches constantly dividing and giving rise to new twigs. In this he was closer to Lamarck's concept of evolution than to either the more generally held Aristotelian idea of the ascent of a straight ladder by a series of jumps, the great chain of being of Leibniz, or to the recently popular polarity theory of the eminent naturalist Edward Forbes. The polarity theory postulated that change occurred from geological periods of fossil abundance to others of poverty, the abundance in the earliest known geological periods and again the abundance in recent times representing the two opposite poles of a sphere which were the Natural Design. The changes originated in the operation of an organizing principle.

Wallace argued against these theories. He stressed on the one hand that living species are usually separated from one another by many intermediate forms and do not, therefore, follow the Aristotelian pattern of separateness, and, on the other hand, that it was impossible to follow Forbes's theory based on abundance and scarcity of fossil species when paleontological knowledge was obviously inadequate for making such a decision.

Those who did believe in the evolution of animals, and they were comparatively few, had tended to concentrate on the large, distinctive groups of animals. They were interested to show that vertebrates had been evolved from insects, for instance, or that Crustacea had given rise to fish, through the intermediate primitive pro-fish fossil, *Cephalaspis*. This concept of the evolution of one dominant group of animals from a pre-existing dominant group as distinct from its evolution from more obscure primitive ancestors was slow to die. Many reputable biologists in the early days of the present century were led to ridiculous hypotheses to account for the origin of chordates from invertebrate ancestors because of their adherence to this doctrine.

Both Wallace and Darwin were interested in the evolution of species, evolution on the small scale, which by its cumulative effect could give rise to large scale changes. Wallace believed that one species divided into two, or more, new species, and the original one then became extinct. The new species evolved not from the most highly specialized species but from "anti-types" that were "the same lower organised species which have served as the antitypes of the former group, but which have survived the modified conditions which destroyed it (the former species). . . . It is evidently possible that two or three distinct species may have had a common antitype, and that each of these may again have become the antitypes from which other closely allied species were created. The effect of this would be, that so long as each species has had but one new species formed on its model, the line of affinities will be simple, and may be represented by a straight line. But if two or more species have been independently formed on the plan of a common antitype, then the series of affinities will be compound, and can only be represented by a forked or many branched line. Now, all attempts at a Natural classification and arrangement of organic beings show, that both these plans have obtained in creation" (1855).

He made these deductions from his own observations of the geographical distribution of species and varieties, and from his knowledge of the vertical distribution of fossils in the rocks. For instance, he had been particularly struck by the fact that in a geographically restricted group, the most nearly allied species were likely to be found in closely adjoining localities, like the groups of monkey, butterfly and fish species he had studied along the Amazon. In very much the same way he argued from the facts of geological distribution, that when the species of any one genus occurred in the same geological epoch they were more closely allied to one another than they were to those separated from them by several geological ages. He argued, too, from his knowledge of speciation on islands, from Darwin's observations on the Galapagos Islands, and in a somewhat curious way from the presence of rudimentary organs in animals.

From all this it seemed reasonable to conclude that the closely related species had arisen from a common antitype or even from one another. The natural law that he enunciated in this paper reads as follows: "Every species has come into existence coincident both in space and time with a pre-existing closely-allied species." A case for the evolution of species from species had been closely and very effectively argued. What caused this evolution remained a mystery to him. He realized that what was needed was an explanation of the mechanism of the phenomenon, but he was not yet able to supply it. At this stage he wished to put on record his conviction that evolution of species did, indeed happen, through natural causes, that the observed facts supported the supposition, and that it was now necessary to find an explanation of the facts. He was prepared for criticism, open to suggestions, but only willing to give attention to arguments based on observable facts such as he himself had collected. He knew his paper would be unpopular. "As his (the writer's) hypothesis is one which claims acceptance solely as explaining and connecting facts which exist in nature, he expects facts alone to be brought to disprove it, not *a priori* arguments against its probability."

The 1855 paper had a disappointing reception, so disappointing, that it seemed to Wallace that it had not been noticed. As he had considered it of "some importance", the almost silent reception was discouraging. One of the earliest comments he received was hardly one to make him enthusiastic. Mr Stevens wrote saying that several naturalists had expressed regret that he was "theorising" when what "was wanted was to collect more facts". Two years later, however, he received, in July 1857, an encouraging comment from Bates who was still collecting on the Amazon. "I was startled at first to see you already ripe for the enunciation of the theory. You can imagine with what interest I read and studied it, and I must say that it is perfectly well done. The idea is like truth itself, so simple and obvious that those who read and understand it will be struck by its simplicity; and yet it is perfectly original.... Few men will be in a condition to comprehend and appreciate the paper, but it will infallibly create for you a high and sound reputation. The theory I quite assent to" (M I 64).

A few months later he received a letter from Darwin with which "I have been much gratified". Darwin had written to him in May: "I agree to the truth of almost every word of your paper; and I daresay that you will agree with me that it is very rare to find oneself agreeing pretty closely with any theoretical paper ... I can plainly see that we have thought much alike and to a certain extent have come to similar conclusions" (M I 129). This was the first letter Darwin wrote to Wallace, and it was the beginning of a long and cordial correspondence.

Later, in answer to a letter from Wallace, Darwin was to write: "You say that you have been somewhat surprised at no notice having been taken of your paper in the *Annals*. I cannot say that I am; for so very few naturalists care for anything beyond the mere description of species. But you must not suppose that your paper had not been attended to; two very good men, Sir C. Lyell, and Mr E. Blyth at Calcutta, specially called my attention to it. Though agreeing with you on your conclusions in the paper, I believe I go much further than you; but it is too long a subject to enter on my speculative notions" (M I 132).

And so, as in many similar cases, recognition of this early paper as a major contribution was long in coming. It was only after the whole mechanism of evolution by natural selection had been accepted that its real value was recognized. Thus, Lyell wrote to Wallace on 4th April 1867: "I have been reading over again your paper published in 1855 in the *Annals* . . . passages of which I intend to quote . . . because there are some points laid down more clearly than I can find in the work of Darwin itself, in regard to the bearing of the geological and zoological evidence on geographical distribution and the origin of species" (M II 21). And many years later Huxley wrote: "On reading it afresh I have been astonished to recollect how small was the impression it made" (Huxley 1903).

But, "That paper is, of course, only the announcement of the theory, not its development," he wrote to Bates in January 1858 (M I 66), and for the next three years Wallace was turning over in his mind the problem of speciation, trying to discover how species evolved from one another and why, in spite of the considerable variability to be found in nature, the species kept distinct, having their own food preferences, habits and habitats, as well as the more obvious morphological characteristics on which the systematist depends for his classification.

Although he was not able, as yet, to determine the causes which underlay the divergence of species, he felt sure that natural causes must be responsible and that those naturalists who denied it were confusing cause with effect. His notebook for 1855 shows him feeling a way towards the solution of this perplexing question. In trying to disentangle this knot he commented on an article which he had read on the number of vertebrae in the necks of birds: "Again how can any man venture to say that, the cause of the different number of cervical vertebrae in different birds is that '*their peculiarities required it*'. Is it not just possible that some totally different causes absolutely hidden from us determined the form and structure of the animals, and that their wants and habits resulted from that structure? It is not easy to see, how a bird could have *habits* and *wants* before it had neck bones, as it must have had if the number of these bones depended on its wants and habits." Later he stated: "the structure of Birds is not varied in accordance with their habits; but that, on the other hand, they are necessitated to adopt certain habits in order to obtain a subsistence in accordance with the peculiar circumstances by which they are surrounded" (Linn. Soc.).

But it was perhaps his increasing knowledge of the distribution of species on islands that provided him with the most insistent proof of speciation. He could not ignore what he observed; he must find an explanation for it. Experience showed that islands had species of their own, but species which were more like those of neighbouring islands than like anything further away.

Two papers written a little later show him putting forward arguments against creation, and in favour of evolution by natural causes on this basis. In *On the natural history of the Aru Islands,* published in 1857, he pointed to the similarity in climate and vegetation of New Guinea and Borneo and concluded that, according to the views of Lyell, the same species should exist on the two islands. This was markedly not so. New Guinea had none of the woodpeckers or trogons of Borneo and Borneo had no cuscuses or cassowaries. But if species were brought into being from pre-existing species by natural causes, they would evolve from those which had inhabited their island in earlier time, and only from those. The further apart the islands, the more different their species might be expected to be, irrespective of climate and vegetation, since they would not have shared a common ancestor for a very long time. The length of time would be more or less correlated with the distance between them. And so, since no ancestral woodpeckers lived on New Guinea there were none today, but far away Borneo, which had been colonized by woodpeckers that had come possibly from nearby Malaya, could be expected still to have them. Wallace was arguing from his own observations that species had evolved from one another and had not, therefore, been created individually.

In 1858 a paper entitled *Note on the theory of permanent and geographical varieties* appeared in the *Zoologist.* In this Wallace argued that the quantitative differences between two species may not be more than between two varieties or between species and variety, and he defined a species as "every group of individuals presenting permanent characters, however slight". On the whole, most naturalists would probably have agreed that varieties had not been specially created. Therefore, he argued, it seemed absurd to suppose that species had been.

And so February 1858 is reached, and the writing of the paper which was to bring the theory of natural selection before the scientific world and which stimulated the completion of the *Origin of Species.*

Wallace was in Ternate, in the Moluccas, suffering from a bad attack of intermittent fever. He had to spend most of every day lying down, and during this enforced idleness, he had nothing to do but think about subjects that particularly interested him. One day he recollected the arguments used by Malthus in his *Essay on the Principle of Population,* the book he had read many years ago when a schoolmaster in Leicester. It was obvious, as Malthus had realized, that many more young animals were produced every year than ever survived to maturity. And so Wallace wondered why some died and others did not. The answer was, again obvious, that those lived which were best suited to the particular environmental conditions in which they found themselves. The most resistant escaped disease and the fleetest of foot escaped being eaten. "Then it suddenly flashed upon me that this self-acting process would necessarily *improve the race*, because in every generation the inferior would inevitably be killed off and the superior would remain—that is, *the fittest would survive*" (I 362).

He considered this idea in relation to the views of Lamarck and those of the author of the *Vestiges* and decided that his ideas supplemented theirs, and smoothed out all the important difficulties which these authors had not been able to overcome. That night and on the succeeding two evenings, he wrote *On the tendency of varieties to depart indefinitely from the original type.* He expanded the thoughts he had had whilst suffering from fever; he considered in more detail the constant natural checks which must occur to counteract the constant overproduction of offspring. "The life of wild animals is a struggle for existence.... Now, let some alteration of physical conditions occur in the district.... The superior variety would then alone remain ... and occupy the place of the extinct species and variety.... Here then, we have progression and continued divergence." He described how, in the field, the members of any one species, although quite distinct from any other species, were different from one another often to a considerable degree. Here, in the wild state, could be seen the variability from which a selection could be made, a situation long recognized in domestic animals where artificial selection had been carried on for years. "Even the peculiar colours of many animals, more especially of insects, so closely resembling the soil or leaves or bark on which they habitually reside, are explained on the same principle; for though in the course of ages varieties of many tints may have occurred, *yet those races having colours best adapted to concealment from their enemies would inevitably survive the longest*."

Wallace sent the manuscript of this paper to Darwin with a covering letter. To send it to Darwin was the obvious thing to do, for he knew, from the two letters he had already received, that not only was Darwin interested in the species problem, but also that he approved wholeheartedly of the articles Wallace had already written. In his letter Wallace expressed the hope that Darwin would find the idea as new as he had himself found it. He asked him, if he thought it sufficiently important, to show it to Sir Charles Lyell.

Darwin received the paper on 18th June 1858 and was completely overcome by this "bolt from the blue". Here, in a nutshell, was his theory of the origin of species on which he had been working since 1839. His terrible disappointment can be imagined—his immediate feelings that nearly twenty years' work had been wasted "so my originality is smashed, though my book, if it will have any value will not be deteriorated" as he wrote to Lyell. It can have been little consolation to him to remember that both Dr Hooker and Sir Charles Lyell had been constantly urging him to publish what he had begun to write in 1844 so that he should not be forestalled in just such a way. At first he decided that Wallace's paper must be published immediately; his own work should take second place, though it naturally disappointed him greatly to be forestalled in this way. Before acting, however, he consulted his friends, Hooker and Lyell, on the best course to follow. They had a better solution, for they were fully aware that Darwin had had this idea of the natural causes underlying species formation probably before Wallace had even collected his first beetle in Leicestershire. In addition, there was written evidence of the trend of Darwin's thoughts, in the unpublished manuscript, and also in a letter which Darwin wrote to the American botanist, Professor Asa Gray, on 5th September 1857.

Lyell and Hooker took it upon themselves, therefore, to decide what action should be taken, so that the rights of both Darwin and Wallace would be protected and each would be given credit for an idea which was of the greatest importance. It says a great deal for the generosity of these Victorian scientists that Lyell should put his name to a communication, the implications of which he did not at this time accept; that Darwin should wish to publish Wallace's paper immediately; and that Wallace, when he heard of the affair (months later), should have equally wished that Darwin had published his work first.

On 1st July 1858 the Linnean Society of London met under the chairmanship of Dr Thomas Bell to hear *On the tendency of species to form varieties; and on the perpetuation of varieties and species by natural means of selection* by Charles Darwin Esq., F.R.S., F.L.S., and F.G.S. and Alfred Wallace Esq., communicated by Sir Charles Lyell, F.R.S., F.L.S., and J. D. Hooker Esq., M.D., V.P.R.S., F.L.S., etc. First a letter was read from Lyell and Hooker pointing out that Darwin and Wallace might both "fairly claim the merit of being original thinkers in this important line of inquiry", and that Lyell and Hooker had thought fit to publish the news in this way, "Both authors having put the matter unreservedly into their hands". This was followed by an extract from Darwin's manuscript, part of a chapter entitled *On the variation of organic beings in a state of nature; on the natural means of selection; on the comparison of domestic races and true species,* in which these words occur: "the amount of food for each species must, *on an average,* be constant whereas the increase of all organisms tends to be geometrical" and "Let external conditions of a country alter . . . in such a case the original inhabitants must cease to be as perfectly adapted to the changed conditions as they were originally". In a variable population those individuals with any small advantage would be the ones that survived. Then follows a short paragraph on sexual selection. After this, an abstract was read of the letter Darwin had written to Asa Gray: "I think it can be shown that there is such an unerring power at work in *Natural Selection,* (the title of my book), which selects exclusively for the good of each organic being." Finally came the paper that Wallace had written in Ternate.

Neither Darwin nor Wallace was present at this meeting, the one owing to family illness, the other because he was some twelve thousand miles away. The communications were read by the Secretary of the Society, as was the custom, and both Sir Charles Lyell and Dr Hooker said a few words. No discussion took place. "The subject was too novel, too ominous, for the old school to enter the lists before armouring," Hooker wrote to F. Darwin (1887).

The old school may have kept quiet in 1858, but there is no doubt that the papers read on 1st July made a deep impression and prepared the ground for the reception of the *Origin of Species* which everyone now knew would appear before long. Even so, the President could say in his address the following year: "The year has not, indeed, been marked by any of those striking discoveries which at once revolutionize, so to speak, the department of science on which they bear" (Bell 1859). There is no doubt that both men gained by the joint publication of their papers. Had Wallace's paper crept unannounced into a scientific journal it might have been ignored, like his paper of 1855, except by Darwin himself who would have found himself forestalled. And there seems little doubt that for Darwin this publication was advance publicity for his great work. Huxley wrote to Hooker, "Wallace's impetus seems to have set Darwin going in earnest, and I am rejoiced to hear we shall learn his views in full, at last. . . . Ever since Darwin and Wallace had made their first joint communication to the Linnean Society in July 1858, expectation had been rife as to the forthcoming book" (Huxley 1918).

Wallace, writing much later (1903), says: "The one great result which I claim for my paper of 1858 is that it compelled Darwin to write and publish his *Origin of Species* without further delay" (I 363).

Although many were awaiting the promised book before taking sides, some were prepared to take up the fight against this new doctrine at once. The Rev. S. Haughton addressed the Geological Society in Dublin in February 1859: "This speculation of Messrs Darwin and Wallace would not be worthy of notice were it not for the weight of authority of the names [Lyell and Hooker] under whose auspices it has been brought forward. If it means what it says, it is a truism; if it means anything more, it is contrary to fact" (Darwin 1887).

Meanwhile, Wallace had heard of the event through letters from Darwin and Hooker, "two of the most eminent naturalists in England, which has highly gratified me." Darwin wrote to him on

6th April 1859: "You cannot tell how I admire your spirit, in the manner in which you have taken all that has been done about publishing our paper. I had actually written a letter to you, stating that I would *not* publish anything before you had published. I had not sent that letter to the post when I received one from Lyell and Hooker, *urging* me to send some MS to them, and allow them to act as they thought fair and honourably to both of us. I did so . . . Hooker . . . is a *full* convert and is now going immediately to publish his confession of faith . . . Huxley is changed and believes in mutation of species: whether a *convert* to us, I do not quite know" (M I 137).

On 24th November 1859 Murray published *On the Origin of Species by Means of Natural Selection, or the Preservation of favoured races in the struggle for life,* by Charles Darwin, M.A.

Natural Selection and Man

The Darwin-Wallace hypothesis was not the first to propound a theory of evolution; Wallace himself had written a paper in favour of the evolution of species in 1855, and in 1852 Herbert Spencer had argued forcibly in favour of a doctrine of evolution in an article, *The Development Hypothesis*. Before this, other scientists had believed in some sort of evolution, and many more had noticed that species grade into one another, the details of which have been examined by, for instance, Lovejoy (1936), Irvine (1955), Eiseley (1959), Himmelfarb (1959) and Glass, Temkin & Straus (1959).

It was not incompatible to believe in evolution while accepting the Aristotelian order of things. Aristotle had divided the animal kingdom into animals with red blood and animals without red blood, and he had thought of the different types of animals as arranged up a ladder within these two major groups, each type being separated from the one below it and from the one above. Any change that might occur in the form of the animals was dependent on an inherent creative force which could advance an animal to a different grade of organization. Such an advancement, not left to chance, was determined. Thus, while there could be change along the Aristotelian ladder, progress from one rung to the next, this change would be sudden and complete and the result of the intervention of a directively creative force. In spite of this possibility, however, most people believed that the ladder of life was fixed and immutable.

Not until the eighteenth century does any great change seem to have occurred in this way of thinking. By then attention was being focused on small structural changes within related groups of plants or animals. Animals might not leap up the ladder but, equally, species might not be immutable. Buffon, in 1749, ventured to state that "these imperceptible differences can be found, not only as differences of size and of form, but also as differences in movements and between succeeding generations of all species". Oliver Goldsmith, who was presumably influenced by the famous French naturalist, wrote in 1776: "Nature is varied by imperceptible gradations, so that no line can be drawn between any two classes of its productions, and no definition made to comprehend them all." In 1790 Erasmus Darwin wondered whether "some animals change their forms and gradually become new genera?"

By the beginning of the nineteenth century there were some who looked for a cause for the changes they supposed to occur in living organisms. In 1803 in *The Temple of Nature* Erasmus Darwin made this clear in rhyming couplets.

> Organic life beneath the shoreless waves
> Was born, and nurs'd in ocean's pearly caves;
> First forms minute, unseen by spheric glass,
> Move on the mud, or pierce the watery mass;
> These, as successive generations bloom,
> New powers acquire, and larger limbs assume;
> Whence countless groups of vegetation spring,
> And breathing realms of fin, and feet, and wing.

Six years later Lamarck wrote in *Philosophie Zoologique* "a change of environment forcing the individuals of a race to change their habits, the less used organs perish slowly, whilst those that are at an advantage develop more and acquire a vigour and a size proportional to their use" and "at the end of many successive generations, those individuals which belonged originally to another *species*, find themselves in the end transformed into a new *species*, distinct from the other". In this, Lamarck, like Erasmus Darwin, retained the Aristotelian concept of a vital impulse: individuals were always striving to become better adapted to their environment. The river bird which did not want to swim but was constantly near water made every effort to stretch and lengthen its legs. Individuals of the species were continually stretching their legs, and in each generation, longer legs were acquired, until the stilt legs of the storks and flamingos were brought into existence.

The movement of internal fluids was considered responsible for bringing about these changes, serving as an intermediary between the changed organ and the reproductive organs.

Lamarck was, in other ways, the first to break away from the Aristotelian dogma. He reclassified the animal kingdom, and for the first time (1800) animals were divided into vertebrates (animals with backbones) and invertebrates (animals without), and the vertebrates were considered to have been derived from the invertebrates. Lamarck arranged the major animal groups into the order in which he considered they had evolved; thus, the majority of worms came before the insects and the polyps before the worms. He maintained that fossils were the precursors of existing species and that species changed into other species when they found themselves in new environments. These changes were the branching of the evolutionary tree, at the species level.

Lamarck believed in organic continuity and he had propounded, like Erasmus Darwin, a theory of the origin of heritable characters, but the mechanism was not generally acceptable. Without an acceptable mechanism it seemed that the world would not be convinced of the likelihood of evolution, would not abandon the creation hypothesis. Sedgwick wrote to Louis Agassiz in Switzerland on 10th April 1845: "... and when they talk of spontaneous generation and transmutation of species, they seem to me to try nature by an hypothesis, and not to try their hypothesis by nature.... But if no single fact in actual nature allows us to suppose that the new species and orders were produced successively in the natural way, how did it begin? I reply, by a way out of and above common known, material nature, and this way I call creation" (Agassiz 1885).

The American Dana in 1857 concurred with this view.

Other European naturalists were influenced by the abstract school of Naturphilosophie, of which Goethe was one of the most fluent exponents and Richard Owen in England was a disciple. The great chain of being arranged the natural world in order. An idea of plenitude tended to keep it static (Lovejoy 1936). But according to Naturphilosophie there could be continuity and change in the organic world as it had been seen by Leibniz. By the nineteenth century the change was seen as variation from or round an archetype, an ideal type, produced by the operation of an organizing principle. This led to theories of serial homology amongst others such that the skull was considered to be a modified vertebra or, recalling the polarity theory of species abundance, the head end and the tail end of animals were homologized. Always some ideal form had been the point of departure for the variations and the guiding force a mystical organizing principle. Comparison with archetypes or of new types with one another was all important, but it remained a comparison as, for instance, in the important observations of the embryologist von Baer that the earlier the stage in development the more closely did fish and mammal resemble one another. From this it followed that each living thing changed from the general to the special during its advance from egg to adult. von Baer made no evolutionary deductions, but it was his observations that later gave rise to the confusion of evolutionary recapitulation in the hands of the Darwinian, Haeckel, and which stimulated Herbert Spencer to his theory of human evolution.

Inorganic evolution, in contrast to organic, was gaining more support during this time.

Kant in *Theorie des Himmels,* written in 1755, had expressed the view that the inorganic world at least could have reached its present state by the working of natural causes, although he was less enthusiastic in applying natural change to the organic world, "from this raw matter and its forces, the whole apparatus of Nature seems to have been derived according to mechanical laws. . . . Yet this apparatus, as seen in organic beings, is so incomprehensible to us, that we feel ourselves compelled to conceive for it a different principle. But it would seem that the archaeologist of Nature is at liberty to regard the great Family of creatures . . . as having sprung from the immediate results of her earliest revolutions, judging from all the laws of their mechanisms known to or conjectured by him."

Others, too, were prepared to entertain the possibility of the evolution of the earth by natural causes whilst dismissing such an explanation for plants or animals. In the Neptunist-Vulcanist controversy the Neptunists considered rocks to be precipitations from solution or suspension, the precipitations occurring once or in succeeding ages. The Vulcanists favoured a dynamic changing earth crust brought about by the interaction of sedimentation and a hot subsurface layer of the earth. Hutton, the founder of Vulcanism, had argued in 1795 in *The Theory of the Earth* that cumulative small effects could produce changes and could supersede the necessity for divine intervention. He neither supported nor denied creation.

It was this general idea that was developed by Lyell in *Principles of Geology* in which he assembled overwhelming evidence in favour of inorganic evolution. Although at that time he did not believe that there was evidence of similar natural causes being responsible for organic evolution, nevertheless, in the second volume of the *Principles* he summarized Lamarck's views on evolution and the mutability of species.

Such evolutionary theories of inorganic change were in direct contrast to those of Cuvier, the most influential of all early nineteenth-century paleontologists. His theory of catastrophes supposed that species were created, overcome by catastrophe, new ones were created until once again catastrophe eliminated them and "none of the agents that she [Nature] now employs were sufficient for the production of her ancient works" (Cuvier 1817).

Mainly then, men searched for absolute design in the universe, and those who took a more relative view or a more dynamic view were the exception. But it is interesting to notice that as early as 1834 the University of Munich had offered a prize for a thesis on the "causes of the mutability of species" (Rádl 1930).

By the middle of the nineteenth century, therefore, only a few seeds of evolutionary theory had been sown. Before the fact of evolution could be acceptable to a wider following, a mechanism had to be postulated. The Erasmus Darwin-Lamarck mechanism had met with a poor response. The Charles Darwin-Wallace mechanism provided an acceptable answer.

There seems little doubt that the formulation of the theory of natural selection was stimulated in both Darwin and Wallace by, on the one hand, their awareness of the selective breeding of domestic animals practised pre-eminently in England since the eighteenth century (Watson & Hobbs 1951), and on the other hand by their awareness from experience in the tropics of the amount of variability between individuals in the wild, and finally by their understanding of the implications of the *Essay on the Principle of Population* written by Malthus in 1798.

Malthus argued mainly from human populations that living beings increasing faster than the food supply are checked by the scarcity of available food and, in extreme cases, by famine. The earth's resources are limited while the inherent tendency of human populations is to increase. By failing to see that both eaten and eaters would be subject to the same problems of scarcity, Malthus himself did not become the originator of a theory of evolution by natural selection.

The newness of the 1858 theory was, therefore, that it provided an acceptable natural cause, natural selection, to account for evolution. This, with the fitting together of so many biological facts, made evolution seem so much the more probable. Natural selection, with evidence from distribution, from domestic breeding, variability, paleontology and general anatomy, made evolution suddenly acceptable to those of a liberal way of thinking. A year later, the *Origin* was sold out on the day of publication (1,250 copies) and caused a revolution in the thought, not only of the biologists, but also of many of the less scientific men of the day, and this in spite of the fact that the book according to Darwin himself "is a very good book, but oh! my gracious, it is tough reading" (Darwin 1887).

The geological principles of Lyell, the embryological observations of von Baer, the many anomalies of geographical distribution, and the findings of the new science of paleontology invented by Lamarck and Cuvier, all fell into a coherent pattern when they were woven into the framework of evolution, and the mechanism for it came from the Malthusian doctrine of population increase and check. "Innumerable well-observed facts were stored in the minds of naturalists ready to take their proper places as soon as any theory which would receive them was sufficiently explained" (Darwin 1887). Dr Hooker and Mr Huxley were immediate converts to the idea of natural selection after the 1858 papers. They were followed by the naturalists, J. Lubbock and H. W. Bates, the American botanist Asa Gray, Robert Chambers of the *Vestiges* and the philosopher Herbert Spencer, whilst many well-known geologists, including eventually Lyell, came to accept the theory. "We wanted not to pin our faith to that or any other speculation, but to get hold of clear and definite conceptions which would be brought face to face with facts and have their validity tested. The *Origin* provided us with the working hypothesis we sought. . . . My reflection, when I first made myself master of the central idea of the *Origin,* was, 'How extremely stupid not to have thought of that!' I suppose that Columbus' companions said much the same thing when he made the egg stand on end. The facts of variability, of the struggle for existence, of adaptation to conditions, were notorious enough; but none of us had suspected that the road to the heart of the species problem lay through them, until Darwin and Wallace dispelled the darkness, and the beacon-fire of the *Origin* guided the benighted," wrote Huxley to F. Darwin (1887).

Opponents of the Darwin-Wallace hypothesis were equally exuberant. Louis Agassiz wrote in 1860: "Until the facts of Nature are shown to have been mistaken by those who have collected them, and that they have a different meaning from that now generally assigned to them, I shall therefore consider the transmutation theory as a scientific mistake, untrue in its facts, unscientific in its method, and mischievous in its tendency." The Rev. S. Haughton maintained that: "the naturalists who have accepted by multitudes the new theory of the origin of species are, as a class, untrained in the use of the logical faculties, which, however, they may charitably be supposed to possess in common with other men" (Darwin 1887). The mathematician Herschel pronounced that "it is the law of higgledy-piggledy" (Irvine 1955), and a botanist that it was "the most short-sighted, the stupidest and most brutal theory imaginable, with which a modern buffoon and bearer of false witness could seek to make himself interesting" (Schimper in Rádl 1930).

In spite of the opposition, the theory of evolution by natural selection was to hold its place in biological thought. One of the implications of this theory and the one responsible for much of the emotional outburst against it was that man was an animal and had come into existence as part of the general evolutionary sequence as a result of the operation of natural selection.

A most enthusiastic convert to the theory was Herbert Spencer, who gave to natural selection the tag "survival of the fittest", and who attempted to apply the doctrine to society as a whole. He argued that each man was responsible for his own and no one else's conduct, the strongest would survive, the weakest would go under. G. E. Moore and Huxley and Wallace himself took a less simple-minded view of the application of the theory to human society. Moore pointed out that there was no way of determining that he who survived in a competitive society, Spencer's fittest, was the Best, nor, even if he could be considered to be the most highly evolved in biological terms, need he necessarily be the Best in social terms. Huxley and Wallace emphasized that man was a social animal and that natural selection became modified to adapt a social group as a whole to new conditions; each animal for itself was not strictly compatible with social life. Furthermore, social life is in some senses only an extreme example of conditions within any discrete population. In neither case is it a question of only the "fittest" surviving. It is the fit that survive.

Soon after the publication of the *Origin,* Huxley had written *Man's Place in Nature* (1863) in which he argued that man should be considered as an animal, not essentially different from any other animal, but more advanced, more complex. In the same year Lyell in *The Antiquity of Man* had traced human fossil remains back as far as he could and estimated that man had probably originated in the pliocene. He made some guarded remarks about the evolution of man: "But will not transmutation, if adopted, require us to include the human race in the same continuous series of development, so that we must hold that Man himself has been derived by an unbroken line of descent from some one of the inferior animals?"

In the following year Wallace brought out a paper in the *Anthropological Review* in which he argued that natural selection applied to the evolution of man, and he showed how it could have operated. He argued that man's physical evolution probably took place first, in the early days, and after that his mental qualities as a social animal became the features on which natural selection acted, the physical characteristics then changing rather little. Upright carriage, in fact, would come before further enlargement of the brain. "But man, under similar circumstances, does not require larger nails or teeth, greater bodily strength or swiftness. He makes sharper spears, or a better bow, or he constructs a cunning pitfall, or combines in a hunting party to circumvent his new prey. The capacities which enable him to do this are what he requires to be strengthened, and these will, therefore, be gradually modified by 'natural selection', while the form and structure of his body will remain unchanged" (NS 314). Wallace had applied natural selection to man. With minor reservations, Darwin was delighted with this statement. "The latter part of the paper I can designate only as grand and most eloquently done. I have shown your paper to two or three persons who have been here, and they have been equally struck with it." Wallace's arguments differ comparatively little in general outline from those used today, with greater knowledge to draw on. That upright carriage evolved before great increase in intelligence is a generally acceptable hypothesis.

In other ways Wallace's views at this time came to be modified. For instance, at first he disagreed with Lyell over the antiquity of man, putting him back to the miocene, on the grounds that it must have taken time for him to evolve. "We have no reason to suppose that mind and brain and skull modification, could go on quicker than that of the other parts of the organization; and we must therefore look back very far in the past, to find man in that early condition in which his mind was not sufficiently developed to remove his body from the modifying influence of external conditions and the cumulative action of 'natural selection'" (NS 323). Later he revised these ideas and came round to the modern view that man must have evolved very rapidly, probably since the early pleistocene as no earlier fossils had been found (1876). Curiously enough, Wallace believed that man originated in Africa, a theory which has had factual basis only since the discovery of Australopithecine fossils in Africa from 1925 onwards (Broom & Schepers 1946, Le Gros Clark 1955, Leakey 1959).

In 1866 Wallace appealed to the Anthropological Section of the British Association to study man scientifically, but in spite of this a gradual change was coming over his own views. Spiritualism and the supernatural, which had interested him years ago in Leicester, were becoming of greater importance in his life. His ideas on the evolution of man gradually became affected by this belief in spirits, and by 1869, they had found expression in print. The following year they were enlarged on further.

This was a great blow to Darwin and Huxley, who felt they had lost their most valuable ally in the campaign for evolution, natural selection, and man as an animal. They agreed with Wallace's early views, that man had evolved as the result of selective forces in much the same way as other animals had done, taking into consideration that man had become a social animal, and that at some stage selection for intelligence had become more intense than selection for other characteristics. But Wallace had changed. He had ceased to believe that natural selection could account for the whole of man. "But there is another class of human faculties that do not regard our fellow men, and which cannot, therefore, be thus accounted for. Such are the capacity to form ideal conceptions of space and time, of eternity and infinity—the capacity for intense artistic feelings of pleasure, in form, colour, and composition—and for those abstract notions of form and number which render geometry and arithmetic possible. How were all or any of these faculties first developed, when they could have been of no possible use to man in his early stages of barbarism? How could 'natural selection', or survival of the fittest in the struggle for existence, at all favour the development of mental powers so entirely removed from the material necessities of savage men, and which even now, with our comparatively high civilisation, are, in their farthest developments, in advance of the age, and appear to have relations rather to the future of the race than to its actual status?" (NS 352). The highly developed artistic and moral qualities of modern man could not be put down to natural selection. For one who followed Robert Owen in his belief that the environment of man was a strong determining force in a man's lifetime this may seem a strange conclusion to reach. And yet it is not necessarily in itself so surprising. It is perhaps difficult to see how natural selection would specifically bring into being artistic and moral feelings, and Wallace's insistence on this has seemed to one recent critic (Eiseley 1959) more reasonable than what he terms the rigidly mechanistic view of other Darwinians.

Wallace, however, did not stop at pointing out the difficulty. He sought an explanation of it. And it was this explanation that was so surprising, coming from one who had not only lost his belief in orthodox religion but who had first suggested that traditions could form part of a cultural inheritance in animals. He proposed that the mental evolution of man had been taken over by a force other than natural selection; a spiritual force. "The inference I would draw from this class of phenomena is, that a superior intelligence has guided the development of man in a definite direction, and for a special purpose. . . ."

Although he says later in the same article of 1869: "I must confess, that this theory has the disadvantages of requiring intervention of some distinct individual intelligence, to aid in the production of what we can hardly avoid considering as the ultimate aim and outcome of all organized existence—intellectual, ever-advancing, spiritual man".

There seems little doubt that Wallace's plunge into spiritualism and its consequent effect on his views on human evolution damaged his reputation amongst many scientific men. Darwin who was preparing the *Descent of Man* at this time wrote to Lyell: "What a good sketch of natural selection! but I was dreadfully disappointed about Man, it seems to me incredibly strange . . . and had I not known to the contrary, would have sworn it had been inserted by some other hand. But I believe that you will not agree quite in all this" (Darwin 1887). And Darwin wrote to Wallace: "But I groan over Man—you write like a metamorphosed (in retrograde direction) naturalist, and you the author of the best paper that ever appeared in the *Anthropological Review*! Eheu! Eheu! Eheu!—your miserable friend C. Darwin!" (M I 251).

In 1871 the *Descent of Man* was published, and Darwin stated his conviction that "I have now endeavoured to shew that some of the most distinctive characters of man have in all probability been acquired, either directly, or more commonly indirectly, through natural selection" and "Natural selection arising from the competition of tribe with tribe, in some large area as one of these, [Australia, Borneo] together with the inherited effects of habit, would, under favourable conditions, have sufficed to raise man to his present position in the organic scale." But in 1889 Wallace still maintained his belief in a subsequent spiritual direction to the course of human evolution even though he was still willing to allow the early stages to have evolved by straightforward natural selection.

The difference in viewpoint between Darwin and Wallace was given a final and very adequate summing up by Wallace in 1905. "On this great problem the belief and teaching of Darwin was, that man's whole nature—physical, mental, intellectual, and moral—was developed from the lower animals by means of the same laws of variation and survival; and as a consequence of this belief, that there was no difference in *kind* between man's nature and animal nature, but only one of degree. My view, on the other hand, was, and is, that there is a difference in kind, intellectually and morally, between man and other animals; and that while his body was undoubtedly developed by the continuous modification of some ancestral animal form, some different agency, analagous to that which first produced organic *life,* and then originated *consciousness,* came into play in order to develop the higher intellectual and spiritual nature of man" (II 17).

In other ways Wallace was very much opposed to complicating the theory of natural selection by the addition of special interpretations to explain special cases, and in no other subject of scientific interest did he allow himself reference to spiritualism.

Speciation

Throughout the whole of his career, Wallace generously attributed the theory of natural selection to Darwin and to Darwin alone. It was probably as much for this reason as for any other that Wallace's own name tends to be forgotten in this context. Wallace insisted to Darwin: "I shall always maintain it to be actually yours and yours only. You had worked it out in details I had never thought of, years before I had a ray of light on the subject, and my paper would never have convinced anybody or been noticed as more than an ingenious speculation, whereas your book has revolutionised the study of natural history, and carried away captive the best men of the present age. All the merit I claim is the having been the means of inducing *you* to write and publish at once" (M I 158). Wallace's consistent use of the term Darwinism to describe the theory culminated in his book *Darwinism,* published in 1889, seven years after Darwin's death.

In *Darwinism* Wallace reviewed the state of the subject up to date. He gave his definitive views on the value of the theory of natural selection as an explanation of problems of animal evolution, ranging from the history of the species concept and its evolution, through problems of animal colour, distribution of animals in space and time, heredity and variation, to the origin of man.

At this time, the cause of variation in animals, both domestic and wild, was not understood. Darwin and Wallace had given a satisfactory explanation of the way in which the total environment could select, from amongst the variety of individuals in a population, those most fitted (best adapted) to survive. But Cope wrote in 1887 "this neat expression [survival of the fittest] no doubt covers the case, but it leaves the origin of the fittest entirely untouched." This was a just criticism. Variability was to be found amongst organisms in the wild state; variability was known in animals and plants under domestication. On this variability natural selection exerted a pressure that resulted in changes of species. But what was this variability and how was it brought about? How do organisms differ from one another? "...If, as I must think, external conditions produce little *direct* effect, what the devil determines each particular variation?" wrote Darwin to Huxley (Darwin 1887). Neither Darwin, nor Wallace nor Huxley could give any explanation.

Lamarck had supposed that the environment had just this direct effect on an animal, and further that the effect of the environment was enhanced internally by the movement of the "internal fluids" which in itself changed them. The more complicated the animal, the more rapidly did these "internal fluids" flow, and the more could the animal change. Darwin was not prepared to go as far as that, and Wallace at first rejected all idea of the inheritance of acquired characters. He maintained that the variability, though admittedly unaccountable, was spontaneous and presumably unrelated to the environment or to the needs of the animal. Darwin worried about the cause of variation, however, and eventually, and reluctantly, he came to accept Lamarck's views on the inheritance of acquired characters, but instead of the "willing and striving" of the animal and the flow of "internal fluids" he put forward his theory of pangenesis in 1868. This, though Darwin seems to have been unaware of it, was a modification of a theory that had been held from time to time through the years since Hippocrates. Darwin imagined pangenes as particles circulating in the body, which took the imprint of the cells in which they originated, were thrown off from these cells, reproduced themselves and, as a result of their distribution round the body became incorporated in all the other tissues including, of course, the gonads. Thus, the environment was able to make its impression on the germ cells, which would pass on this impression to the next generation.

When Wallace first read *Variation in Animals and Plants* he was delighted with pangenesis, because it was "a positive *comfort* to me to have any feasible explanation of a difficulty that has always been haunting me" (M I 196). But in spite of the comfort of pangenesis, neither Wallace nor Darwin was particularly enthusiastic about it. Although both of them accepted it as a working hypothesis they were prepared to reject it in favour of a better one, should such be found.

On reading summaries of the work of Weismann in 1886 Wallace immediately rejected pangenesis. Weismann studied the development of coelenterates and, as a result of his observations, maintained that the germ cells were laid aside early in life and were distinct from the body cells of all animals. The body cells played no part in the propagation of the species, and they had no inheritable effect on the germ cells. Therefore, changes in the adult body brought about in response to the environment could not affect the germ cells and could not be directly inherited. This theory appeared to dispose of Lamarckism and pangenesis.

In *Darwinism,* Wallace returned to his original views on the spontaneous nature of variation, making the observation that, on the whole, selection (the environment) works towards uniformity and harmony, variations supplying the diversity. These grounds alone, he argued, would be sufficient to reject any theory of the inheritance of characters acquired in response to an environmental stimulus. But he never put forward any theory to account for variation, although he recognized that natural selection could act only "through the universal facts of heredity and variation" (M II 101). What were these universal facts? Wallace saw that they had something to do with cross-fertilization, exemplified in sexual reproduction, and that they had something to do with inheritance. "This [mingling of characters] occurs in each generation; hence every individual is a complex result reproducing in ever-varying degrees the diverse characteristics of his two parents, four grandparents, eight great-grandparents, and other more remote ancestors; and that ever-present individual variation arises which furnishes the material for natural selection to act upon. Diversity of sex becomes, therefore, of primary importance as the *cause of variation*" (439). But the understanding of the causes of this variation, produced by cross fertilization, eluded him. Indeed, like so many others, he tended to become confused over the causes of variation and the causes of evolution.

Whenever a new theory was put forward to account for the causes of variation most nineteenth-century biologists regarded it as an alternative to natural selection. And like them Wallace would be up in arms, defending natural selection and showing how selection itself would cause differences to come about. Although this was true, there must still be a cause for variation in the first place; it must originate and it must be perpetuated. Wallace and Darwin had been the first to show that natural selection could only work on variability. But just as so many believe that Lamarckism is an alternative to Darwinism, when in fact Lamarckism would itself be useless without selection, so the various nineteenth-century theories about variation were considered to be alternatives to Darwinism. Admittedly, most of these theories were not convincing—fundamental laws of growth and decay (Geddes 1886), spontaneous variability (Bennett 1870) or Lamarckism under a new guise—but they all appeared to be an attack on Darwinism, and were in fact usually put forward with just such a purpose. But Wallace did not seem to see that causes of variation and natural selection were not antagonistic, and that each was essential to the other. Darwin and he had seen it when they accepted Lamarckism and pangenesis, for Lamarck's theory provided a cause for variability not for the whole of evolution, but somehow this seemed to get forgotten. It was probably because of this fundamental confusion that the work of Gregor Mendel was overlooked when it was first published in 1865.

In 1900, the works of Mendel were discovered and their value was recognized at once by many who were working on the problems of heredity. Mendel had argued in 1865, that an organism possesses factors which determine each of its characteristics and which exist in pairs. Each member of a pair, though it may not have exactly the same effect as the other member, is concerned in the determination of the same characteristic as its fellow member. Every organism contains many pairs of factors. Only one of a pair of factors is passed into any one germ cell so that the progeny of a mating receive half their factors from their mother and half from their father. The factors retain their individuality and are passed on from generation to generation "those characters which are transmitted entire, or almost unchanged in the hybridisation, and therefore in themselves constitute the characters of the hybrid, are termed the *dominant,* and those which become latent in the process *recessive*" (Bateson 1909). The factors were shown to be inherited in an orderly and predictable way and assorted and shuffled independently of one another. "The constant characters which appear in the several varieties of a group of plants may be obtained in all the associations which are possible according to the laws of combination, by means of repeated artificial fertilisation." By the inheritance of these numerous factors the progeny would retain a general resemblance to their parents but would be likely to vary from them and from one another to some degree by reason of the shuffling and chance combinations of the pairs of factors.

A little before Mendel's work was discovered, de Vries had proposed a theory of mutation in which he suggested that random heritable changes occurred in the germ cells. These changes he called mutations. They were large and sudden changes in hereditary material, spontaneous in origin, and the cause of the appearance of entirely new forms, even of new species, in one dramatic jump. According to this theory, evolution would proceed in explosions instead of in the smooth continuous way envisaged by Darwin and Wallace.

Wallace, who was nearly eighty by this time, did not see that the Mendelian and de Vriesian theories might be exactly what the natural selection theory of evolution needed for its completion. Once more he, and others, looked on rules of variation as alternatives to natural selection, not as the missing link in the whole argument. It was in this frame of mind that he wrote in 1908: "The claim of the Mutationists and Mendelians as made by many of their ill-informed supporters, are ludicrous in their exaggeration and total misapprehension of the problem they profess to have solved." He also urged that neo-Lamarckism and Mendelism in no wise affected the truth and stability of the natural selection theory. In attacking those who rejected natural selection in favour of Mendelism or mutation, he himself failed to see the importance of these new ideas. But he did not reject them outright. His main attack was against the abandonment of natural selection in favour of the new theories, and his failure was in not adding them up into the modern conception of the process of evolution. He was willing to admit that the laws of Mendel explained the inheritance of certain factors, but to him it seemed that they did not provide for enough variability. This was understandable, because no one knew how many Mendelian factors there were in an organism, but Wallace knew from experience how much variability there was amongst the members of a species. It was not until many years later that it was shown that there are thousands of factors involved in the make up of an organism and that these can be assorted, shuffled and dealt in so many ways, through sexual reproduction, that they can give rise to immense variety from which the environment can select. "But the essence of Mendelian characters is their rigidity. . . . Moreover, when crossed they reproduce the same pair of types in the same proportions as at first and therefore without selection; they are antagonistic to evolution by continually reproducing injurious or useless characters," he wrote in 1909 (M II 92). And, of course, in a sense this is true, but only half true.

According to Mendelian laws, inheritable factors are all the time being mixed by sexual reproduction so that quite often injurious or useless characters may show up. But these either will be weeded out or kept at a low frequency by natural selection, so that they will not be damaging to the species as a whole. The multiplicity of the Mendelian factors and their variability provide a reserve from which new combinations are being thrown up to be tested by natural selection. Every now and then a superior combination will be thrown up and favoured by selection at the expense of others. And so this will go on, new environments selecting out new combinations of factors. A species must have a reserve of variability, in the form of Mendelian factors, if it is to survive changes in environment, changes in the direction of natural selection. Selection is a conservative force as many earlier naturalists, such as Lyell and Buckland, had observed. Mendelian factors and their mode of inheritance, together with mutation, are a diversifying force. Thus the two are antagonistic, but such an antagonism is necessary for the establishment of a dynamic equilibrium which forms the basis of evolution.

Neither Wallace nor Darwin lived to see the emergence of what has been called neo-Darwinism, the welding together of Mendelian and Darwinian theories and the expansion of both to take in new developments. De Vriesian mutations proved a misunderstanding of the material, but mutations on a much smaller scale have been shown to be responsible for increasing the diversity of the genetic material of a species. But mutations do not normally lead to explosive bursts of evolution as de Vries believed; they can be small enough to produce only small changes. The gradualness of Darwinism is not jeopardized by the acceptance of the theory of mutation. The Darwinism of 1889 has been enormously added to.

Although Darwin's great work was called *On the Origin of Species by Means of Natural Selection*, he never actually defined a species, and still less did he provide an acceptable hypothesis to account for the actual formation of a new species. Both he and Wallace were much more interested in the general implications of their theory: that evolution could be brought about by natural means; that species could slowly change their form in time. Within a species there were varieties, or as Darwin called them "incipient species" which could gradually form into species themselves. One variety within a species would gradually become adapted to a slightly different set of conditions from another variety within the species. When the intermediate and original types became extinct because they were not adequately adapted, two new species had been made out of the one.

Wallace pushed the definition of a species further. In 1864 he concluded that "when the differences between two forms inhabiting separate areas seems quite constant, when it can be defined in words, and when it is not confined to a single peculiarity only, I have considered such forms to be a species . . . contact without intermixture being a good test of specific difference" (NS 142). Most definitions of species are based on a criterion of fertility or sterility. Members of a species are all fertile with one another and sterile with members of other species. Such definitions obviously have both theoretical and practical limitations. As Wallace made clear, fertility is the sort of quality that cannot usually be tested in the wild, and still less when a species is determined from one dead specimen.

Modern definitions recognize that species, at any given moment, are at all stages of evolution from their relatives, and the definition needs to fit such a dynamic situation. Some species have diverged from their nearest relations much more than others have done. Some, therefore, will show no possibility of interbreeding with their relatives, whilst some may show only partial sterility. To some extent it is just a matter of time whether two groups will or will not interbreed. But a species can be defined for convenience as a group of organisms which does not normally interbreed with its nearest relatives, a definition which is practically the same as that adopted by Wallace in 1889 (167). The origin of a new species, therefore, involves the coming into existence of a group of animals or plants which do not only look different from their nearest relatives but which also do not interbreed. In theory it is not necessary for the groups to look distinct, although in practice it is usually found that they do have some morphological differences.

It is implicit in the *Origin* that new species can evolve from varieties in a large freely mixing population, but how this is brought about was not considered in any detail. But the question of whether a large population could actually break into two parts, each part ceasing to breed with the other, formed a subject for considerable correspondence between Wallace and Darwin. Wallace pointed out, and Darwin agreed, that if two varieties in a population interbreed freely then there can be no possibility of two species being formed from them. He then suggested to Darwin that if there were partial sterility between the two forms, the hybrids would be less effective (be fewer in number and leave fewer offspring) than the two parent varieties, and eventually the two forms, adapted each to a slightly different environment, would form two species. "It appears to me that, given a differentiation of a species into two forms, each of which was adapted to a special sphere of existence, every slight degree of sterility would be a positive advantage, not to the *individuals* who were sterile, but to *each form*". A month later he wrote: "It is admitted that *partial sterility* between *varieties* does occasionally occur. It is admitted the *degree* of this sterility *varies*. Is it not probable that Natural Selection can accumulate these variations and thus save the species" (M I 205, 196).

Darwin did not agree; he took the view that anything that lowered the fertility of the original population as a whole would be at such a disadvantage that it would be weeded out by natural selection and could never become established to divide up the population into two separate species. "Lessened fertility is equivalent to a new source of destruction," he wrote (M I 207). Wallace did not feel strongly enough about it to carry the argument any further. He took the view that Darwin was probably right, although there might still be some cases where his own proposals would work, in particular in cases where very many offspring were produced and where a slight reduction in fertility could hardly matter.

Today the subject is in much the same state. There are more biologists on Darwin's side than on Wallace's, but the question is still open. Whilst it is generally agreed that sterility as such is not very likely to be favoured at once by natural selection, there may be circumstances when it can be established in an otherwise more or less interbreeding population. Selective mating, changes in reproductive behaviour for instance, might lead effectively to a cessation of interbreeding which might not be eliminated if it did not lower the fertility of the two groups as a whole. The fertility would only be markedly lowered if mating took place regularly between the two varieties. But if such mating were prevented by change in behaviour pattern there might not be so much wastage (Carter 1951). This is a question that has not been decided and waits on experimental evidence which is at present too sparse to provide an answer. What does seem to be true, however, is that very high fertility is not always a necessity for survival. Wallace believed "that number of offspring is not so important an element in keeping up population of a species as supply of food and other favourable conditions, because the numbers of a species constantly vary greatly in different parts of its area, whereas the average number of offspring is not a very variable element" (M I 210). Whereas Darwin believed that "I look at the number of offspring as an important element (all circumstances remaining the same) in keeping up the average number of individuals within any area. I do not believe that the amount of food by any means is the sole determining cause of numbers" (M I 207). Modern work on fluctuations in numbers of birds has suggested that food is probably the most important determining factor but, curiously enough, the fertility, the actual number of eggs laid, is adjusted to the amount of available food (Lack 1954). As Wallace implied there is often a reserve of fertility.

If then there is still no agreement on the evolution of sterility in a continuous population, what is the modern concept of species formation, and did either Wallace or Darwin have any alternative views? The modern answer, according to Rensch (1933), Mayr (1940, 1942), is that before two species can be formed out of one population, the population must be divided into two by physical barriers. Mayr takes the view that sterility cannot arise in the one population effectively to break it into two. There must be geographical isolation of the two groups, as for instance on islands. The two groups then go their own ways, becoming adapted to their different circumstances and sterility factors may or may not accumulate between the two; but there will not be any selection in their favour, they will merely be the result of divergence to suit other conditions (Moore 1955).

Both Darwin and Wallace were well aware of conditions prevailing on islands. Darwin had noticed that distinctive finches of the genus *Geospiza* occurred on the different islands of the Galapagos Archipelago; Wallace had observed of the jewel thrushes, *Pitta,* in the Molucca Islands: "They are interesting as showing the permanent modifications in form of these semi-terrestrial birds, in islands within sight of each other" (1862). He observed: "Here [Oriental region] we find all the conditions favourable to the development of a rich and varied fauna. The land is broken up into great peninsulas and extensive islands; lofty mountains and large rivers everywhere intersect it; while along its northern boundary stretches the highest mountain range upon the globe" (T N 319).

In spite of these observations the nineteenth-century naturalists did not ascribe to such physical isolation the prime importance that tends to be accorded to it today, in the process of species formation. Darwin conceded that evolution of species isolated on islands had occurred: they had changed because the environment was different on each island. He concluded, however, that, on the whole, evolution in a small population, such as could be found on a smallish island, would not be as likely to occur as in a large population on a continent. "Lastly isolation, by checking immigration and consequently competition, will give time for any new variety to be slowly improved; and this may sometimes be of importance in the production of new species. . . . Although I do not doubt that isolation is of considerable importance in the production of new species, on the whole I am inclined to believe that largeness of area is of more importance" (Darwin 1859). There is much truth in this assertion, for a small population may indeed be too small to produce enough variability for selection. On the other hand, in a large population the variability tends to be swamped. Mathematical estimates of the optimum size for a rapidly evolving population favour a medium-sized one, the size which might easily be found on a fairly large island (Wright 1943).

Wallace was more emphatic about the effects of geographical isolation than Darwin had been, and by 1889 he was writing: "Complete isolation, as in an oceanic island, will no doubt enable natural selection to act more rapidly for several reasons. In the first place the absence of competition will for some time allow the new immigrants to increase rapidly . . . while, of course, any intercrossing with the original modified stock would be absolutely prevented" (D 145). Wallace realized that if there were geographical isolation the evolution of species would probably follow but he did not think the converse to be necessarily true, that without geographical isolation there could be no speciation

He further realized that once varieties had been isolated in this way it was fortuitous whether they did, in fact, evolve into separate species, as Moore (1955) has shown to be true of frog species. "On the whole, then, we conclude that, while isolation is an important factor in effecting some modification of species, it is so, not on account of any effect produced, or influence exerted by isolation *per se,* but because it is always and necessarily accompanied by a change of environment, both physical and biological" (D 150).

Geographical isolation is not the only form of isolation that may exist between closely related species. There may be colour differences, behavioural differences, ecological differences, seasonal differences or differences depending only on incompatibility of the genes or chromosomes. Twentieth-century biology regards these isolating mechanisms as secondary. That is to say that they become important only when two species come to occupy the same territory once more, after the original geographical isolation has broken down (Blair 1955). The secondary types of isolation serve to keep the new species apart, by preventing any wasted effort going into useless attempts at mating, for instance. Wallace recognized several of these isolating factors, colour differences, and the tradition of learnt song in birds, but to him they were just as important as geographical isolation and could be responsible in themselves for separating two species. "The idea that either infertility or geographical isolation is absolutely essential to the formation of new species, in order to prevent the swamping effects of intercrossing, has been shown to be unsound, because varieties or incipient species will, in most cases, be sufficiently isolated by having adopted different habits or by frequenting different stations; while selective association, which is known to be general among distinct varieties or breeds of the same species, will produce an effective isolation even when the two forms occupy the same area" (D 185). Some naturalists would agree with him, but most follow Mayr in requiring an initial physical separation.

The origin of new species then depends on four main factors. There must be variability between individuals of the original group of organisms (shuffling of genes, changes in genes or in the chromosomes). There must be geographical isolation of the incipient species which is subsequently reinforced or replaced by other types of isolation, such as physiological or psychological incapacity to interbreed. There must be selection pressure exerted by the environment in which the groups live. Selection pressure may take the form of increased competition for food, increase in predators, change in climate or attacks from disease, or any form of competition between individuals or groups of organisms. Finally, there must be plenty of time. It may take something of the order of 500,000 years for a new species to be formed (Zeuner 1950).

Darwinism as expounded by Darwin and Wallace went a very long way to considering these problems. In fact, it is astonishing how few of the points they missed. They may not have known of the causes of variation nor have had much idea of the time involved in the evolution of species, but they realized that there must be variation, that natural selection worked on this and they came near to realizing the importance of isolation. Modern developments along all these lines have given rise to the modern theory of the origin of species—to neo-Darwinism.

London 1862 to 1869

Early in 1862 Wallace had returned from the east, assured of recognition by at least the more progressive of the leading biologists of the day. His paper on the theory of evolution by natural selection had given him a place in biological thought. He could be sure of ready admission to scientific societies, of meeting eminent scientists, of an interested audience for anything further he might like to write or say on natural history.

Publication and sale of his books was equally certain. Most of all he was pleased that he would be accepted by other scientists as one of themselves. But he had given little thought to lecturing, or writing on a big scale. For some reason he felt that he had no verbal ability, a defect which would make writing and lecturing both laborious to himself and uninteresting to his readers.

The proceeds from his Malay collections had exceeded his most optimistic expectations. They had been invested by Mr Stevens in Indian Railways and they could be expected to yield about £300 a year. In addition, he had his private collections in reserve which could be sold to provide another two or three hundred a year if necessary. He could afford to live without worrying about additions to his income. His immediate plans, therefore, were to sort out his collections and describe his many new species and, at the same time, illustrate the points of special interest shown by the animals of the islands of the Malay Archipelago so that one day he might produce a complete fauna of the area.

It took him some time to settle down. His health was poor, and the sheer hard work of unpacking and sorting thousands of specimens of birds and insects was a daunting prospect. In spite of this, by the beginning of May he was preparing a lecture for the Zoological Society. The live birds of paradise he had brought home had aroused a great deal of interest amongst those who saw them in the Society's gardens, and it was about them and his adventures in search of them, in New Guinea, Aru and the Moluccas that he spoke to the Zoological Society.

Membership of scientific societies, living in London and working frequently in the British Museum brought him in contact at this period with many of the leading intellectuals of the day, so that he could number amongst his friends and acquaintances a good proportion of the well-known names of Victorian England. In the first version of *My Life* he devoted five chapters to these people because, he said, it was during the ten years after his return from Malaya that he lived his most social life and, more important, it was during this time that the course of his life and his future work was largely determined. Many of the influences which were thus responsible were the results of discussions or of correspondence with other biologists.

Today, much of the interest of Wallace's friendship with his contemporaries lies in the correspondence that resulted. This is particularly true of his relationship with Darwin. Their surviving correspondence is large. It extends over the period 1857 to 1881 and covers discussions of many of the biological problems in which they were both interested. It becomes particularly detailed over those problems on which they did not agree, such as sexual selection, the evolution of man and the distribution of plants and molluscs. Published in their entirety in 1916 by Marchant, these letters form an instructive commentary on the course of biological thought in the middle years of the nineteenth century.

With no one else did Wallace have such a constant correspondence on mainly biological matters, although there remain letters written between him and Sir Charles Lyell, discussing problems of animal distribution, and between him and Herbert Spencer on the subjects of natural selection and land nationalization.

The writings of Herbert Spencer had so impressed both Wallace and Bates, that, some time during 1862, they called on the philosopher of evolution and natural selection to ask what he thought on the subject of the origin of life. "He was very pleasant, spoke appreciatively of what we had both done for the practical exposition of evolution, and hoped we would continue to work at the subject. But when we ventured to touch upon the great problem, and whether he had arrived at even one of the first steps towards its solution, our hopes were dashed at once"

(II 23). Throughout the following years Wallace occasionally visited Spencer in his Bayswater boarding house; he met him at Huxley's or at Lubbock's and he corresponded with him until his death in 1903. Wallace expressed his admiration for the philosopher in a letter to Darwin written in 1864: "I am utterly astonished that so few people seem to read Spencer, and the utter ignorance there seems to be among politicians and political economists of the grand views and logical stability of his works. He appears to me as far ahead of John Stuart Mill as J.S.M. is of the rest of the world, and, I may add, as Darwin is of Agassiz" (M I 150).

Ten years later, it was to Wallace that Spencer turned when he wanted someone to read the proofs of the first part of *The Principles of Sociology,* asking him for criticism "alike as naturalist, anthropologist, and traveller" (M II 27). At this time Wallace was greatly influenced by Spencer's outlook on social conditions. He had been impressed by his early works as long ago as 1853, and he was even more impressed by the way Spencer had taken up the advocacy of natural selection and applied it to the economic and social spheres. He was, indeed, so much impressed by Spencer's term "survival of the fittest", with its obvious appeal to the ordinary man, that he suggested to Darwin that it might be a good idea for them to use it in their future writings. "Natural Selection is, when understood, so necessary and self-evident a principle that it is a pity it should be in any way obscured; and it therefore occurs to me that the free use of 'survival of the fittest', which is a compact and accurate definition of it, would tend much to its being more widely accepted and prevent its being so much misrepresented and misunderstood" (1866 M I 172). Darwin agreed, remarking: "It is, however, a great objection to this term that it cannot be used as a substantive governing a verb; and that this is a real objection I infer from H. Spencer continually using the words 'Natural Selection'."

Very soon after Wallace came to live in London, T. H. Huxley invited him to his house, and a lifelong friendship began between them, although on many biological matters Wallace confessed to feeling overawed and inferior to Huxley. "This was due, I think, to the fact that the enormous amount of Huxley's knowledge was of a kind of which I possessed only an irreducible minimum, and of which I often felt the want. . . . With Darwin and Lyell, on the other hand, although both possessed stores of knowledge far beyond my own, yet I did possess *some* knowledge of the same kind, and felt myself in a position to make use of their facts and those of all other students in the same fields of research quite as well as the majority of those who had observed and recorded them" (II 39).

Huxley, his contemporary, became a personal friend. Probably Lyell, twenty-six years Wallace's senior, had the greatest influence on his future development as a biologist however. It was to Lyell that Wallace turned most frequently for advice at this time, and it was from Lyell's published work that Wallace sought help in the elucidation of animal distribution problems. It was Lyell, even more than Darwin, who encouraged Wallace to indulge in what the nineteenth century called biological philosophy and which was looked on as a very dubious occupation.

Wallace found the task of sorting and describing his collections much less attractive than he had anticipated. Even though the specimens themselves were a constant source of delight and wonder and even though they recalled the pleasures and the pains of his solitary wanderings, the numbers involved, some 3,000 bird skins of 1,000 different species, and insects by the thousand, began to appear too formidable a task to complete within a reasonable length of time. The theoretical approach to biology seemed more rewarding work.

As he sorted and classified his collections, he occasionally gave displays of bird skins which were much admired; and during 1863 he managed to write eleven separate scientific papers, mostly about birds. In this same year he gave an address to the British Association, an address in which he talked briefly on the geographical distribution of animal life.

At this time he began to think of his financial position. By 1864, he was giving a few lectures, and reviewing books, but it did not occur to him then that he would be able to live by writing or talking. He disliked lecturing, and the small success of his Amazon books did not encourage him to take up writing as a profitable career. In any case he did not feel that he had any aptitude in either direction, so when the secretaryship of the Royal Geographical Society fell vacant he applied for the post. Bates was the only other applicant, and Bates was successful. Wallace was not disappointed. He did not like the idea of regular employment, and he was genuinely pleased that the post should go to Bates. Not only did he consider that Bates was the better man for the job, but also he was pleased that it would bring his friend to live in London. Wallace himself would have more time for studying his collections. He was far too busy to give any further thought to money for the next five years.

He was still publishing descriptive papers regularly. The birds were being followed by the results of work on the butterfly and beetle collections. In 1864 and 1865, however, some of his most interesting theoretical scientific papers appeared.

In 1864 he wrote on the parrots of the Malay Archipelago, in the following year on the pigeons of the area. In both papers, he considered the factors at work in bringing about the diversity of these two groups of birds. In each case the richness in number of species in the Archipelago was far greater than in any other part of the world, in each case there were birds with exceptional colourings, and each group had species confined to particular islands. Two groups of widely different birds showed strikingly similar trends in adaptation.

In colour, the parrots were generally green varying into yellow, grey and red, "but as soon as we reach the Moluccas and New Guinea we find a new type of coloration appearing in both groups. Among the lories we find vivid red and crimson, sometimes with a remnant of green on the wings and tail, but often covering the whole plumage, varied with bands or patches of equally vivid blue or yellow, while the red sometimes deepens into a blackish-purple" (I 399). Similarly, the soft lilacs and browns of the pigeons turned to creamy white on New Guinea, golden green on Batchian and green grey on Aru. Different orders of birds thus showed similar outbursts of variation in an area largely remarkable for being an archipelago. Wallace explained this variation by applying to the pigeons and the parrots the laws of natural selection.

If natural selection were to account for the colours of these two groups of birds, what was the selective agent? What force could explain the outburst of colour on some islands or the sudden occurrence of decorative crests on both pigeons and parrots in New Guinea? What was the selective agent that caused otherwise brightly coloured birds to become black or white on some islands? There were black cockatoos on Aru, black lories and white pigeons on New Guinea.

Wallace saw in these parallel trends a negative force at work. He attributed the main phenomena not to any positive selective agent but to the total absence from the eastern part of the Malay Archipelago of arboreal carnivores, especially monkeys. The birds were not being eaten, and they could establish themselves over the area; therefore they did not need protective colouring which kept them more uniformly green or lilac in other areas, but they could radiate into new plumage adapted to a new set of environmental factors: "who would ever have dreamed that monkeys influenced the distribution of pigeons and parrots." At this time Wallace was not ready to suggest what other environmental factors might influence the colour variations. It was a subject to which he was to return.

Of equal interest was a similar survey of the Malay Papilionidae. Darwin commented on this: "I cannot conceive that the most firm believer in species could read it without being staggered. Such papers will make many more converts among naturalists than long-winded books such as I shall write if I have the strength" (M I 167). In this paper Wallace discussed at length the different species of papilio butterflies that occurred in the Archipelago, from the azure-winged *ulysses* of the easterly isles to the golden green *adamantius* (*macedon*) of Celebes and the tailed *coön* of the west, their relationship to one another, the curious phenomena of polymorphism and mimicry which they exhibited and their anomalous distribution within the area. He argued that all these curious features could be explained by the theory of natural selection and in no other way.

Although he was now writing important papers, praised by his friends, his work tended to be confined to particular groups of animals for which he had a personal preference. Everyone was waiting for something on a bigger scale. Darwin continually urged him to write a book about his experiences in the Malay Archipelago, a book that would be comparable to Bates's *The Naturalist on the Amazons*. The idea attracted Wallace, but he felt that the time had not yet come for the enterprise. "As to my 'Travels', I cannot bring myself to undertake them yet, and perhaps never shall, unless I should be fortunate enough to get a wife who would incite me thereto and assist me therein—which is not likely" (M I 166).

During these years Wallace's outside interests were still as wide as they had been when he first returned to England. His interest in the economics of Mill and Spencer continued, and any humanitarian project could be almost sure of his support. Thus, along with many of his scientific friends, he supported the Jamaica Committee of which Mill had become chairman. In 1865 Governor Eyre had put down a Negro uprising in Jamaica with great violence and had hanged a Negro Baptist minister. This had sharp repercussions in England; it divided the British public almost as much as the Jamaican. The radicals, liberals and humanitarians were horrified at the brutal murders, the Tories and Empire builders felt that Eyre was only upholding British power and prestige. The affair gave rise to an extraordinary amount of ill-feeling. "Goldwyn Smith called Ruskin 'a sentimental eunuch', and . . . the father of Herbert Spencer, dying of an overdose of laudanum, spent his last moments dreaming furiously of the whole affair" (Irvine 1955). Mill became the chairman of the Jamaica Committee which sought to indict Eyre for murder and had the support of Darwin, Wallace, Huxley, Spencer, Frederic Harrison, Leslie Stephen, John Morley, Goldwyn Smith and the working class leaders and radicals. In opposition to this committee the Tories formed the Governor Eyre Committee, under the chairmanship of Carlyle, and with the support of Ruskin, Tennyson, Kingsley and Dickens. The affair lingered on until 1868, and at the end of it the Jamaica Committee could claim nothing more than a theoretical victory.

It was only exceptional circumstances, however, that brought Wallace into active political life. Outside his scientific work his main interest became spiritualism and mesmerism. He visited mediums, made friends with convinced spiritualists, even arranged séances at his house in St Mark's Crescent, and he tried to interest biologists in the subject. For the most part they found this whim of his a bore and were not interested. He wrote to Huxley ". . . We meet every Friday evening, and hope you will come sometimes, as we wish for the fullest investigation, and shall be only too grateful to you or anyone else who will show us how and where we are deceived." Huxley replied: "I am neither shocked nor disposed to issue a Commission of Lunacy against you. It may be all true, for anything I know to the contrary, but really I cannot get up any interest in the subject. I never cared for gossip in my life, and disembodied gossip, such as these worthy ghosts supply their friends with, is not more interesting to me than any other" (M I 187).

Wallace was not discouraged by lack of support from those whom he would have liked to interest in the subject. Instead, he collected together the evidence of miracles and supernatural phenomena from as many sources as possible and published them in 1886 under the title *The Scientific Aspect of the Supernatural.* The book was not well received. Those of his friends who made any comment merely wished that he had taken an experimental approach to the subject and had written about his own experiences instead of collecting together ghost stories and unexplained phenomena of animal behaviour. They dismissed the event as one of Wallace's fads. To many who had welcomed natural selection as a good materialist philosophy, the defection of one of its originators to the spiritual world was a sad blow. Rather than reject natural selection, many of them rejected Wallace as a result. Wallace himself had not rejected natural selection. He had only added spiritualism to the last phases of man's evolution, put spiritualism in the place of the religion he had rejected long ago, finding in it a useful explanation of phenomena he did not understand and for which he could find no other explanation.

Then in the spring of 1866 Wallace, at the age of forty-three, married the eighteen year old Annie Mitten. With her, and later with his father-in-law, William Mitten the botanist, Wallace took many walking holidays in the hills of England, Wales, Scotland and, in the following year, Switzerland. Walking had always been one of his favourite relaxations. He usually walked with a purpose, however; either to study the natural history of a district, to look at some geological formation, or to look for evidence of glacial erosion.

He had become deeply interested in the problems of glaciation, problems not well understood at the time. Because of his observations during these walking holidays, he came to the conclusion that many of the valleys, ridges and lakes of North Wales had been formed by the grinding down action of glaciers and were not a result of water erosion, as most people believed. These observations were published in 1867, and they formed the basis of his more extended theories of glaciation, which later came to be applied to problems of animal distribution.

At this time too, through the persuasions of friends, he altered the distribution of his investments, laying the foundations for continual financial worries that were to be the stimulus for much of his most important scientific work.

In 1867, therefore, there seemed to be no reason to delay

work on his *Travels*. He had a wife, a home and, for the time being, money. He had already published several papers on the distribution of animals and on the geography of the Malay Archipelago. His interests were not concentrated yet on this major work, however. Talking to fellow biologists, working on his insect collections, he kept on being distracted by new ideas. This time he felt he had something to add to the theories of protective colouring. He first wrote a short, popular account of the disguises of insects, and in 1867 he published a paper which amplified the theory of mimicry put forward by H. W. Bates five years earlier.

It was at about this time, too, that he decided finally that he would not himself describe many more of his specimens but would hand them over to other people and concentrate instead on the fascinating theories which had emerged from his own studies of animal life. "I might have spent the rest of my life upon similar work, for which my own collection afforded ample materials, and thus settled down into a regular 'speciesmonger'. For even in this humble occupation there is a great fascination; . . ." (I 403).

In 1868 he was awarded the Royal Medal of the Royal Society for his "labours in practical and theoretical zoology" and the following year his narrative of travels was finished and published. *Malay Archipelago* was dedicated to Darwin "not only as a token of personal esteem and friendship but also to express my deep admiration for his genius and his works". *Malay Archipelago* gave Darwin great pleasure. He was pleased with the dedication, delighted that the pages were cut and gilded and, above all, full of admiration for the contents. Wallace had tried to persuade his publisher to issue the whole edition with cut pages, but "I could not persuade Mr MacMillan to cut more than twenty-five copies for my own friends, and he even seemed to think this a sign of most strange and barbarous taste" (M I 235).

Malay Archipelago was greeted with enthusiasm. Darwin wrote: "I shall be astonished if your book has not a great success; and your splendid generalisations on geographical distribution, with which I am familiar from your papers, will be new to most of your readers . . . let me congratulate you heartily on having written so excellent a book, full of thought on all sorts of subjects. Once again, let me thank you for the very great honour which you have done me by your dedication" (M I 237). Lyell and Kingsley expressed their admiration and compared the book to

Darwin's *Voyage of the Beagle*. Professor Strasburger of Bonn declared that "Through his 'Malay Archipelago' a new world of scientific knowledge was unfolded before me" (M I 121). By June of the same year, several European countries were requesting translation rights, and eventually it was translated into all the main languages. In English, it ran through a dozen editions. *Malay Archipelago* was the most successful of all Wallace's works.

Wallace's Line

Until Wallace began to contribute to the theory of the distribution of animals, little attention had been paid to the fact that whilst some groups were abundant in a given locality, others were scarce or entirely absent and yet had areas where they, too, were abundant. For one thing, the areas more distant from Europe had not been intensively explored until the beginning of the nineteenth century, so that although the more outstanding animal representatives of the continents had been described by early travellers, very little detail was known of their faunas. South America had been vigorously guarded from intrusion by the Spaniards until the middle of the eighteenth century; the interior of Africa was unknown until the nineteenth century; and except for the spice islands of the Malay Archipelago, Australasia was little explored until this time.

That there were some outstanding faunal differences between the continents had already been observed, but most of the early writers had accepted them as unquestionable facts. Providence had decreed that these differences should be. "For the God of heaven and earth greatly providing for mankind, would not that all things should be found in one region, to the ende that one should have neede of another," wrote Edward VI in a letter missive for Sir Hugh Willoughby adventuring to the mighty Empire of Cathay in 1553 (Hakluyt 1903-05). Yet some were puzzled. "If we say then that all these kindes of creatures were preserved in the Arke by Noah, it followes that those beasts, of whose kindes we finde not any but at the Indies [America], have passed thither from this continent, as we have saide of other beasts that are knowne unto us. This supposed, I demand how it is possible that none of their kinde should remaine heere? and they are found there, being as it were travellers and strangers. Truly it is a question that hath long held me in suspense" (Acosta 1608 ed). Acosta's work, *Historia natural y moral de las Indias,* first published in 1589, was in great demand in Europe where, although there was an insatiable appetite for descriptions of the New World, there were few works to meet the demand. But in spite of the intense interest in the natural history of America, most men were prepared to accept the story of the Ark without question, without wondering how animals otherwise unknown had got into the New World. Only few gave it any further thought. "Why so many strange birds and beasts proper to America alone, as Acosta demands, were they created in the six days, or ever in Noah's ark? if there, why are they not dispersed and found in other countries?" asked Robert Burton in 1628. There was no answer forthcoming. Nor was there an answer to the equally interesting problem of why many apparently suitable animals were altogether absent from America, a point made by Sir Thomas Browne fifteen years later when he wrote in *Religio Medici,* "... that is, not only how the distinct pieces of the world, and divided Island, should be first planted by men, but inhabited by Tigers, Panthers, and Bears. How America abounded with Beasts of prey and noxious Animals, yet contained not in it that necessary Creature, a Horse, is very strange. By what passage those, not only Birds, but dangerous and unwelcome Beasts, came over; how there be Creatures there, which are not found in this Triple Continent; (all which must needs be strange unto us, that hold but one Ark, and that the Creatures began their progress from the Mountains of Ararat:) they who, to salve this, would make the Deluge particular, proceed upon a principle that I can in no way grant; ..."

But to most men these differences were fixed by divine law. If other reason for them was needed it could be found in the differences of climate in the continents, though Buffon (1761) observed that climate alone was not responsible for the present distribution of animals, for if this were so it would be reasonable to expect to find elephants in the New World. "But for whatever cause this difference comes, being a product of the time, the climate or the earth, or dating from the moment of Creation, it is none the less real. Nature, I aver, is in a continual state of flux." Continuing this line of thought, he made the first constructive attempts to explain the differences and similarities between the great continents of the world. Comparing the Old with the New, he suggested that many of the animals of the two had once been shared and that the two continents had been continuous, the animals only becoming isolated when the seas irrupted to divide the land.

Linnaeus faced the problem of distribution by supposing that the habitable world had been limited to one small tract, all the original animals being congregated there. As the primaeval ocean subsided and the land increased, so the animals dispersed.

For most naturalists, however, animals and plants had not only been created in the places where they are found today, but also in the exact numbers. Louis Agassiz, the Swiss paleontologist, wrote to Sedgwick in 1845 : "I have also tried to show the direct intervention of a creative power in the geographical distribution of organised beings on the surface of the globe when the species are definitely circumscribed." Even Humboldt concluded that a Divine Idea determined the numerical relations of flowers and animals in any one region. To most natural philosophers, animals had also been created almost entirely for the benefit of man "doubtless for those beings who are alone endued with reason" (Kidd 1833). Thus the elephant had been created in a region where it could find suitable food for itself, and it had been created docile so that man could use it in that region.

By the beginning of the nineteenth century attempts were occasionally made to elucidate the problems of organic distribution. Lyell had followed Buffon and expanded his observations to cover New Holland, maintaining that "The numbers and distribution of particular species are affected in two ways, by changes in the physical geography of the earth. First, these changes provide or retard the migrations of species; secondly, they alter the physical conditions of the localities which species inhabit" (1832). But the most important attempt was made by Edward Forbes in 1846. He analysed the provenance of the flora of the British Isles and showed how geography and climate influenced the distribution of plants and animals.

The observation of peculiarities and irregularities in animal distribution made a deep impression on both Darwin and Wallace. In both cases it was one of the major influences that led to their formulation of the theory of evolution by natural selection. Darwin had been impressed by the odd fauna of the Galapagos Islands, which he visited in 1835; Wallace by the peculiarities in distribution of Amazonian and East Indian animals. Darwin was puzzled by the absence of mammals from the Galapagos Islands and by the presence of many specialized finches and large reptiles; reptiles and finches distinctive of each island "... the Spaniards can at once pronounce from which Island any tortoise may have been brought" (Barlow 1945). There was no apparent reason, climatic or vegetational, why mammals should not have been created on the Galapagos; no apparent reason why each island of the group should have recognizably different turtles and finches; no apparent reason why the fauna should be more like that of America than of anywhere else in the world if it was all owed to the Creation. All these anomalies could be explained only later when the theory of common descent, of evolution, had been accepted.

The facts of animal distribution were used by both Darwin and Wallace as an argument in favour of the evolution of animals one from another. Once evolution had been accepted, the argument could be inverted and the theory of evolution used to explain the observed facts of the geography of animals, zoogeography. If animals, which are closely related, occur in widely different parts of the world, how did they get there by natural means? If strange animals occur in remote parts of the world, why are they thus confined? Where are their nearest relatives? What has been their probable history? Why are tapirs found only in South America and Malaya, elephants only in Africa and India, sloths in South America and kangaroos in Australia?

Wallace had turned his attention to the geographical distribution of animals during his journeys up the Amazon and Rio Negro, and he had realized the importance of observing the exact localities where specimens were caught. But it was not until he observed and recorded in the islands of the Malay Archipelago that he made any original contributions to what was to be his major work.

The subject of zoogeography in its modern form may be said to have been "invented" by Wallace, for he was the first to base the subject on the theory of evolution. Accept the fact that animals have descended one from another instead of being created *in situ,* species by species, and the whole interpretation of the geography of animals is revolutionized.

Wallace was revolutionary in other ways, too. He realized that zoogeography was not a subject concerned only with collecting facts about present-day faunas, classifying them and comparing them; it was also a study of the history of the animals, their evolution, and the history of the land masses of the world. Zoogeography was not only a method of pigeon-holing regions, it was also a story of changes through geological time. Zoogeography must reveal the ways in which animals had come to occupy their particular geographical positions. With this realization Wallace turned to the available paleontological information, studied the problems associated with the dispersal of animals and based it all on the then recent geological theories of Lyell (1830-33) on the antiquity and permanence of the continents.

But like the animals and the continents, Wallace's theories evolved slowly. At first he worked on the detailed but difficult problems of the zoogeography of the Malay Archipelago while travelling amongst the islands, but it was only much later (1876) that he applied to the whole world what he had learnt. Wallace was never content with the mere accumulation of facts, the description of species or of faunas. After a very short time in the East Indies he began to theorize not only on the origin of species but also on the reasons for the somewhat unexpected differences in the faunas of nearby islands. He turned from the respectable practice of description to the less reputable occupation of theorist, and although this change was disapproved of by many, it was welcomed by Darwin who wrote to him in December 1857: "I am a firm believer that without speculation there is no good and original observation. Few travellers have attended to such points as you are now at work on; and indeed the whole subject of distribution of animals is dreadfully behind that of plants" (M I 131).

The Malay Archipelago was an ideal part of the world for the study of zoogeography. The islands may not have been so unique as the Galapagos Islands, but they had peculiarities and they lay between two continents which differed markedly in their faunas. The explanation of their peculiarities was not as simple as for the Galapagos, but in solving the difficulties Wallace gained a remarkable insight into the many factors that affect the distribution of land animals.

After two years of travelling, mainly in the western part of the Archipelago, Wallace wrote to Bates who was still in South America, that he thought that Malaya, together with the islands of Sumatra, Java and Borneo formed one zoological province, "... the majority of species in all classes of animals being common to two or more of these countries". In 1858 he wrote again to Bates: "I believe the western part [of the Archipelago] to be a separated portion of continental Asia, the eastern the fragmentary prolongation of a former Pacific continent" (M I 67). The first realization of these differences came to Wallace in 1856 when he had the startling experience of travelling straight from the island of Bali to the island of Lombok. It seemed as though he had passed completely out of an Indo-Malayan region across a mere twenty miles of sea into an Australian region. He had expected the fauna near Australia to differ from that of Asia, but he had not expected the change to be so abrupt, nor so far to the west. Hitherto, writers on Indian zoology had tended to include within their range the fauna of the Malay Peninsula and all the islands of the Archipelago (Pennant 1791). The Australian fauna had been assumed to be confined to that continent or, at the most, to have spread to a few eastern islands (Péron 1807, Prichard 1826). A faunal break to the west of Celebes and Lombok had not been anticipated.

Further observations of the island faunas confirmed this first impression that the break was comparatively far to the west, and that it was sharply defined.

In 1858 P. L. Sclater contributed to the Linnean Society of London a paper on *The general distribution of members of the class Aves*. In it he put forward a scheme for dividing up the world into regions, on the basis of similarities or dissimilarities in their bird populations. The areas, once established, could be considered fixed and more or less ordained because ". . . as a general rule, every species of animal must have been created within and over the geographic area which it now occupies". Sclater showed that whilst such birds as pheasants and jungle fowl were widespread throughout what he called the Indian region, they were absent from the Australian region where cockatoos, cassowaries and birds of paradise were confined.

This contribution from Sclater stimulated Wallace to undertake a detailed investigation into the boundary between these newly proposed zoological regions. In 1859 he wrote a paper from the field on *The Geographical Distribution of Birds*. He accepted Sclater's regions, but suggested small emendations, and then he made out a very convincing case for the positioning of the line of demarcation between the Indian and Australian regions, of which Sclater had said "It is not yet possible to decide where the line runs which divides the Indian zoology from the Australian." Wallace suggested a line running between Borneo and Celebes in the north and between Bali and Lombok in the south. He was not convinced of the affinities of Celebes and the Philippines, and at this stage he did not commit them more than tentatively to either the Indian or the Australian region. At the end of the year, however, further work brought a larger and more detailed paper on the zoogeography of the Malay Archipelago, and it was sent to the Linnean Society by Darwin. In it, Wallace showed that not only birds fell into geographically defined regions but also other animals, particularly mammals.

By this time he had come to the conclusion that the Philippines should with some qualifications be put into the Indian region, leaving the position of Celebes undefined. New Guinea he considered to have been part of Australia, the Aru Islands part of New Guinea. He noticed that insects are of less value in the classification of regions than birds or mammals because not only are they more easily distributed over water and mountains but also they are a much older group. Besides, they are very much affected by local circumstances. Thus the climate of an island will determine its colonization by plants and insects to a very much greater extent than it will determine the success of at least some mammals and some birds, animals which are often very much more adaptable as individuals than invertebrates are.

Having classified the various islands of the Archipelago into one or other of the zoological regions, the next step was to interpret these facts in the light of what was known of the geological history of the area or, alternatively, to argue from the facts of animal distribution to the paleogeography of the area.

Influenced by the new geology which stressed the general permanence, but evolution of the continents, as well as the instability of volcanic regions, Wallace realized that if the world could be divided into zoological areas it was not because it had been created in that way but because the continents, although having this general permanence, had been joined to one another in different ways at different times. These connexions might have been only small and temporary, or they might have amounted to larger land bridges.

Very little was known of the paleogeography of the Malay Archipelago, so that an interpretation of the zoological facts could not be based on detailed geological knowledge. Wallace, therefore used the second method of argument. From what he knew of the fauna of the islands he tried to reconstruct their geological history. Unfortunately, he could derive little help from fossils as almost none was known from the area.

In London in 1863 Wallace read a paper to the Geographical Society on the geography of the Malay Archipelago. He showed how the islands of the eastern division were separated from one another by only shallow seas, whilst deeper seas lay, for instance, between Borneo and Celebes. He maintained that the occurrence of volcanoes and coral islands suggested that the Archipelago was a region that might well have undergone considerable change during recent geological epochs. He supported this contention with a review of the natural histories of these regions, and he committed himself for the first time to a definite boundary line between Indian and Australian regions. This line separated a region on the west, characterized by the presence of such animals as monkeys, orang utans, elephants, tapirs, sunbirds, cuckoos and pheasants, from a region to the east whose peculiar fauna included forms such as kangaroos, the duckbilled platypus, birds of paradise, cockatoos and cassowaries. The line of demarcation passed to the east of the Philippines, as he had previously suggested, southwards, and now decisively to the west of Celebes and further south between the islands of Bali and Lombok.

In the same contribution he took the subject further and suggested some of the changes in land formation that might have occurred in the comparatively recent past. From the characteristics of the fauna he deduced that Java was the island which had been isolated longest from the Malayan mainland and that the small island of Banca must have been cut off from Sumatra before Sumatra lost its connexion with Borneo. He concluded, "it shows in a most forcible manner how impossible it is to understand . . . geographical distribution of animals, without taking into consideration all the probable and possible changes which may have recently taken place in the distribution of land and water on the earth's surface."

The two regions into which the Malay Archipelago fell in the "comparatively recent past had each been part of a larger land mass, but had not had any connexion with one another during the Tertiary [cenozoic] epoch." The line that Wallace drew between these two regions became known as Wallace's Line after

T. H. Huxley had referred to it by that name in 1868. Unfortunately, the line drawn by Huxley differed from Wallace's in passing to the west of the Philippines, but this error has not prevented the original line from being accepted as Wallace's Line by later workers.

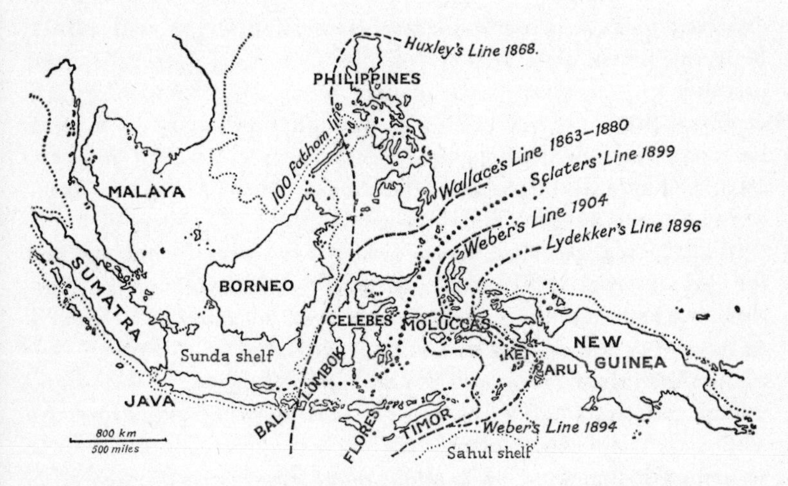

Fig. 3. Lines suggested for separating Oriental and Australian faunal regions 1868-1904.

Wallace regarded his dividing line as a matter of convenience. It most satisfactorily divided an Indian fauna from an Australian one, when the greatest number of animal species had been taken into account. At the same time, it gave some reality to the history of the region. But to most naturalists of the nineteenth century the line had to mean that all lands to the west of it had been recently connected with one another and similarly those to the east. There were naturalists who believed in creation, and there were those who accepted evolution. On the whole, however, they all still required a theory of land bridges to account for the distribution of animals. They also required that the line should be absolute, and that it should define a real faunistic and floristic break, for the sake of neatness and utility.

Wallace never considered that his line fulfilled these stringent conditions. Malaya, Java, Sumatra and Borneo seemed, on faunistic grounds, to have once been united; likewise Australia, New Guinea and the Aru Islands. In contrast the Moluccas,

Celebes and Timor to Lombok formed an intermediate area which had not been connected, in cenozoic times at least, with either the eastern or the western land masses, or with one another. Wallace considered, therefore, that this group of islands had received its fauna by chance immigrations of animals from nearby land. Those islands near to the continent of Australia would be expected to have a predominantly Australian fauna, and should lie therefore in that region for the sake of convenience. But this did not necessarily mean that they had been joined in cenozoic times to that continent, though they might well have been separated by much narrower straits than today. The Molucca Islands, Timor and Lombok could thus be classified, but the island of Celebes was a more difficult problem.

Wallace realized that Celebes must have been isolated either for the whole of the cenozoic period or at least for a very long time. Although it lies comparatively near to Borneo, it seemed to have very few species in common with that island, nor had it many Australian animals. On the contrary, its fauna was individual and characterized to some extent more by the absence of common Archipelago forms than by their presence, although it was obvious that some of its animals had come from the Malayan region and others from the Australian. Many of these animals had then diverged into species peculiar to the island. Wallace listed eighteen species of butterflies of the genus *Papilio,* nine species of mammals and ninety-four species of birds, their large number suggesting long isolation from neighbouring lands. This was further supported by the finding among the birds and mammals of endemic genera as well as species.

Celebes would appear then to have been a separate land mass for longer than most other Malayan islands, obtaining its fauna by chance overseas migrations. To Wallace in 1880 it should "ever remain a mere matter of opinion with which [region] it should properly be associated". Eventually he came to believe that it might have been joined to Borneo long ago, losing this connexion by early cenozoic days. If this were so, Celebes would be better classified with the western Malayan islands, even if its exact status were not clearly defined.

Therefore, it might be argued that, as he himself wrote, "Wallace's line must be drawn east of Celebes and the Philippines" (1910). Usually, however, the line known by his name is the one of 1863, and the fact that he revised the position of Celebes serves mainly to emphasize that he considered it to have been a separate island for a longer time than the others in the area.

How far has Wallace's Line stood up to modern research into the geology and paleontology of the Malay Archipelago? In the middle of the last century for one reason and another alternative proposals were already being put forward to separate the Indian and Australian areas in different ways. The majority of dividers tried to distribute just one group of animals satisfactorily and, whilst birds seemed to fall readily into some groupings, mammals seemed better fitted by other arrangements.

In 1868 T. H. Huxley had drawn what he erroneously called Wallace's Line, to the west of the Philippines to mark off the limits of the Indian birds. In 1894 Weber suggested, on oceanographic grounds, that a line drawn east of Celebes (fig. 3) divided the Australian region from the Indo-Malayan in a more satisfactory way than "this unfortunate line" of Wallace. In 1896 Lydekker drew a line further to the east of the Moluccas than Weber had done, and he accepted Wallace's Line in the west, leaving an intermediate zone in between. Three years later, the Sclaters drew their definitive line, which was the same as Wallace's except that it put Celebes into the Indian region. Five years later still Pelseneer defined a line which was based on Weber's oceanographic observations and took into account the distribution of the molluscs and the mammals. This line (fig. 3) passed between Timor to the west and the Kei and Aru Islands to the east. Pelseneer called it Weber's Line.

The two lines which still merit serious consideration are those which bear the name of Wallace and Weber, in spite of the fact that the *Encyclopaedia Britannica* referred in 1911 to "the now exploded Wallace's line".

Until recently, and certainly in Wallace's day, the paleogeography of an area was deduced from the zoology and then the anomalies of animal distribution were resolved from this reconstructed geographical history. This was inevitable when nothing was known of the paleogeography of the area, and it was not a method to be despised; it gave rise to fundamental conclusions which have not been revised even in the light of greater knowledge. Today, a little is known of the cenozoic history of a considerable part of the world, but, in spite of intense geological and oceanographic research, it has not been easy to reconstruct the history of the Malay Archipelago. Several Dutch expeditions in the 1930's worked over the area very thoroughly and a tentative account of the history of the area has been given by Umbgrove (1949).

On the map it can be seen that Wallace's Line runs along the eastern edge, the Sunda Shelf, of an area whose separate islands are joined by stretches of comparatively shallow sea, less than 200 metres in depth. A similar continental shelf, the Sahul Shelf, runs along the western edge of an eastern group of islands, including New Guinea, separated from one another by an equally shallow sea. The "land" to the west of the Sunda Shelf and that to the east of the Sahul Shelf consists of rocks of great age which would not be affected by the extensive folding processes which produced the islands of the deep sea between Asia and Australia. Sunda-land and Sahul-land were almost certainly in existence in the mesozoic. Whether the area between these two ancient land masses has always been sea and islands or whether it was ever continuous land is a more difficult problem to solve, the evidence being conflicting. Cretaceous fossils have been found fairly continuously from Asia to Australia, and this might be considered evidence of land connexion during the mesozoic (Kuenen 1935) but it is not conclusive. If there were continuous land between the two continents, and the general concensus of opinion is against it, it had certainly become broken up by the eocene.

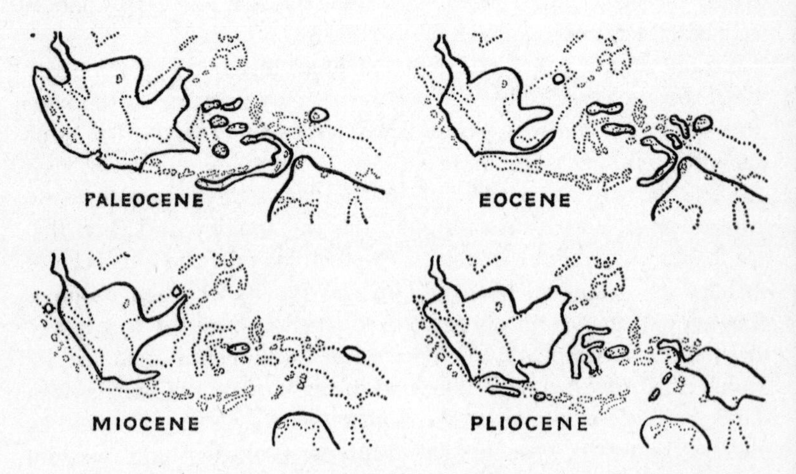

Fig. 4. Cenozoic paleogeography of the Malay Archipelago (after Umbgrove 1949).

According to Umbgrove, an eocene map (fig. 4) would show an extensive Malayan region in the west, including what is now Borneo, Sumatra and Java, extending into the China Sea and, in the east, a second land mass made up of Australia and the Arafura Sea. In between, there were probably parts of Celebes and an arc of land running from Bouru through the Kei Islands to Timor. By the miocene some thirty million years later, the sea had invaded many of the old land nuclei and the western continent had become smaller and differently shaped: New Guinea and its associated islands had probably sunk below the sea leaving only the Australian continent in the east. Between these two there may have been land in the area of the modern Sula Islands, but the rest of the intervening space was probably filled by sea only. By the pliocene Sundaland had extended, and Bali had appeared above the sea. New Guinea had become dry land again, and Celebes had appeared as an island. Finally, during the pleistocene, the deep expanse of sea between the two main continents was broken up by the other islands known today, none of which seems to have had any land connexion with the continents since then.

This reconstruction of the history of the area provides a useful working hypothesis in comparatively good agreement with the evidence, but it is not the only possible interpretation of the observed phenomena. Another interpretation has been deferred to a later chapter as its implications spread further afield than the Malay Archipelago.

There seems, then, to be some geological evidence for Wallace's Line and also for the Sahul Shelf line. Sumatra, Java, Borneo and Bali, together with Banca, almost certainly obtained their fauna from remote times from the Indian region, with which the precursors of the present day islands were in direct physical association. Only in the late pliocene did these islands become separate and allow for a certain amount of faunal differentiation, such as is found to have occurred in Java where, for instance, the Malay deer has differentiated into a Javanese species. On the eastern side, New Guinea and the Aru Islands may have obtained their fauna through direct connexions with, or close approximations to, Australia, becoming separated and differentiated at a later date. Plant distribution in this area makes it difficult to believe, however, that New Guinea was ever actually part of the Australian continent.

There is, then, not one geographical break between the western and eastern regions of the Archipelago, as earlier writers had all assumed, but two. One to the west is more or less Wallace's Line and one to the east runs along the edge of the Sahul Shelf, approximating roughly to Weber's Line. The islands in between had a varied cenozoic history. Geologically, there seems to be no evidence for land bridges connecting the intervening islands with either of the continents or with Celebes since the beginning of the cenozoic, or even earlier.

Geographically the "middle islands" do not fall automatically into either of the great zoogeographical regions. Modern paleogeography leaves them in their anomalous position. If a line is to be drawn, its position must be decided on faunistic grounds.

The intermediate islands are particularly noteworthy for the poverty of their fauna. Their colonization has been a chance affair. For this reason, it could be argued that it is pointless to draw one line between these islands, and that a more rational solution would be to leave Wallace's Line in the west and Weber's Line in the east and elevate the intermediate islands to a region of their own. This latter solution had been favoured by Lydekker, Weber himself (1902) and again by Dickerson and others (1928) who called the new region Wallacea. One of the main objections to this, however, is that Wallacea has very little homogeneity within itself (Stresemann 1939), each island being very different from the others and almost ranking as a region of its own. Excessive breaking down of regions in this way reduces the whole idea of zoological regions to absurdity, and the usual practice is to try to classify even oceanic islands in the region to which they show the greatest faunistic affinity. Wallacea serves better as a term "applied informally as a descriptive attribute" (Mayr 1944b), than as the name of a separate region. On the other hand, its use does underline the differences in the histories of the islands and the mixed nature of their fauna.

Which line separates the Indian and Australian regions most satisfactorily in the light of the faunistic work of the last seventy years? Or, which direction did the fauna of these middle islands come from if they had no continental connexions? Although they might be supposed to have obtained their invertebrates from Asia in mesozoic ages, most of the early fauna, except perhaps for a few relicts on mountain tops, would have been eliminated during the miocene era if Umbgrove is correct in assuming there was a general submergence of the islands at that time (fig. 4). They would then have to be repopulated from the pliocene onwards. Both east and west have contributed something, but is the fauna predominantly Australian, as Wallace maintained, or Malayan, as Pelseneer (Weber's line) preferred?

Wallace believed that many of these intermediate islands had more Australian elements in their fauna than Indian. It was a consideration of these proportions that led him to draw his line in a westerly position. Since the middle of the last century, however, there has been a great increase in knowledge of the fauna of these islands. Where Wallace listed 118 species of bird on Timor, for instance, some 168 are known today; where he knew five species of reptile, forty are known today (Mayr 1944a); and the same is true of other animals, particularly the invertebrates which have been increasingly studied.

Wallace to some extent, and most other observers after him, based their conclusions on the distribution of what might be called "indicator" animals. For instance, the presence on Celebes of marsupial phalangers, typical products of Australia, tended to carry more weight than the fact that there were at least sixteen species of placental mammals to contrast with these two marsupial species. The presence of white cockatoos on Lombok tended to be more impressive than the fact that some 70 per cent of all the birds on the island have Indian affinities (Mayr 1944b).

Arguments for and against the faunistic reality, or convenience of Wallace's Line, have been based mainly on descriptions of those animals which had or had not transgressed the line. Should it be considered more important that *Tarsius, Cynopithecus* and civets have crossed the line, or that elephants, bears and hedgehogs have not (Raven 1935)? Some species of Lepidoptera extend across the line, others do not (Zeuner 1942). Celebes has no indigenous freshwater fish (Norman 1942). In contrast to freshwater fish, reptiles do not conform to Wallace's Line (Keast and others 1959). The verdict in these cases depends on what the author considers to be the most important "indicator" animals or, alternatively, depends on the result of the analysis of the particular group on which he is working.

It could be argued that the only possible criterion for a boundary line on faunistic grounds should come where there is roughly a fifty-fifty mixture of faunal elements from the two regions, a half and half mixture of all the animals taken together. But this again is not an easy criterion to work to. On many islands the fauna is not yet known in its entirety, and thus only one or a few groups can be counted. Of these few, some achieve the fifty-fifty mark on one island and others on another. For instance, on Wetar Island, just north of Timor, the birds are more than 50 per cent Australian, but in all other groups the western element prevails as it does on Timor itself. It would seem reasonable to put Wetar in the Indian region on the basis of this estimate, but some authorities would give more statistical weight to the well-known bird class than to groups whose numerical appraisal is not more than an informed guess. Further, some would give more statistical weighting to ancient species than to recent ones. However, in spite of the difficulties, it seems reasonable to work towards a statistical estimate for the determination of the faunistic boundary between two regions.

Although Wallace may have been unduly influenced by "indicator" animals, he was the first and almost the only one of the early zoogeographers to try to apply such a statistical test. Unfortunately his information was less comprehensive than it is today. For example, Wallace estimated that on Timor the Australian birds outnumbered the Indian, whereas a more recent appreciation (Mayr 1944a) shows 62 per cent of the species to have western affinities and only 30 per cent eastern, the remaining 8 per cent peculiar to the island.

The most up to date counts of various groups of animals in the Archipelago indicate that, on the whole, the western element is much larger on the intermediate islands than Wallace supposed, showing not unexpectedly a gradual decrease towards the east. Thus three-quarters of all the known Celebesian species are of western origin, 67.6 per cent of the birds (Mayr 1944b) and 88 per cent of the reptiles (Rensch 1936), and much the same is true of Flores.

Where should the fifty-fifty line be drawn in the light of the most recent information? Obviously it must lie much further east than Wallace's Line. But does it lie on Weber's? Some authorities estimate that it corresponds more closely with Weber's Line than with any other, running west of the Moluccas, Bouru, Ceram, Aru and Kei and east of Timor (Mayr 1944b), but others (de Beaufort 1951) would push the line even further east to correspond with Lydekker's eastern line.

It must then be concluded that, although Wallace's Line has a paleogeographical significance, it no longer seems to provide the best line for marking off the western from the eastern fauna. To travel eastwards from Asia appears to have been more usual than to travel west. The reason for this may be either that population pressure has been consistently greater on the Asiatic continent than it has been on the Australian, or that the Asiatic animals having become more successful than the Australian, through close competition, have succeeded in securing places on the islands ousting Australian forms or by getting there first. Finally, it may be because the western intermediate islands are nearer to Indo-Malaya than the eastern intermediates are to the Australian continent.

The fauna of Wallacea has come from both Asia and Australia by island-hopping, along what Simpson (1953) has called a "sweepstake" route, to stress the chance element. The island hoppers could have travelled along any string of islands and most routes have been suggested at some time (see Croizat 1958 for instance). The two most favoured are the route along the equatorial rain belt from Malay to Borneo, thence to Celebes, the Moluccas and New Guinea (Zeuner 1942) and, more likely, since Borneo and Celebes are so different, birds, at any rate, may have used the Philippines, Celebes, Flores, Timor route (Stresemann 1939, Wallace 1863).

The peculiar fauna of Celebes would then be derived mainly from the Philippines in the west, as Wallace believed and Stresemann has since confirmed, with fewer immigrants coming from Borneo and from the Molucca and Sula Islands. The dwarf buffalo of the island is related to a buffalo in the Philippines and, with the babirussa and an extinct genus of elephant, it has been found in pleistocene deposits on Celebes. Probably all the Indian mammals of Celebes came from the Philippines by chance sea crossings, whilst the Australian phalangers may have come from the Moluccas. Some of the more archaic animals may have come from the Sula Islands, close neighbours to Celebes, and islands which represent the remnants of an old land arc of which they alone remained above sea level during the whole of the cenozoic era. This might explain, for instance, the presence of three species of Australian mountain toad *Oreophryne*. The amphibia are bad sea voyagers, and it is not clear how these toads were able to get on to an island that has apparently always been an island. They may have survived on the Sula Islands when the rest of the Archipelago was below the sea during the eocene-miocene, and later they may have managed the crossing to Celebes, which is only some fifty miles of island-filled shallow sea. Alternatively, it has been argued, the Celebes toads are relicts of a still more ancient fauna acquired during the mesozoic when there may have been an even greater tract of land in the area. It is argued that being mountain toads, they were able to survive on peaks which remained above the sea when the rest of Celebes was submerged. *Oreophryne* are not the only amphibia of the Celebes fauna, which contains some ten species of Asiatic frogs and toads. These species are not, however, distinctive of the island but are identical with those of Borneo, and it is likely that they have been introduced recently (Darlington 1957).

Whatever the explanation of these anomalies, the most usual conclusion on the status of Celebes is the same as Wallace's; that Celebes has always been an island and has obtained its fauna by chance immigration and it should be put into the Indian rather than the Australian region. There seems no reason to follow Weber in actually attaching Celebes to Malaya at any time during the cenozoic. Of the other islands, Lombok, Flores, Timor and the Sula Islands should probably also go into the Indian region, whilst also remaining anomalous islands in Wallace's sense, colonized across the sea.

The final conclusion must be that, as a line dividing western and eastern faunas, Wallace's Line has no statistical basis. It can no longer be regarded as the fifty-fifty, Indian-Australian, faunal line. Weber's Line happens to come much closer to providing a suitable faunistic boundary.

Paleogeography and zoogeography must still be interested in Wallace's Line and Wallacea. As a delineation of a geological break during the cenozoic and probably earlier eras, Wallace's Line emphasizes the history of the area, and this history, inevitably, influenced present day animal distribution.

Wallace drew another line through the Malay Archipelago to mark the division between the Malayan and Papuan types of men. This line ran further to the east than his zoological line, passing between Flores and Sumbawa in the south, through the Moluccas and to the east of the Philippines in the north.

Presumably man's colonization of the area was considerably later than for the majority of modern mammals, for it is unlikely that modern man had evolved before the pleistocene. He made up for his lateness by his conscious ability to cross natural barriers.

There is thus little differentiation of man into distinct races, and boundaries between geographical variants tend to be blurred. With these reservations, there seems to be some justification for the dividing line that Wallace drew. The Melanesian Papuans, to the east of the line, may have come from an Australoid and African negro-white ancestry, whilst the Indonesian Malays are thought by many to have come from negro-white-mongoloid progenitors. Modern blood group analysis shows that whilst the distribution of some groups is independent of Wallace's Line others give support to his hypothesis. West of Wallace's Line in Malaya, Java and Borneo the proportion of the M blood group is approximately 60 per cent whilst east of the line the proportion drops sharply to 43 per cent and is as low as 20 per cent in New Guinea (Mourant 1954). This adds interest to the possibility of a human Wallace Line.

Man has had a very mixed history and can cross the seas more easily than other animals. Anthropologically, therefore, the most that can be said for the line is that it may represent the easterly limit reached by one particular wave of colonization, other waves having spread further. It cannot be taken as proof that the Malays came from the west and the Polynesians from the east, as some authors believe (Heyerdahl 1952).

From Malay Archipelago to the Geographical Distribution of Animals 1869 to 1876

With the publication of *Malay Archipelago* in 1869 Wallace had completed the preliminary study of animal distribution in the light of the theory of evolution by natural selection. His next major contribution was not written until seven years later.

During these years his published writings were on a variety of subjects, some stimulated by his efforts to find paid employment, some by his interest in social problems and a few on specific aspects of the problems of animal distribution and on the meaning of colour in the animal world.

To solve his financial problems Wallace, encouraged by Lyell, applied in 1869 for the directorship of the Bethnal Green Museum, whose foundation as an art and natural history centre had been accepted in principle by the Government. After making his application, he crystallized his ideas on the management of museums in an article published in *Macmillan's Magazine*. He regarded museums as a means of stimulating the interest of the ordinary man, and as a means of teaching both the specialist and the non-specialist. But, if there should be a conflict of interest, it was the ordinary man who should be considered first.

He advocated a scientific layout of the specimens, but at the same time he stressed the need of an aesthetically satisfying arrangement. As for the principles of arrangement, he not unnaturally gave a prominent place to locality. The geography, geology, paleontology and fauna and flora of the district within which the museum was situated should be stressed. Structure and classification in general should be accompanied by suitable illustrations of geographical distribution. But above all, a museum should be a place where animals, plants, fossils or other objects could be studied to their greatest possible advantage. A specimen in a museum, according to Wallace, should catch the eye. "Two of the great evils of museums are, crowding and distraction. By the crowding of specimens, the effect of each is weakened or destroyed, the eye takes in so many at once that it is continually wandering towards something more strange and beautiful, and there is nothing to concentrate the attention on a special object. Distraction is produced also by the great size of the galleries, and the multiplicity of objects that strike the eye" (SSS II 14). Wallace was suffering from the cluttering, wholly inefficient effects of Gothic revival architecture which made of so many museums a hopeless welter of objects. He could have had in mind any one of several big museums when he wrote: "In designing museums, architects seem to pay little regard to the special purposes they are intended to fulfil. They often adopt the general arrangement of a church, or the immense galleries and lofty halls of a palace. Now, the main object of a museum-building is to furnish the greatest amount of well-lighted space, for the convenient arrangement and exhibition of objects which almost all require to be closely examined." He also advocated seats in museums so that displays could be studied in comfort.

No striking improvements have been made until very recently in the form of display, and most of the museums of today can improve only within the chaos of acanthus leaves and coloured brick provided by their nineteenth-century architects. In 1869 Wallace was too far ahead of his times to have any influence on the majority opinion of the nineteenth century.

Curiously, Wallace was averse to government money being spent on museums or other scientific projects, on the grounds that they were of interest only to a few specialists. In the first volume of the scientific periodical *Nature,* with whose foundation Wallace was concerned, he expressed these views on government aid to science.

In spite of both strong support from influential scientists and the serious thought he had given to the matter, the question of the directorship of the Bethnal Green Museum dragged on until, in 1872 when it was built, the Government decided not to appoint a director.

In the meantime, to augment his income, Wallace had become an examiner in physical geography at the rate of £60 a thousand papers. This experience, which lasted until 1897, gave rise to articles on the iniquities of teaching, in particular of religion. He believed that education could be a positive force in the betterment of mankind, but he also knew from experience that teaching was not an easy profession. Although he realized that teachers fell short of even the minimum requirements, this was not the worst of the system in his eyes. The worst aspect was that teachers were compelled to teach subjects of which either they were ignorant or in which they were uninterested. This, according to Wallace, applied in its most vicious form to religious teaching.

He believed that there should be complete freedom to adhere to any religion whatever, and he wrote to Lyell: "... it is a disgrace to civilization and a crime against posterity that the great mass of the instructors of our youth should still be those who are fettered by creeds and dogmas which they are under a penalty to teach.... It is equally the duty of the State to disqualify as teachers, in all schools and colleges under its control, those whose interests are in any way bound up with the promulgation of fixed creeds or dogmas of whatever nature" (I 431).

When the agitation for the disestablishment of the Church of England was at its height, he wrote a long article in *Macmillan's Magazine* against such a move. He did not believe in one religion for all, he did not himself believe in any of the orthodox creeds, but he did believe that everyone should be entirely free to choose his religion. His suggestions for reforms within the National Church were therefore revolutionary. He suggested using the National Church more as a super cultural and educational body than as a religious sect. The Rector would be the ideal cultured man, giving advice and instruction to parishioners and having an overall control of the church buildings within the parish. Rectors would not themselves be preachers nor teachers of any particular religion, but they would see that all religious sects should have the use of the church and access to the people of the parish. There would be complete freedom of religious choice under the great umbrella of the National Church. The National Church would be a cultural and educational organization. These revolutionary ideas do not seem to have caused any kind of a stir. They were clearly too Utopian to be taken seriously and did not appear relevant either to those who advocated disestablishment or to those who preferred to keep things the same as they had been.

During this period of spasmodic writing, attempts to ease his financial situation, and the building of his house at Grays in Essex in anticipation of the Bethnal Green Museum directorship, Wallace became involved in an unfortunate controversy that pursued him for many years.

In January 1870, Mr John Hampden, who believed in a flat earth, challenged scientific men to prove the convexity of the surface of any inland water, offering to stake £500 on the result. Whether from annoyance, need for money, love of controversy or some other unknown reason, Wallace unfortunately accepted the challenge, with the approval of Sir Charles Lyell. In March, with the aid of telescope and a surveyor's level, Wallace proved to his own and an umpire's satisfaction that a six mile stretch of the Old Bedford Canal near Downham Market, between Welney Bridge and Old Bedford Bridge, was not flat. The experiment, sketched by the two men's referees and an umpire, was published in various issues of *The Field*, and it was decided that Wallace had won the challenge. But Mr Hampden refused to accept the decision and demanded back the money he had deposited with the umpire. He was legally correct to do this because the law does not recognize bets. Unfortunately neither Wallace nor the umpire knew this. Not recovering the money, Hampden began a systematic persecution of Wallace that lasted for the next sixteen years or so. He abused him to all his friends, to scientific colleagues and even to his wife. It was an altogether regrettable affair, one in which Wallace felt wronged and irritated, to judge by the amount of space and detail given to it thirty-five years later in *My Life*.

In spite of these distractions Wallace's scientific work was making progress. He had written an important paper on the theory of birds' nests, and this led to a long correspondence with Darwin on the question of the bright colours of male animals and, with the earlier paper on mimicry, laid the foundations for his developing views on the meaning of colour in general.

These two papers, together with the famous early papers on speciation and others on natural selection and on man, were collected and published as *Contributions to the Theory of Natural Selection* in 1870. His main reasons for publishing this collection which had been written over a period of fourteen years, was to make clear that Darwin, not he, was the major contributor to the theory of natural selection, and yet at the same time to point to important differences which had developed in their separate points of view.

Contributions to the Theory of Natural Selection was well received, except for the final chapter on man which introduced metaphysics and spirits into evolution. He was accused of saying that " 'our brains are made by God and our lungs by natural selection', that, in point of fact 'man is God's domestic animal' " (WL 315). This was considered to spoil an otherwise excellent book.

The distribution problem was not being neglected. In 1871 his presidential address to the Entomological Society was concerned with the insect faunas of islands and, in particular, with the beetles of Madeira. He had no first hand experience of Madeira, but in the course of his studies on geographical distribution he had become acquainted with the various faunistic works of others. From a neglected work on the insects of Madeira by Wollaston he was able to reconstruct the possible methods of colonization of the island. He followed Darwin, against almost every other naturalist, in maintaining that many islands had been colonized by chance migrations across the sea. He would not subscribe to the generally held view that all islands with animals on them must once have had a land connexion with a continent. He was becoming more emphatic on this point which had become significant to him by his study of Celebes and other Malay Archipelago islands.

This subject was elaborated five years later when, as president of the biological section, he attended the British Association meetings for the last time as a regular participant. His address on the relations of living things to their environment, with a short discourse on the antiquity of man, drew evidence from island faunas, and he discussed, amongst other things, the tendencies shown towards unusual colouring in insular animals and appealed for more information from students of island floras and faunas. As far as the antiquity of man was concerned, his opinions had altered over the last ten years. Whereas earlier he dated man's origin in miocene days, he was compelled to admit that the evidence now pointed to a more recent date for his origin, sometime just before the onset of the ice ages, a view which has been held until the present day.

The elucidation of the biological problems connected with the colonization of islands had formed the basis of Wallace's work on the geographical distribution of animals. Beginning in the far eastern islands, culminating in the publication of *Malay Archi-*

pelago, it was extended to islands in other parts of the world. But islands, forming only a comparatively small part of the earth's surface and constituting specialized problems in distribution, were not the major problems in the world distribution of animals.

Already in 1869, Wallace was considering extending his range from islands to the whole world, but it was not until 1872, in response to the persuasions of Professor Newton and Dr Sclater and with the encouragement of Darwin, that he began to work seriously on the subject. He undertook to review the world problem of animal distribution; present day distribution, past distribution and the factors governing this distribution.

His personal knowledge of four distinct regions of the world, Europe, South America, Malaya and some of the Australasian islands, together with his own geological observations, made him well qualified to undertake this work. But, even for a man with such powers of shaping seemingly formless material, it was a formidable task. He soon realized that it would be impossible to take into consideration all groups of animals; therefore, he concentrated his attention mainly on the mammals and birds, applying his deductions from these two classes to reptiles, freshwater fish, molluscs and some of the insects. Plants he hardly considered at all; nor the other groups of invertebrate animals. In the event he was mainly concerned with giving a comprehensive account of the mammals.

He collected his evidence into two categories, the first to provide information and interest to the naturalist and traveller, and the second for students of particular groups of animals. He described the regions and subregions of the world and their characteristic animals, and then he went systematically through the different groups of animals and discussed their distribution. It was fortunate that "... my special tastes led me to some work which involved a good deal of reasoning and generalisation" (II 94).

No one before him had attempted to describe the present day world distribution of all major groups of terrestrial animals, no one had taken into account the evidence of fossil forms and, above all, no one had based such a survey on the principle of evolution and adaptation, of animals and of land masses. The concept was new.

In 1876 when the *Geographical Distribution of Animals* was published in two large volumes, the modern science of zoogeography came into being.

Geographical Distribution of Animals

Wallace described *The Geographical Distribution of Animals* as a book bearing "a similar relation to the eleventh and twelfth chapters of the *Origin of Species* as Mr Darwin's *Animals and plants under Domestication* does to the first chapter of his work" (GD *xv*). He had, in fact, at one time suggested that Darwin should write such a book and in 1867 had written to him, "I have been reading Murray's volume on the Geographical Distribution of Mammals. He has some good ideas here and there, but is quite unable to understand Natural Selection, and makes a most absurd mess of his criticism of your view on oceanic islands. By the bye, what an interesting volume the whole of your materials on that subject would, I am sure, make" (M I 181).

But it fell to Wallace to write the work, and it might be considered, from the success he achieved, that *The Geographical Distribution of Animals* should be compared more with the *Origin* itself than with *Animals and Plants under Domestication* as a contribution to biological philosophy.

The Geographical Distribution of Animals was the first comprehensive study of the problems of zoogeography.

Several works devoted almost entirely to vertebrates have appeared (Beddard 1895, Heilprin 1887), others, even more exclusive, concerned with the geography of mammals only (Lydeker 1896, Sclater & Sclater 1899). Atlases of distribution have been published (Bartholomew and others 1911, Joleaud 1939), and further general works on the distribution of vertebrates (Jeannel 1942, de Beaufort 1951, Darlington 1957, Croizat 1958, Furon 1958, George 1962). But *The Geographical Distribution of*

Animals has not been surpassed. It stands supreme because "in all geographical and geological discoveries the great outlines are soon reached; the details alone remain to be modified" (M I 288).

The reception of *The Geographical Distribution of Animals* was warm. Darwin wrote, "I must have the pleasure of expressing to you my unbounded admiration of your book . . . it is a memorable book, the basis of all future work on the subject. Reviewers think it necessary to find some fault, and if I were to review you, the sole point which I should blame is your not giving very numerous references." Wallace replied, "I confess the justice of your criticism. But I am dreadfully unsystematic" (M I 286, 295).

In *Nature* the book was reviewed: "Mr Wallace has already registered many claims on the gratitude of naturalists present and future. In their interest he has explored the tropics of the east and the wildernesses of the west, and has brought home numberless novelties. He has written one of the best and most instructive books of naturalists' travels ever yet issued. . . . But beyond all these scientific feats—and they are no mean ones—he has accomplished a task that will extend his fame even more widely amongst those who love science, as the author of the first sound treatise on zoological geography." And Hooker addressing the British Association in 1881 commented, "It remains to allude briefly to the most important general works on distribution which have appeared since the foundation of this Association. Of these the two which take the first rank are Professor Alphonse de Candolle's *Géographie Botanique* and Mr Wallace's *Geographical Distribution of Animals*."

The book consists of discussions of the problems of animal dispersal, the distribution of extinct animals, the characteristics of the chief faunal regions of the world, and the distribution of the main families and genera of terrestrial animals.

Of course, the catalogue of the distribution of the various land animals has been very much modified since 1876, and it is now chiefly of historical interest, as being the first attempt to make such a survey. Knowledge of fossil forms has also increased considerably since Wallace's day. But considering the small amount of fossil evidence he had at his disposal, it is remarkable that he was able to use it so persuasively. He laid down the broad principles. Only the details have changed, as he himself had anticipated. The regions and fundamental principles underlying their colonization, their geological history and the evolution and dispersal of animals remain in their broad essentials the foundations of modern zoogeography. By synthesizing several branches of natural history, geology, paleontology, zoology and the theory of evolution by natural selection, Wallace succeeded in classifying the world, as he had originally classified the islands of the Malay Archipelago. And whatever the changes in detail that have been made, or will be made, to the subject of zoogeography, it will ever remain true to say that it was Wallace who gave the subject its modern basis.

Before Wallace the subject had been static; Wallace used the theory of evolution, a theory of change, to explain present day distribution. He introduced the concept of time, emphasizing that distribution depended on the previous history of animals and on the previous history of land and oceans. In 1876 zoogeography became dynamic. It was in this that his *Geographical Distribution of Animals* was revolutionary.

Wallace was not the first to divide the world into zoological regions. As early as 1778 Fabricius had classified the world into eight climatic regions for the insects. Various later attempts had been made to locate zones for molluscs and crustacea. Latreille (1815) made zoological climates for the insects and arachnids. Each climate was worth twelve degrees of latitude either oriental or occidental. Prichard (1826) followed the latitudinal method for mammals, but he differentiated also Australia and the Pacific Islands. In 1835 Swainson defined five geographical provinces based on a study of the distribution of animals, mainly mammals and birds but including also references to reptiles, amphibia and land invertebrates. Neither temperature, food, foes nor habitats determined these provinces, but the will of the Almighty. Agassiz in 1850 had recognized six natural provinces based mainly on climate, with easterly and westerly subdivisions. It was Sclater, however, who in 1858 classifying the world into regions to account for the distribution of modern birds, provided the basis on which Wallace built the modern science of zoogeography.

Sclater divided the world into six regions according to the map shown in fig. 5, giving them the names: *Palearctic*, Europe, N. Asia and Africa north of the Atlas Mountains; *Ethiopian*, Africa and part of Arabia and the surrounding islands; *Indian*

(*Oriental*), India, Malaya, the Philippines, Borneo, Java and Sumatra; *Australian,* Papuan islands, Australia, Pacific islands and probably New Guinea and New Zealand; *Nearctic,* Greenland and North America to the centre of Mexico; and *Neotropical,* South America.

Many others after Sclater divided the world to suit the particular group of animals in which they themselves were interested but little attempt was made either to consider all animals together or to interpret their distribution in the light of past history. Günther (1858) fitted reptiles into Sclater's areas, Murray (1866) preferred to unite North and South America into one region and Africa and India into another to "explain" mammalian distribution, whilst in 1868 T. H. Huxley decided to divide the world into northern and southern hemispheres to account for the distribution of birds. Others made many subdivisions. Sclater revised his regions to fit in with mammalian distribution in 1874, and J. A. Allen (1871) produced a theory of circumpolar distribution and divided the world into zones distant from the north pole by varying degrees. Blyth (1871), taking mammals and birds as the criteria, made seven regions, including a Lemurian and one large northern region.

After a consideration of all these proposals, Wallace adopted Sclater's original classification, with his own amendments, including the renaming of the Oriental region. He considered

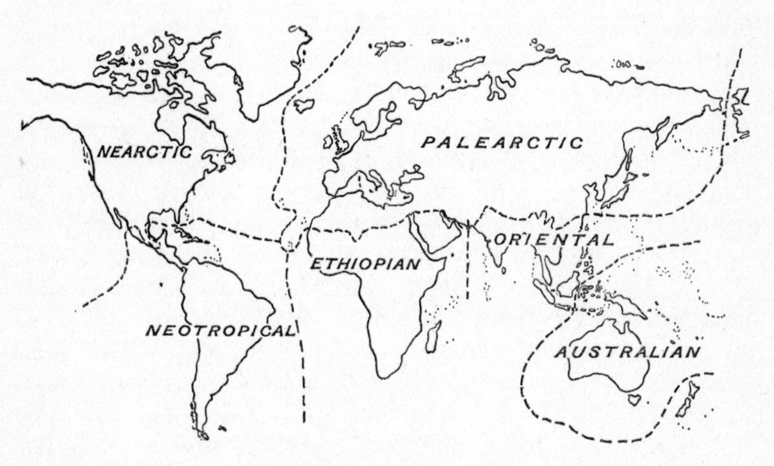

Fig. 5. The zoogeographical regions of the world defined by Wallace in 1876.

that Sclater's regions were the most appropriate to account for the greatest number of facts. For Wallace based his theories on a study of all the well-known groups of animals, even though he was guided to his conclusions mainly by the facts revealed in the study of the distribution of the mammals of the world, and to a lesser extent by the birds.

Whilst every effort was made to divide the world into faunal regions, each of which could be considered to have a distinctive history resulting in characteristic types in each region, Wallace considered that this classification should be regarded primarily as a convenience for naturalists, an approximate classification of a historical process. Moreover, he maintained that many regions could not be rigorously circumscribed unless they were bounded by ocean. "The land boundary between two regions will be, not a defined line but a neutral territory of greater or less width, within which the forms of both regions will intermingle, and this neutral territory itself will merge imperceptibly into both regions" (GD I 184).

He divided the world, then, into six main regions, and in the third part of *The Geographical Distribution of Animals* he described each region and its subregions. At the end of each regional section he listed the families of mammals, birds, reptiles, amphibia, freshwater fish and diurnal lepidoptera, indicating in which other regions they were to be found. In this way an invaluable check list of the distribution of the land vertebrates was provided. The mammals and birds were further detailed, being listed in the same way at the generic level.

He started by describing the Palearctic region because as "it is both more extensive and much better known than any other, it undoubtedly forms the most convenient starting-point for our proposed survey of the zoological history of the earth" (GD I 175). He described its geographical characteristics and climate. Then he discussed the land and freshwater animals of the whole area, as well as giving an account of four subregions. He showed that the Palearctic has representatives of most of the main orders of placental mammals, although no order is restricted to the region. There are the families of moles, shrews and hedgehogs, bears, hyenas, rabbits, squirrels and mice, as well as horses, pigs and camels, all of which are well-known animals of the region, but none of which is confined to it. But he characterized the region more particularly by its deer, bovids, beavers, badgers, pheasants and ruffs and by the peculiar desmans, or water-moles (*Galemys* and *Desmana*).

In the main, the characteristic animals of Wallace's Palearctic are the characteristic animals of modern zoogeographers, although some changes have been made (Ellerman & Morrison-Scott 1951, Vaurie 1959). Some genera which Wallace thought were restricted to the area have now been shown to have a wider range. Changes in classification have also made alterations necessary. But perhaps even more striking are the additions that have been made to his list. To the few families of butterflies that Wallace listed, a wealth of information on other terrestrial invertebrates can be added. A new family of small rodents, the Seleveniidae, came to light in Kazakhstan in 1938, and they are believed to be restricted to the Palearctic. To the families of reptiles, amphibia and freshwater fishes can be added not only more families, but also a comparatively detailed survey of genera and species. Out of this more detailed knowledge perhaps the most striking fact that emerges is the diversity in the Palearctic region of some of the amphibia. The urodeles, or tailed amphibia, are characteristic of the region, a feature which Wallace did not appreciate, through lack of knowledge. Almost all the salamander family and the related Hynobiids, for instance, are confined to the Palearctic.

Adjoining the Palearctic, south of the Sahara, lies Wallace's Ethopian region, with which he included Madagascar and the adjoining islands. Whilst noting the presence of some very distinctive forms in this area, he also observed that many otherwise widespread groups were absent from it. There are no bears, camels, deer, or common moles. One mammalian order, represented by the aardvark *Orycteropus*, is confined to this region. The hippopotamus family, the giraffe family (which includes the okapi), the lemurs (Madagascar only), the golden moles and the elephant shrews are not found in any other part of the world. But where Wallace listed nine endemic families, twelve can be counted today, all the additions being amongst the rodents and largely the result of reclassification (Ellerman 1953, George 1962). Amongst the birds of the Ethiopian region there are fewer pigeons, parrots and pheasants than might be expected in a tropical country, but six families, including secretary birds and ostriches, are found nowhere else. Reptiles are common; they include both typical tropical families and a few confined to the region, amongst which are a family of pleurodire or side-neck turtles. These turtles, which are more primitive than the cryptodires, are confined to the southern continents. Africa lacks tailed amphibia, but amongst freshwater fish there are several curious genera: for instance birchirs *Polypterus*, and *Protopterus* one of the three genera of living lungfish (the others are in South America and Australia). Wallace summed up, "perhaps none of the great zoological regions of the earth present us with problems of greater difficulty or higher interest than the Ethiopian" (GD I 285).

Eastwards of the Ethiopian region lies the less obviously defined Oriental region, which includes the westerly islands of the Malay Archipelago. Again Wallace describes it in four subregions, characterizing the whole region by, above all, its primates (apes, monkeys, lorises, tarsiers and tree shrews) and by its pheasants. In illustrations of the region occur also a flying colugo *Cynocephalus,* a tapir, a panda *Ailurus,* a chevrotain *Tragulus,* hornbills and drongo shrikes *Dicrurus*. To the three families of mammals, which he considered to be confined to the area, tarsiers, tree shrews and flying colugos, can now be added the spiny dormice Platacanthomyidae. Wallace listed many families of snakes and lizards, as well as crocodiles and the fish-eating Gavialidae; but he thought the gavials occurred also in North Australia, whereas today they are believed to be an endemic oriental family. A family of freshwater turtles Platysternidae, also confined to the region, was unknown to him.

Further east still, amongst the islands of the Malay Archipelago lies the boundary of the Australian region. With the easterly islands of the Archipelago and Australia Wallace included the Polynesian islands and New Zealand. The most outstanding feature of this region is the absence from it of all but a very few placental mammals, and the presence in their place of the monotreme and marsupial orders of mammal. "They [marsupials] are classed in six distinct families, comprising about thirty genera, and subserving most of the purposes in the economy of nature, fulfilled in other parts of the world by very different groups" (GD I 391). Only bats, mice and pigs and the dingo dog represent the placental land mammals in Australia, apart from recent introductions like the Palearctic rabbits. There are no native pheasants, but instead the region has confined to it birds of paradise, cockatoos, lyre birds and three of the flightless ratite families, emus, Dromaeidae, cassowaries, Casuariidae, and kiwis, Apterygidae (New Zealand only). One order of reptiles, represented by *Sphenodon,* the tuatara lizard, is found only in New Zealand; several genera of snakes and lizards, though related to Asiatic forms, are themselves confined to the Australian region. The second living family of pleurodire turtles live in the Australian region, occurring otherwise only in the Neotropical. There are no tailed amphibia, no toads of the genus *Bufo,* though for some reason Wallace considered that these did inhabit Australia, but there are a great many tree frogs, a genus of which is shared with the Neotropical and two northern regions. The freshwater fish fauna is poor. There are no members of the widely distributed carp family, but there is a lungfish *Neoceratodus.* "The Australian is the great insular region of the earth. As a whole it is one of the best marked, and has even been considered to be equal in zoological value to all the rest of the globe; but its separate portions are very heterogeneous, and their limits sometimes ill-defined" (GD I 387).

In the western hemisphere, in the New World, there are two zoogeographical regions, the Nearctic and the Neotropical.

In the north, the Nearctic resembles the Palearctic in climate and physical geography. In fact, the two regions have many land animals in common, such as moles, bears, wolves, beavers, squirrels, rabbits, goats, sheep and deer. But there are also striking differences; there are no hyenas or native horses, but four more or less restricted families. Grouse and large bovids appeared to Wallace to be chiefly characteristic of the region, together with the four restricted families, the pronghorns Antilocapridae, the pocket gophers Geomyidae and the pocket mice Heteromyidae (combined in one family in the nineteenth century) and the sewellels Aplodontidae. Just as the Nearctic has animals in common with the Palearctic, so it has some which are more typical of its other neighbour, the Neotropical, such mammals as opossums and nine-banded armadillo, and birds such as humming birds and cardinals. Knowledge of Nearctic reptiles was limited in 1876 but, in fact, North America has a number of characteristic members of this class of vertebrate. There are the garter snakes *Eutaenia,* horned iguanid lizards *Phrynosoma*; and the rattlers and Gila monster; there are snapping turtles Chelydridae and musk and mud turtles Kinosternidae. Like the Palearctic, the Nearctic has many tailed amphibians. Indeed, the greater part of this amphibian order occurs in the two northern regions. In a few mountain streams of north west America lives the primitive frog *Ascaphus,* unknown to Wallace, and related closely to a faraway New Zealand frog. "Though not very rich, and having many disadvantages of climate and of physical condition, it is yet sufficiently well characterized in its zoological features to rank as one of the well-marked primary divisions of the earth's surface" (GD II 122).

Finally, there is the Neotropical region, South America, part of Mexico and the Antilles. The Neotropical fauna is perhaps the most striking of all the regions. "Richness combined with isolation is the predominant feature of Neotropical zoology, and no other region can approach it in the number of its peculiar family and generic types" (GD II 5). The Neotropical, like the other southern regions, has an order of terrestrial mammals confined to it. The Nearctic and Palearctic are the only regions that do not have this distinction. In the Neotropical, the distinctive order is the Xenarthra, which includes sloths, anteaters and armadillos. Of the several modern genera of this order only one modern armadillo has left the region to colonize the Nearctic. A good deal of reclassification of this group has obscured the essential correctness of Wallace's observations of 1876. There are two endemic families of monkeys, Cebidae (spider monkeys and howlers) and Callithricidae (marmosets); vampire bats; many families of rodents including guinea pigs, capybaras and agoutis; and an odd family of marsupial rats Caenolestidae, only one of which was known to Wallace, and wrongly classified. The peccary family only just reaches the Nearctic. There are llamas whose nearest relatives are the Palearctic camels, and several species of tapir, related to Oriental tapirs. Otherwise there are, amongst others, raccoons, otters, bears, cotton-tail rabbits and opossums (marsupials). The Neotropical has no indigenous oxen, sheep, bison or horses. Of its many birds, the toucans, hoatzins, humming birds, tinamus and the American ostrich *Rhea* are the most outstanding. Boas and iguanas are conspicuous amongst the reptiles, and the whole family of teiid lizards and the short-nosed crocodiles, the caimans, are restricted to the area. The caimans were not recognized as distinct from alligators by Wallace. But he was aware that the Neotropical had side-neck turtles related both to those in Africa and others in Australia, although he did not realize that they were more primitive than the other turtles of the world, nor that they constituted two separate families. There are many tree frogs, and the Surinam toad *Pipa* related to *Xenopus* of Africa. Voracious

Alfred Russel Wallace, aged 39 (Singapore)

piranhas, electric eels and the third lungfish *Lepidosiren* are confined to Neotropical fresh waters.

In discussing the characteristics of the six main zoogeographical regions, Wallace had taken his classification further. He had defined subregions of the regions, areas which could be distinguished as often as not for climatic reasons. Thus there would be the European, Mediterranean, Siberian and Manchurian subregions of the Palearctic. But as these are dependent on climate to so great an extent, and have been many times altered, they are not amongst the most important zoogeographical contributions that Wallace made. They serve to stress, however, the important fact that, within a main region, animals are not uniformly distributed but are affected by climate, vegetation and other physical factors, as well as their own interdependence. Wallace's main purpose was not simply to relate animal distribution to climate and vegetation but, on the contrary, to explain why regions which had indeed similar physical and climatic features, yet had such different animals. His thesis was to show why, for instance, the fauna of Africa is not more like South America than it is, considering its size, shape and climate.

Wallace had preceded his survey of the distribution of most of the living land animals, of which only a few examples have been given, by a discussion of the problems of dispersal and a review of fossil forms. From an interpretation of all the evidence, he was then able to suggest a scheme of the probable history of the continents, which in its turn would explain their zoological characteristics.

He stressed four factors to influence the distribution of land animals. Geological, meaning that unless stretches of land were above water and within easy reach they could not be colonized by land animals. Zoological, in the sense that only those animals that had already evolved would be available as colonists at a given time. Dispersal, in that some animals are more easily dispersed than others: birds and bats can fly across water, but amphibia find salt water crossings difficult. Ecological, comprising all the climatic and biological conditions an immigrant could meet on entering a new locality: ecological conditions could prevent an animal species establishing itself in an area, even though it had arrived there.

To Wallace's four factors is now often added replacement, a special feature of the ecological factor. In a settled community most ways of life are filled. An invading animal to be successful must first supplant the occupant of the suitable niche. The replacement factor is, however, of limited influence in the early colonization of new islands.

Because Wallace believed in evolution, the theory of change, he realized that animals might not have been in the past in the same places as they are found today: "in establishing our regions we have depended wholly upon their *now* possessing a sufficient number and variety of animal forms, and a fair proportion of peculiar types; but when the validity of our conclusions on these grounds is disputed, we may supplement the evidence by an appeal to the past history of the region in question" (GD II 122).

If animals had not been created once and for all in their zoological regions, their former distributions must be discovered before any explanation of present day arrangements could be arrived at. It was only a study of the geographical distribution of fossils that could provide this information.

To study fossils as though they were equal in importance to living animals was revolutionary and by no means generally acceptable, for it must be remembered that it was only since the recognition of a process of evolution that fossils had been regarded as of any direct significance to the ancestry of present day animals, although their organic origin had long been realized in some circles (see Lyell 1830).

Cuvier (1812) had regarded fossils as representatives of groups of animals, which had been created and which then met with catastrophe and were eliminated. Others had supposed that fossils had been gathered in the middle east by the crusaders, who dropped them in the course of their homeward journeys (Voltaire 1746). Fossils, before evolution, had nothing to do with modern animals. Even in 1876 there were many, such as Richard Owen, who had not accepted the theory of evolution and its implications for the interpretation of fossils.

In 1876 the best fossil record was provided by mammals and it was, therefore, mainly on mammals that Wallace based his paleogeographical theories. For the first time, all the fossil records of the cenozoic period were assembled and related to modern zoology and to geography.

Wallace found, for instance, that representatives of the genus *Tapirus*, the tapirs, had been found in pliocene and earlier deposits of France, and yet modern tapirs were confined to remote

Geological Time Scale, in Millions of Years since the Beginning of Each Epoch (Holmes 1960).

Era	Millions of years	Epoch	
	0	recent	
	1	pleistocene	first fossils of man
	10	pliocene	
cenozoic	25	miocene	
	40	oligocene	
	60	eocene	
	70	paleocene	
	135	cretaceous	
mesozoic	180	jurassic	first bird fossils
	225	triassic	first mammal fossils
	270	permian	
	350	carboniferous	first reptile fossils
paleozoic	400	devonian	first amphibian fossils
	440	silurian	
	500	ordovician	first vertebrate fossils
	600	cambrian	

parts of the eastern and western hemispheres. Finds in the miocene of India and pliocene of North America confirmed the supposition that this animal must once have been widespread.

It was comparatively easy to interpret this case of discontinuous distribution. There were records of fossil tapirs through the whole area from the Neotropical to the Oriental regions. The only assumption that had to be made was that by the end of the pleistocene the tapirs of the Palearctic and Nearctic had become extinct, leaving widely separated modern representatives. This was a new outlook in the nineteenth century. It replaced the idea that tapirs, for instance, had been created in South America and Malaya and nowhere else, as the result of some Divine Plan. It provided natural causes for discontinuous distribution, and it used fossils for tracing both the ancestry of the group and the former range of the group.

Similarly Wallace explained the modern distribution of the camel family. Camels are restricted to the Palearctic, and llamas to the Neotropical today. Fossil evidence made it seem likely that the family had originated early, in the Nearctic, whence it had spread both south and east. Sometime after the end of the pliocene it appeared, from the fossil evidence, that the family had died out in the place of its origin, leaving only the present day arrangement. With very considerable increase in the knowledge of fossil camels this argument has not been improved upon, although the time of origin of the family in the Nearctic has been pushed back to eocene days (Simpson 1945, Romer 1945).

Another of the mammalian families which had a fairly well documented history by the nineteenth century was the horse family. Wallace knew of several fossil horses from North America and from the Palearctic, from which he argued that horses had evolved in the Palearctic, spread to the New World and then become extinct in their new homes. In this instance, a formerly widespread group had contracted to leave representatives only in the Palearctic and Ethiopian regions. Although the principles of Wallace's argument were sound, in this case the details have had to be modified in the light of increased knowledge. It would appear that the horses actually originated in the Nearctic (Simpson 1951a).

Other distributional problems were not quite so easy to elucidate from the known fossils, but Wallace used the same sort of arguments to reconcile the facts, as he had done for the better authenticated histories. Lack of complete evidence was not enough to make him fall back on creation, nor to manufacture a new theory. If there were gaps, they could be left for future zoogeographers to fill in. In the meantime, he would provide a hypothesis.

Marsupials had been found in miocene deposits of Europe and in the pliocene strata of North America, though living marsupials are confined to the Australian region and South America, with the exception of the Nearctic opossum. To Wallace it seemed reasonable to suppose, therefore, even though no fossil marsupials were known from the Oriental region, that the group had been formerly widespread and later, when the northern representatives died out, had been left as two separated and restricted groups: another example of discontinuous distribution of an earlier widely ranging group. Although many more and earlier marsupial fossils have been found since 1876 none has so far come from the Oriental region and Wallace's hypothesis still awaits proof.

But one of the most difficult problems that Wallace had to solve was that of the edentates. In the nineteenth century this group of animals, called misleadingly toothless, was made up of the anteaters, armadillos and sloths of the Neotropical region, the pangolins of the Ethiopian and Oriental regions and the aardvark of Africa. A few fossils had been described from miocene Europe, pliocene South America and late pliocene North America, purporting to be related to the edentate group. The problem was to explain how the group could have become distributed from the Orient to South America by pliocene times without evidently living in North America until much later. To get over this difficulty Wallace suggested that edentates must have spread through Eurasia and the Nearctic in early cenozoic times, whence they could have spread south into the Ethiopian, Neotropical and Oriental regions. Soon after this flourishing period, he argued, the Nearctic edentates died out; the South American forms prospered, sending a few into the Nearctic again; and the remaining representatives gradually diminished. Wallace was not very happy with this interpretation, but it was the best he could do with available knowledge, and the only way of avoiding some form of connexion between South America and Africa, to which he was absolutely opposed.

This may not have been a very convincing argument, but it was typical of the sort of reasoning he undertook in *The Geographical Distribution of Animals*. It is also an example of his refusal to be deterred by awkward seeming facts, and of his determination to find a consistent explanation for all distribution. He would not devise new theories to fit each new awkward case, which was the tendency of most of the nineteenth-century zoogeographers.

And certainly in the case of the edentates his reasoning was amply justified by later developments, developments which included a reclassification of the group. Today it is realized that the nineteenth-century edentates do not really form a naturally related group, their similarities being due to their similar habits of eating ants and termites. Thus the Neotropical anteaters, sloths and armadillos have become the order Xenarthra. The pangolins (Weber 1904), the aardvark and all the fossils that Wallace knew are not closely related to these Xenarthra; further, the pangolins and the aardvark are not closely related to one another either. The problem that faced Wallace does not exist. The reappraisal of the group and further fossil finds have made it possible to suggest that the Xenarthra radiated in South America from northern paleocene ancestors, later sending back occasional migrants to the north, and that the other anteaters arose either in Eurasia or Africa. The anomalies of distribution have disappeared with the reclassification of the group and, with additions to the ancient fossil lineage, the explanation can now follow closely along Wallace's line of reasoning.

From his study of such examples of mammalian history, in spite of the limitations of the time, Wallace concluded that many animals which are now restricted to one or a few parts of the world once had a much wider distribution, like the tapirs, the camels and the marsupials. Others, like the horses, had spread and then contracted again.

He further concluded that the main groups of land mammals, at any rate, had originated in the northern hemisphere, in the temperate zone. "I have given what I believe is the first connected sketch of the relation of extinct Mammalia to the distribution of living groups and have arrived at some very interesting and suggestive results" (GD I *viii*). He considered that most terrestrial mammals had been dispersed by migration across land, although a few might have taken to the water and crossed comparatively small gaps. With the increase in population pressure as successful groups expanded and further types evolved, the excess would have to move away from the centre of origin. If the centre of origin were the northern hemisphere, then obviously at least part of the spread would be to the south on normal statistical grounds of probability. There was uncolonized land to the south and congenial habitats, so that a great part of the spread would be certain to be southwards. As the northern climate cooled during cenozoic days, many animals would be forced gradually southwards with the changing climate, and this tendency would be exaggerated to its maximum in the pleistocene when the northern lands became covered in ice. Many northern forms would become extinct. The occurrence of the ice ages in the pleistocene had only recently been discovered, and Wallace emphasized its influence in pushing animals southwards, a view which he later expanded still further.

As a result of his survey of the present day distribution of animals and of their distribution in the past, he was able to conclude part three of *Geographical Distribution* with the important generalization: "If our views of the origin of the several regions are correct, it is clear that no mere binary division—into north and south, or into east and west—can be altogether satisfactory, since at the dawn of the Tertiary [cenozoic] period we still find our six regions, or what may be termed the rudiments of them, already established. The north and south division truly represents the fact, that the great northern continents are the seat and birthplace of all the higher forms of life, while the southern continents have derived the greater part, if not the whole, of their vertebrate fauna from the north; but it implies the erroneous conclusion, that the chief southern lands—Australia and South America—are more closely related to each other than to the northern continent. The fact, however, is that the fauna of each has been derived independently, and perhaps at very different times, from the north, with which they therefore have a true genetic relation; while any intercommunion between themselves has been comparatively recent and superficial, and has in no way modified the great features of animal life in each" (GD II 159).

On the basis of this general hypothesis, Wallace was able to give an account of how the various continents had been colonized during the cenozoic by succeeding waves of mammals, and from this he was able to reconstruct the cenozoic history of the continents.

Thus, he considered that marsupials had once been widely spread over the northern hemisphere and had found their way into the southern hemisphere at the end of the mesozoic. They had travelled through the Oriental region (leaving no fossil evidence) and made their way into Australia either by way of the island chain or, less likely, by a direct land connexion between Australia and Asia which had then been broken. Isolated in Australia for the whole of cenozoic times, the marsupials had prospered, free from competition, to give the present day variety which is found nowhere else in the world.

In the early days, South America, too, was receiving its first migrants, but according to Wallace these were not marsupials but mainly the ancestors of the Xenarthra, rodents and South American monkeys. The connexion with the north was not lost until mid-eocene days, according to Wallace's deductions. Then South America enjoyed a period of isolation, comparable to but not so permanent as the Australian, during which her original mammalian fauna flourished and diverged. Xenarthra and rodents and monkeys radiated widely, and so also did a very curious group of mammals, the protoungulates.

By 1876 Wallace knew fossils of some of these protoungulates. They were indeed like Cuvier's catastrophes, having no obvious relationship with modern mammals. There were, for example, enormous toxodonts, something like a cross between a rhinoceros and a bear: "They are allied at once to Rodents, Edentates and the aquatic Sirenia, in so puzzling a manner that it is impossible to determine to what order they belong" (GD I 147). Toxodont fossils had been collected by Darwin during his *Beagle* voyage, and they were almost as important a stimulus to his thoughts on the origin of species as were the birds and turtles of the Galapagos Islands.

In addition to the toxodonts which Darwin and Wallace knew, there have been found since then many other more curious South American herbivores of various shapes and sizes (Scott 1937). A fair imitation of both a three-toed and a one-toed horse is now known to have existed, as well as a large animal resembling in some respects both the modern camels and the tapirs. These South American protoungulates are no longer living today, but instead the more modern ungulates, such as tapirs, llamas, peccaries and deer, occupy the Neotropical region. From the fauna Wallace knew he concluded that South America had regained a connexion with the North American continent in pliocene times. This allowed the entry of the more modern animals from the north who competed successfully with the protoungulates and supplanted them.

Equally surprising in the story of South America was the early radiation of a stock of marsupials, almost comparable with that of present day Australia. When Wallace was writing, it appeared that the pliocene was the earliest stratum to provide marsupial fossils in South America, and so he assumed that the opossums of modern South America must have been latecomers from the north. But since then a large and varied fauna of marsupials has come to be known from the paleocene to the pliocene of South America (Osborn 1910, Simpson 1951b). It included not only ancestral opossums, but also a varied collection of carnivores, including one that was very like the placental sabre tooth tiger. These formed the carnivore complement to the protoungulate herbivores, and like them the marsupials were unable to compete successfully with the northern carnivores which invaded the Neotropical region in the pliocene. But Wallace was unaware of this interesting feature of his Neotropical region.

By arguing from what he did know of fossils and present day distribution, however, he deduced the way in which South America had been colonized by mammals from the end of the mesozoic to the present day. From the facts, he assumed that South America must have had a long period of isolation from the north, during the middle part of the cenozoic. This would explain the Neotropical fauna of today. Only the edentates would not fit into his picture.

Following the same arguments, he explained the fauna of Africa, but because African connexions were with Eurasia and not, like the Neotropical, with North America, and at different geological times, the end result was distinctly different. Africa, according to Wallace, was cut off sometime in the eocene from the rest of the world after receiving a collection of primitive mammals, mainly insectivores, ancestral primates or lemurs, and a few primitive carnivores.

There is no disputing Wallace's deduction that Africa, too, had a history of isolation during much of the cenozoic; but a recent survey of the available geological evidence suggests that Africa may have been separated from the north much earlier than Wallace had thought, even as early as the cretaceous (Moreau 1952). If this is true, Africa could have received, during the cretaceous, insectivore, condylarth and possibly marsupial mammal immigrants. Towards the end of the cretaceous, it is suggested, the land connexion was severed, and for several million years the only access to Africa would have been by island hopping over the Tethys Sea, a method of colonization which could have been used by early primates and, less likely, by carnivores. A connexion with Asia was then re-established sometime during the early cenozoic and from then, until the deserts became almost impassable, Africa could receive the more modern northern animals. Both the break from the north and the subsequent reunion were, therefore, much earlier than those of the Neotropical with the Nearctic.

Wallace considered the Eurasia-Africa connexion, through Arabia, to have been always an arid area, so that only prairie living forms crossed over. He suggested a special small corridor of forested land to let in the elephant and rhinoceros. This general aridity of the Arabian corridor might account for the absence of deer and bears in Africa and the presence of many antelopes. But it now seems likely that in the miocene and early pliocene the connexion between Africa and Asia was forested, and that it only became dry in the late pliocene. This would account for the absence of bears, as Wallace thought, because bears did not evolve until the corridor had become too dry for them, but it is more difficult to account for the absence of deer, except by supposing that, although they had evolved in time, they did not disperse widely until much later, or that their habitat had already been occupied by antelopes.

It was in the north that the main evolutionary advances were being made, according to Wallace. What of its history then? What of its differentiation into two separable regions? Have they been more alike than they are today or were they less alike at some remote epoch? According to Wallace and to present day zoogeographers, the northern land mass had evolved from a comparatively uniform area in mesozoic times into two regions which had been frequently, but not always, connected. Thus at some times the Palearctic and Nearctic were more distinct than they are today (eocene and miocene according to Wallace, pliocene according to Simpson 1943a, 1947a, b), at other times they were more uniform. The connexion between the two regions had probably been across the Bering Straits, but Wallace did not rule out the possibility of some more extensive connexion by way of Greenland and Europe. But Wallace did not enter into a detailed discussion of the making and breaking of the northern connexions.

During the great earth movements of the miocene and the pliocene, the Himalayas came to cut off the Oriental from the Palearctic region. The last of the regions could begin to develop its own characteristics. Before this time, fossil evidence has shown, that, apart from climatic and local differences, the Oriental region was almost indistinguishable from the Palearctic. From the pliocene onwards, the Oriental region developed its typically tropical fauna distinct from the cooler Palearctic.

This reconstruction of the general geographical history of the main terrestrial components of the world was based by Wallace largely on the study of mammals, both living and fossil. A considerable number of mammal fossils was already known, and land mammals, being somewhat restricted in their movements round the world, provided excellent material for the purpose. Mammals have only been in existence since the later part of the mesozoic, so that their history is mainly cenozoic, a period for which some attempt can be made to reconstruct the history of the land masses. Wallace was not prepared to speculate on the happenings of the mesozoic or the paleozoic.

There was very much less known of other vertebrate groups, and although, apart from the birds, they are of much greater antiquity than the mammals, Wallace did make a cursory attempt to fit their cenozoic representatives into the scheme which he had arrived at from the study of mammals.

Thus he suggested that birds, like mammals, had evolved in the north and spread southwards, although there was little fossil evidence to support it. Nevertheless, Wallace concluded that the flightless birds, the ratites, had once had a world wide range and "represent a very ancient type of bird, developed at a time when the more specialised carnivorous mammalia had not come into existence, and preserved only in those areas which were long free from the incursions of such dangerous enemies", that is, in the three southern continents (GD II 371). Flying birds presented him with greater difficulties, however. Even so, he was able to say of the parrots, for example: "Some primeval forms may have entered the Australian region with the Marsupials, or not long after them; while, perhaps at a somewhat later epoch they were introduced into South America. In these two regions they have greatly flourished, while in the two other tropical regions only a few types have been found, capable of maintaining themselves, among the higher forms of mammalia, and in competition with a more varied series of birds. This seems much more probable than the supposition that so highly organised a group should have originated in the Australian region, and subsequently become so widely spread over the globe" (GD II 331).

Reptiles and amphibia are much older groups and they are even more difficult to assign to a centre of origin, though the present distributions may be products of cretaceous and cenozoic events only. For these an early Old World distribution has been tentatively suggested (Darlington 1957). Wallace, too, assumed a widespread early distribution and subsequent extinction in some areas, but he could not consider the reptiles and amphibia in detail because knowledge of fossil forms was even more limited than it is today.

This then was Wallace's thesis as it appeared in *The Geographical Distribution of Animals* in 1876. Animals or, at any rate, mammals originated in the north and spread over the world. They migrated southwards into comparatively unoccupied countries as and when these countries were connected with the north, the flow becoming more rapid when the north cooled and finally became covered in ice in the pleistocene.

Objections to Wallace's synthesis were not long in coming. His line, his regions, his theory of dispersal from the north and his reconstructions of the histories of the continents were challenged. Modifications to his original thesis have been made. Many points are still subjects for debate.

Among the first objections were those that queried the reality or the status of zoogeographical regions. The position of the demarcation line between the Australian region and Oriental region was a case in point. Another protracted discussion has been taking place over the status of the Nearctic and Palearctic regions. Already the matter had been raised, even before the publication of *Geographical Distribution*, by both Huxley (1868) and Blyth (1871) who preferred to unite the two northern regions into one. After careful consideration of the arguments, Wallace had decided against this. The question was raised again by Heilprin (1883) who united the two regions into a Holarctic because of the similarities of their mammals and their climate.

Wallace gave much thought and reconsideration to this problem. He maintained (1894 SSS I) that, since the climate of the two regions is so similar and since they may have been united recently, it is very surprising that the faunas are not more alike than they are. Yet the differences are more fundamental than the resemblances, and he showed this to be true numerically, by counting the number of forms common to both, and the number of forms which are distinct. He found that, of six common orders of mammals, only 27 per cent of the genera were common to both Palearctic and Nearctic. Wallace concluded, therefore, that these regions were more different from one another than the Ethiopian from the Oriental. These regions qualified for full regional status since they fulfilled the requisite utilitarian conditions.

Wallace was constantly reiterating the point he had made in earlier statements, that the actual boundary of a region was a matter of convenience. Zoogeography, in his view, served two purposes, a classification of present day faunas, and a history of the faunas and regions. If the two did not give exactly the same answer, then that was of little importance.

A recent estimate of the number of fossil mammals common to the Nearctic and Palearctic shows that in the early eocene they had 45 per cent of their genera in common, but by the pliocene only 15 per cent (Simpson 1943a). A study of the birds of the Nearctic led Mayr (1946) to conclude: "It is not justifiable, as far as birds are concerned, to include North America either in a 'Neotropical' or in a 'Holarctic' region." There is not complete unanimity amongst zoogeographers today. Many would agree with Mayr that Wallace's Nearctic and Palearctic, on the evidence of present day faunas, should be kept as separate regions. Others would agree with de Beaufort (1951), for example, uniting them into a Holarctic because they have been physically separated from one another only more recently than any of the other regions.

The difficulties encountered in classifying the Nearctic and Palearctic regions are undoubtedly the result of their history. Geographically the two regions are separate today, but they cannot always have been so, and faunistic differences depend on the length of time for which adjacent regions have been separated from one another. So far no independent method of reconstructing the history of the northern land masses has been devised, and it must still be inferred from a study of the distribution of fossils.

Further fossil finds have amplified the history a little. Where Wallace assumed in a general way that breaks and joins had occurred through the cenozoic, today's zoogeographer would go so far as to say that the two regions were joined from the mesozoic until the oligocene, with the exception of a short break during mid-eocene (Simpson 1947b). This would account for the uniformity of the early fauna.

There may have been a break and a rejoining in the miocene, and another break and rejoining in the pliocene, the final break occurring some time during the pleistocene. This intermittent highway is generally supposed to have been across the Bering Straits, although there is no direct evidence for this prior to the pliocene-pleistocene connexion. On zoological evidence alone, Wallace and later zoogeographers Matthew (1915) and Simpson (1947), for example, have argued strongly in favour of this site.

The alternative route through Europe, the British Isles and Greenland is unlikely on both geological and zoological grounds.

Even though the Bering Straits connexion is generally acceptable on the available evidence, a further difficulty remains. It is not clear whether its far northern situation would provide land and climate suitable for the migration of all those animals which do indeed seem to have made the journey, in particular those of the tropics.

The bridge area is unlikely to have been wholly tropical, the absence from it of fossils of tropical forms seeming to confirm this contention. But, in spite of this, it may have been warm enough, and it may have extended far enough south to make it passable by ancestors of animals which are confined today to the tropics. Mammals, at least, can live within a wide range of climate and, during times of overpopulation or food shortage in their home area, may have extended to comparatively uncongenial lands (Matthew 1915, Simpson 1943a), to pass gradually from one zoogeographical area to another (George 1962).

Whether the latitude of the Bering Straits was subtropical through the cenozoic, or whether the ancestors of today's tropical animals were better adapted to a temperate climate, subsequently evolving in parallel, the Bering Straits remains the most favoured position for an intermittent Nearctic Palearctic connexion. Given the history of the two regions and their present day faunas, there seems no reason against giving each full regional status in accordance with Wallace's classification.

The status of Wallace's Neotropical region has never been seriously questioned, but many informed speculations have differed in the interpretation of the geological history of the Panama Isthmus, and taxonomists have queried the position of the boundary line. Geological evidence and modern zoological knowledge have combined to indicate a longer period of separation between the Neotropical and Nearctic regions, a separation that started not in the mid-eocene, as Wallace supposed, but in the paleocene, and extended on into the late pliocene. Moreover, the geological history of the isthmus seems to have been more complex than Wallace and his contemporaries had realized. Whilst there was effective separation of the two continents from the paleocene to the pliocene, parts of the isthmus had been submerged and elevated at different times to provide a changing sequence of islands between the two continents (fig. 6).

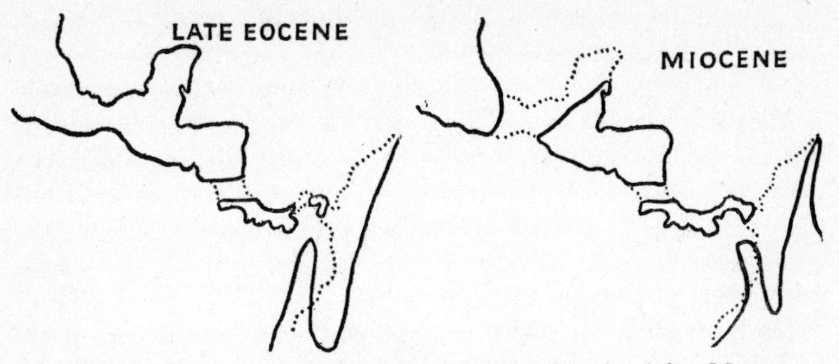

Fig. 6. Cenozoic paleogeography of Central America (after Mayr 1946).

Therefore, Simpson (1951b) has modified Wallace's interpretation of the colonization of South America, by supposing, from fossil evidence, that whilst the region did indeed receive its early xenarthra, protoungulates and marsupial ancestors from the Nearctic at the end of the mesozoic, the rodents and monkeys came in later by island hopping. This would accord well with their sudden appearance in South American oligocene and miocene deposits respectively. Being small, and some of them arboreal, they might be expected to have had more chance of success along such a sweepstake route than any other Nearctic animals of the time. But all this, in reality, is only an amplification of Wallace's thesis.

Taxonomists have argued that Wallace drew the line between the two regions along an ecological rather than a geographical break, along the northern edge of the rain forest belt, and that this boundary is, therefore, neither more meaningful nor more striking than one which could be drawn along the Canadian forests to cut off a circumpolar region. But this argument, although it may fit the facts of bird distribution, seems not to have general application. It remains true, however, that the exact demarcation of the boundary line is difficult. There has been considerable migration of recent animals in both directions along the piece of land that is Central America, so that the boundary becomes even more blurred than it does between some of the other adjacent regions of the world.

Wallace was in complete agreement with this. He emphasized that it was largely a matter of convenience where the line was drawn, because all regions would be separated from their neighbours by a larger or smaller neutral zone where the typical faunas of the two regions intermingled.

It can be concluded therefore that little improvement has been made on Wallace's classification of the world into regions according to the distribution of the better known land animals. The modifications that have been made are modifications in detail only. Today, almost all biologists base discussions about zoogeography on Wallace's six regions even if they do not accept his interpretation of their colonization.

The classification of the world into zoological regions on faunistic grounds was the sort of biological concept which was readily acceptable to nineteenth-century naturalists. It did not matter whether a man believed in creation, as their inventor Sclater did, or whether, as Wallace, he accepted evolution. They could still argue the desirability of a particular classification in more or less the same language. But when it came to a discussion of Wallace's reconstruction of animal histories, they found themselves arguing from different premisses.

Sclater, for instance, would accept the regions of *Geographical Distribution* but he found himself unable to accept Wallace's solution of the problems of discontinuous distribution. Sclater believed in special creation and, therefore, he could not accept the hypothesis that some animals had once had an entirely different range from that of their modern representatives. In 1878 Sclater put forward some particularly difficult examples of discontinuous distribution, and suggested that they could not be explained on Wallace's hypothesis. He asked, amongst other things, why lemurs (the lemurs and the lorises of modern classification) were to be found only in Africa, Madagascar and Malaya, giant tortoises only on the Galapagos Islands and the Mascarene Islands, and how the distribution of the little blue magpie *Cyanopica cyanus* could be explained, as it was found only in Spain in the west and in Japan and a few parts of eastern Asia in the east.

Wallace (1879) pointed out that lemur-like animals existed as far back as the eocene in North America and Europe. He supposed, therefore, that they had spread during the cenozoic to cover most of the Old World, including Madagascar. Deterioration of climate or other extraneous cause had led to their eventual extinction in the north, leaving today's discontinuously distributed groups. Free from competition in Madagascar, they had flourished there more than anywhere else.

The giant tortoises belong to the genus *Testudo,* which is of considerable antiquity and wide range. Continental species tend to be small, but according to Wallace are as closely related to the giant island forms as the island forms are to one another. Their gigantic size is therefore a result of parallel evolution in similar habitats; they are not an example of discontinuous distribution. Only one feature of the distribution puzzled Wallace. How did they get to the islands? Probably, he thought, by floating either as adults or eggs across straits which might formerly have been narrower. This view has lately been supported by Simpson (1943b).

The little blue magpie, a former more widely distributed bird, according to Wallace, had become restricted by climatic conditions, becoming extinct in uncongenial areas, those areas lying between its present homes.

Birds do not provide good fossil material, and so there is no paleontological evidence either for or against this view. But Wallace's explanation is generally acceptable. It is unlikely that any modern zoogeographer would quarrel with his statement that "the only mode of explaining the existing distribution of living things is by a constant reference to those comparatively slight but often important changes of sea and land, which the most recent researches show to be alone probable; and, what is still more important, by recognising the undoubted fact that every group of animals whose distribution is discontinuous in now more or less in a fragmentary condition, and has, in all probability once had a much more extensive range, to which its present distribution may offer no clue whatever" (SSS I 282).

Increasing knowledge has abundantly justified Wallace in his explanation of the principles underlying examples of discontinuous distribution. Fossils of camels, of side-neck turtles, of lungfish, have indeed provided evidence of former wide range and subsequent extinction. But although the principles have proved correct and acceptable, it does not follow that the details are equally valid. One of the most important details of Wallace's thesis was the then entirely new conception of a northern origin for mammals (and probably other vertebrates too), and the importance of the northern ice ages in the extinction and, therefore, partition of once continuous populations.

Matthew (1915) urged the acceptance of the north as the birthplace of the mammals, and on the whole it was not until recently that the idea was seriously challenged by new fossil evidence. Today it begins to seem too sweeping a generalization. There is good fossil evidence that Africa has been the birthplace of several groups of mammals. The earliest ancestral type of mastodon and elephant, *Moeritherium,* has been found in late eocene deposits of Egypt. The coneys (Hyracoidea) probably evolved in Africa and have spread only very little from their place of origin. There is evidence to suggest that man also originated in Africa. The earliest man-like forms, the Australo-pithecines, have been found in Africa, and only in Africa.

But it seems clear, as Wallace maintained, that the Bovidae (cattle, sheep, antelopes, etc.) arose in the Palearctic, probably in southern Asia, and expanded until they had covered most parts of the world. Additional paleontological evidence also supports Wallace's Nearctic origin for the camels and, although the horses have now been assigned to the Nearctic, there is yet no reason to doubt their northern origin.

Thus the orders and families of mammals may, as it turns out, have different areas of origin. Though it may be true that the majority arose within one large land mass, according to some in the Old World tropics, according to others in the north (Darlington 1959, Keast and others 1959).

But what of the first mammals? The earliest remains which have been ascribed to the mammals have been found either in European or North American deposits. Docodonts are known from upper triassic beds of Somerset, Glamorgan and Switzerland (Parrington 1941, Kermack & Mussett 1959); a symmetrodont from the trias of Somerset (Kühne 1950); and many other early types of mammals were widespread over the northern lands by late jurassic days (Simpson 1928 and 1929). There are earlier mammal-like reptiles which are known from deposits in Europe, North America and Africa (Watson 1921, Broom 1932, Romer 1945, Kühne 1956), but this is probably pushing the story back too far.

One of the difficulties in making definitive statements about the distribution of animals in past ages is that the finding of fossils is chancy. It depends on suitable conditions for preservation in past ages; it depends on conditions of the rocks today; it depends on the chance of quarrying activities in the right place or on the chance distribution and assiduity of paleontologists. Much more fossil evidence is needed before the complete story of the mammals is known, but it seems likely that the first mammals may have evolved in the north, but that subsequent evolutionary advances were made in different parts of the world. But if the northern origin is not entirely acceptable, all sorts of possibilities are opened up for explaining animal distribution in other ways than those propounded by Wallace.

In arriving at his conclusions, Wallace had tried to base his interpretations of animal distribution on geological principles. He had followed Lyell in assuming that the land masses of the world had been more or less as they are today, extensive land in the north and separate southern continents, changing in profile but not in general plan. But Lyell provided him with few details and, therefore, many of Wallace's descriptions of the state of the continents in past ages were deduced from what he knew of the distribution of fossils.

From similar evidence, other zoogeographers have arrived at different interpretations of some of the most striking examples of discontinuous distribution. They have put aside a northern origin, even though it seemed more likely in the nineteenth century than it does today. They have put aside Lyell's thesis of slow evolution of land masses. They have, instead, summoned up vast tracts of land from under the sea to explain every difficulty of distribution, to join islands to continents and continents to other continents: for each problem a new continental land connexion.

Already in 1776 Buffon had speculated on the possibilities of a connexion between Africa and South America, between Ireland and North America, between England and France, on account of faunal similarities. In 1846 Edward Forbes relied on land bridges to explain all the anomalies of the British flora regardless of any geological evidence which there might be to the contrary. A land bridge had been proposed to connect the Galapagos Islands with South America. Land bridges stretched to St Helena and the Azores. Land bridges were fashionable, and it was against this fashion that Darwin wrote in 1859, "I cannot honestly admit Forbes's view on continental extensions which . . . would lead to the belief that within the recent period all existing islands have been nearly or quite joined to some continent."

The most striking alternatives to Wallace's hypothesis were, however, the widely held beliefs in east-west land connexions between the southern continents. Australia, South Africa (Karroo) and Brazil were found to have similarities in their permian-jurassic rock structures, and this, together with the faunal similarities, lungfish, side-neck turtles and flightless birds, seemed to indicate to nineteenth-century naturalists a vast southern continent which was called Gondwanaland by Suess (1888). Gondwanaland was separated from Northland by the Tethys Sea. It was argued, therefore, that evolution in these two land masses had occurred independently until connexions were established from north to south sometime in the cenozoic.

Whilst there is no reason to doubt the existence of the Tethys Sea, which is today in part represented by the Mediterranean, there is little substantial evidence in favour of Gondwanaland in periods more recent than the jurassic (Termier & Termier 1960). According to their own particular preferences, zoogeographers have advocated either a continent in the south Atlantic between Africa and South America, or a continent in the Indian Ocean between Africa, through Madagascar and Ceylon to India. South Atlantis was supposed to account for the presence in Africa and South America of monkeys, porcupines, ostriches, side-neck turtles, lungfish and other freshwater fish; and Lemuria, in the Indian Ocean, had been invented by Sclater to account for the distribution of lemur-like animals and had been raised to regional status by Blyth (1871).

Darwin expressed his doubt of continents in a letter to Wallace, "... I do not say the most valuable point is your protest against sinking imaginary continents in a quite reckless manner, as was stated by Forbes, followed, alas, by Hooker, and caricatured by Wollaston and Murray ... I have lifted up my voice against the above view with no avail, but I have no doubt that you will succeed, owing to your new arguments and the coloured chart" (M I 286).

Wallace did toy with the idea of Lemuria at first, but eventually he dismissed it and concluded: "In the Southern Hemisphere there appear to have been three considerable and very ancient land masses, varying in extent from time to time, but always keeping distinct from each other, and represented, more or less completely, by Australia, South Africa, and South America of our time. Into these flowed successive waves of life, as they each in turn became temporarily united with some part of the northern land" (GD II 155).

Having dismissed Gondwanaland, Atlantis and Lemuria, there was still a difficult distributional problem to be faced. How was it that Australia and South America had certain animals in common? Marsupials, chelyid turtles and the tree frog *Hyla,* for instance. To explain similar distributional problems in the plant world, Hooker had suggested an antarctic route between the two continents, and zoologists like Hutton (1873) were quick to take up this as an explanation of the zoological anomalies. Although Wallace himself preferred a unified explanation for all distribution (northern origin and southward spread with subsequent extinction), he could not rule out the Antarctic route, particularly as there were no marsupial fossils in the Oriental region, and no *Hyla* in either the Oriental or Ethiopian regions to confirm his own hypothesis.

Little advance has been made towards a solution of the Antarctic bridge problem, except for the confirmation that a continuous continent, once warmer than today, exists below the ice. Fossil leaves of the southern beech have been taken from the continent (Cragg 1959, Couper 1960), but so far no fossils of the higher animals. Until this paleontological evidence is forthcoming it is difficult to make a judgment on the Antarctic bridge theory. In the meantime, it seems reasonable to regard the Antarctic continent, linked by chains of islands to South America and Australia, as a likely route for invertebrates and even for early vertebrates but too early in geological time to provide a highway for modern mammals (Kuschel 1960).

If there are to be no continent-sized land bridges, can all the similarities in the faunas of the southern lands be explained in accordance with Wallace's hypothesis? In some cases they can. For instance, there seems no reason to doubt that side-neck turtles and lungfish were once widely spread, dying out in the north but maintaining populations in the south.

Some of the puzzling similarities in the southern faunas have been shown to be superficial. South American monkeys (Hemprich 1820) and porcupines (Wood 1950) are no longer thought to be closely related to their African counterparts. Their similarities are the result of parallel adaptations to a similar environment, from an ancient common ancestor from the north. The same argument can be applied to many of the flightless birds of the southern continents. Natural selection has evoked the same response more than once, as in the similar case of the anteaters. The superficial similarities have deceived zoologists for years.

There are still certain similarities between the southern continents, however, which cannot be easily explained, either by differential extinction or by appeal to parallel evolution. What is the correct history of the marsupials? How do they come to be in South America and Australia and yet have left no fossils in the Oriental region? How is it that South America and Australia share a genus of tree frogs? It is possible that a single continental land bridge might be sufficient to solve these problems. Instead of continental links between each continent and its neighbour, a unitary link in the south through Antarctica, together with the known northern link, would provide the simplest bridge hypothesis to account for the distributional anomalies.

In the early part of this century a different theory was put forward which had the advantages of all the continental bridges but was, at the same time, a unitary theory. This was the drift hypothesis put forward in 1924 by Wegener. Instead of unknown continents going up and down, the known continents pulled apart sideways. Wegener proposed that the world was all one land mass

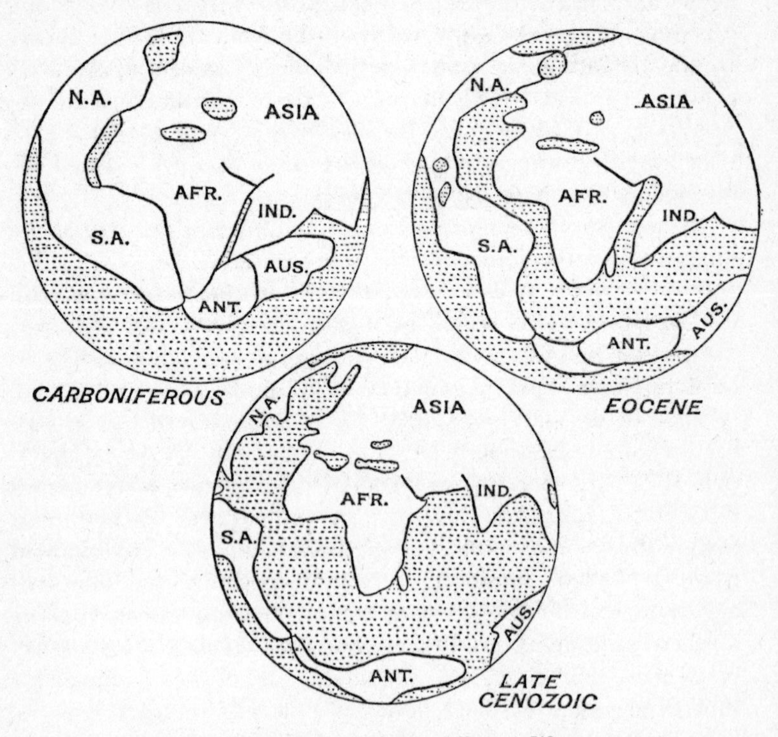

Fig. 7. Continental drift according to Wegener.

in the carboniferous (fig. 7). Gradually this mass split into pieces which drifted apart. Africa and South America drifted away from one another, losing touch in the eocene. Australia was at this time still joined to South America, only separating after the pleistocene. Thus the marsupials were able to spread between South America and Australia, as well as tree frogs, lungfish and side-neck turtles. Why the xenarthra and protoungulates did not spread with them is not explained.

Wegener's drift hypothesis would account for the similarities between the southern continents, but it makes it difficult to interpret the dissimilarities. Not only are there differences in the eocene faunas of South America and Australia, but Australia also has a small Oriental component in its fauna dating from the miocene. By the miocene at the latest then, Australia must have been in a position to receive migrants from Asia.

Certain botanical facts have been adduced to support the drift hypothesis, such as the presence of glacial floral remains in the southern continents and changes in the location of forests (Chaney 1940). And there is the unexplained presence in both South America and Africa of similar triassic reptiles (Neaverson 1955).

But even if Wegener's drift hypothesis is correct (du Toit 1937), it would appear from most of the evidence that the unity of the land mass must have been broken before the jurassic or very little later and, therefore, it could hardly explain the distribution of any but the earliest of the modern land vertebrates.

The coastlines of South America and Africa, when their continental shelves are considered, fit together reasonably well. The geological strata of the adjacent coasts are similar. On the east point of South America and the west bay of Africa there are similar paleozoic and early mesozoic rock formations. The likenesses do not extend, however, to more recent times. Similarly, although the floor of the south Atlantic is unstable and volcanic, suggesting considerable changes over the ages, there is both seismic and gravitational evidence that some parts at least have remained unaltered since the jurassic (Caster 1952). This would again put the latest date for east-west drift back to mesozoic days.

Recently, new physical measurements have reawakened interest in the drift hypothesis, and there seems to be a possibility that the problem will eventually be solved one way or the other. By measuring the orientation of magnetic rocks at different epochs and in different parts of the world, it has been possible to suggest that displacement of certain land masses has occurred. Thus India, Africa and Australia seem to have moved relative to one another since the mesozoic (Blackett and others 1960, Irving 1957). Assuming that the northern lands were more or less stationary then the southern continents would have drifted northwards (Nairn 1956).

The evidence of paleomagnetism is very suggestive, but it is based on certain assumptions which have not yet been proved. Should paleomagnetism prove that the continents have floated apart or that the ocean floor has expanded (Dietz 1961), alterations may have to be made in the interpretation of animal distribution. Until more precise dating and positioning is calculated, however, little can be done. Meanwhile, the general opinion that the southern continents have been further south than they are today might seem to lend support to an Antarctic bridge or Antarctic island stepping stone theory.

Drift is still an open question but it could provide an alternative for part of Wallace's distribution hypothesis.

Whatever the outcome of the drift dispute, it remains true that the basic principles of zoogeography that Wallace laid down in 1876 are still the foundations of the subject. The details may change, but his regions are still regarded as sound and a convenient way of classifying the world fauna. Knowledge may increase, but the principles involved in his synthesis of fossil material and present day distribution to account for changes in past distribution are fundamental to zoogeography. His acceptance of zoological and geological evolution, and his correlation of the trends, was revolutionary, and they must necessarily form the basis of all zoogeographical work.

Animals may not all have originated in the north, but wherever they started, they either became widespread, crossed uncongenial habitats without staying, or stayed at home. Some of those that were widely dispersed became extinct in some parts of their range, others remained ubiquitous. Their spread would depend both on themselves and on the nature of the obstacles they encountered, ecological, geographical or climatic. Whatever the final verdict on the permanence or impermanence of the position of the continents, these general principles will apply.

Wallace's contributions to biological thought in writing *The Geographical Distribution of Animals* were fundamental to the subject of zoogeography. He had indeed laid the foundations, and only the details have altered. But although the principles were revolutionary, the claims he himself made for his conclusions, that there are six main zoogeographical regions of the world, were very much more modest. "Zoological regions are those primary divisions of the earth's surface of approximately continental extent which are characterised by distinct assemblages of animal types. Though strictly natural, in the sense already pointed out, they have no absolute character as equal independent existences, since they may have been different in past ages, but are more or less conventional, being established solely for the purpose of facilitating the study of the existing geographical distribution of animals in its bearing on the theory of evolution" (1894a).

Surrey 1876 to 1880

Even before *The Geographical Distribution of Animals* was published, Wallace had begun to regret his isolation from the meetings of scientific societies in London. Although he had gone no more than twenty miles from London, he had effectively cut himself off from such activities. What had seemed the ideal state six years before was beginning to pall, and so he decided to sell *The Dell* at Grays "—mainly for two reasons; drought and wind prevent the satisfactory growth of all delicate plants; and I cannot stand being unable to attend evening meetings and being obliged to refuse every invitation in London" (M I 288).

Wallace and his family moved to Dorking. From there he was able to meet his friends in London and yet enjoy the countryside. He had no plans for further scientific work, and he seemed to have no inclination to develop any of the questions that had come up during the writing of *Geographical Distribution*. With this enormous undertaking he felt he had said his say on natural history, and he did not envisage ever writing anything more. As he wrote to Darwin : "I am amazed at your continuous work, but I suppose, after all these years of it, it is impossible for you to remain idle. I, on the contrary, am very idle, and feel inclined to do nothing but stroll about this beautiful country, and read all kinds of miscellaneous literature" (M I 297).

But he was not idle for long. During 1877 he wrote several book reviews, articles for the *Encyclopaedia Britannica* and an important paper on the affinities of the fauna of Madagascar; and before long he was preparing a new book.

Tropical Nature was published in 1878. In it he discussed the climate, vegetation and animal life of tropical countries, showing why the climate differed from the temperate regions, and the consequences of this difference. A great deal had been written about tropical countries, but as he wrote in the preface, "so far as I am aware, no one has yet attempted to give a general view of the phenomena which are *essentially* tropical, or to determine the causes and conditions of these phenomena. The local has not been separated from the general, the accidental from the essential, and, as a natural result, many erroneous ideas have become current as to what are really the characteristics of the tropical as distinguished from the temperate zones." He described humming birds as a particularly good example of the luxuriance of tropical nature, and then he added a few chapters on colour, in which he put forward his views on the meaning of warning colours, mimetic colours, and male colour and plumage, views which had been gradually taking shape for many years, and which had been published in a series of papers during this time. The book finished with a brief survey of the factors affecting animal distribution. There was little new in *Tropical Nature*. It was in some ways similar to *Contributions to the Theory of Natural Selection,* in so far as most of the material had been published before, including the presidential address to the biological section of the British Association (1876). *Tropical Nature* brought together the papers which illustrated the characteristics of the tropics. Only the working out of the causes of the climatic differences between tropical and temperate regions was new.

The Wallaces did not settle in Dorking. An American medium, treating Wallace for some complaint, suggested in one of his trances, that Wallace's young son was in danger and needed a more bracing place to live. Early in 1878 they moved to Croydon where they stayed for three years.

But money was becoming a continual source of anxiety. Wallace had never had much confidence in his writings as a reliable source of income and, therefore, he felt compelled to try again for a salaried occupation.

Epping Forest had been recently acquired for the public, and Wallace applied for the post of superintendent. But he was not successful, although he was supported by many leading naturalists, whose views were represented by the editor of *Nature* when he wrote: "We are sure no one can be better fitted than Mr Wallace to perform the duties attaching to such an office, and as, so far as we know, no more suitable candidate has appeared, the duty of those who have the filling-up of the appointment is plain" (1878). And one of Wallace's neighbours in Essex, a Mr

Mongredien, wrote a testimonial which shows the methodical way in which Wallace worked at things he was interested in. He was much more like Darwin in his perseverance, than like the mercurial Huxley. But he was unlike Darwin in not having the singleness of mind and purpose to go from one piece of work to another without the stimulus of need and the persuasion of friends. Mongredien wrote: "I have had the pleasure of knowing Mr A. R. Wallace for several years; and from having been engaged jointly with him in an undertaking connected with arboriculture, I can vouch unreservedly, not only for his extensive knowledge of hardy trees and shrubs and of their cultivation, but also for his excellent habits of business and his steady activity in the performance of whatever duties he undertakes. In the small estate which he had laid out and planted at Grays and which I have visited, he showed great taste and judgment both in the choice of the site and in the manner in which he made the most of its capabilities."

Wallace was more disappointed to lose the superintendency of Epping Forest than he had ever been over any of his other unsuccessful applications. Once he had made up his mind to apply for a post, he gave to it his wholehearted interest and serious thought. He had considered, therefore, what he would do with Epping Forest if he was given the opportunity, and he expressed his idea in a long article published in the *Fortnightly Review*. It described the present state of the forest, the characteristics of temperate zone forests in general, and made suggestions for improving badly denuded areas. He proposed to establish: "Several distinct portions of forest, each composed solely of trees and shrubs which are natives of one of the great forest regions of the temperate zone" (SSS II 82). In this way he thought people would be able to get an idea of the associations of trees seen in other parts of the world, for instance in the United States. They would also be able to form an idea of what the forests of this country might have been like if they had not been denuded of species by the pleistocene glaciations. This was a novel idea for reafforestation, an idea which could hardly have been expected by the commissioners, and an idea which could hardly have come from anyone but the pioneer of organic distribution. Perhaps it was too ingenious to appeal to the committee of the Corporation of London whose duty it was to make an appointment; perhaps it was also too costly. But whatever the reason, they did not appoint Wallace, and Epping Forest did not become a lesson in the geography of trees.

Wallace's financial problem was not solved. Luckily, a distant relative came to his immediate rescue, and transferred to him money enough to bring in about £50 a year. For the rest, he was forced to go on writing and lecturing during the following two years. He accepted invitations to lecture in Manchester and other cities; he wrote a volume on *Australasia* for Stanford's *Compendium of Geography and Travel,* as well as writing articles on many different subjects. Some of his articles were important contributions to scientific theory, for example on the evidence for glacial epochs in the northern hemisphere, others were on social problems.

Of the articles on scientific subjects, two may perhaps be considered more important than the others in so far as they were of direct significance to the theory of evolution. One was a defence of evolution with respect to problems of geographical distribution, and the other took the species problem one stage further on.

Evolution and the Distribution of Animals was published in 1879 in reply to Sclater's criticisms of the explanation of discontinuous distribution as expounded in *Geographical Distribution of Animals,* (see p. 146).

The Origin of Species and Genera (1880) was concerned with actual species formation, and the evolution of the higher categories of animals. After defending Darwin's theory of evolution by natural selection, he went on to discuss species formation, to dispel various misconceptions that had arisen, and to find causes of the origin of genera. He pointed out that there was far more variation within wild populations than anyone, including Darwin, had ever believed and that selection, although acting on individuals, needed this wide range of variability within the population to work on. Further, he stressed the importance of geographical isolation in species formation. "If this change of conditions should extend over the whole area occupied by the species, this one extreme form will replace all the others; while, if the area should be cut in two by subsidence or elevation, the conditions of the two portions may be modified in opposite directions each becoming adapted to one extreme form" (SSS I 298). This article followed much more nearly along the lines of the 1855 paper on species than along those of 1858 when he, like Darwin, was mainly concerned with establishing a generalization, the principle of natural selection.

After the question of species formation, Wallace raised the

problem of genus formation, and the higher categories of animal classification. Was it true to say that natural selection working on a variable population, with the breaking up of the population into two or more groups, was adequate for all evolution? Did it account for the whole sequence throughout the animal kingdom, or was it only the explanation of the coming into existence of species? Would it account for the evolution of vertebrates from invertebrates, or only for the divergence of the horse genus into the zebra, quagga and ass species? Wallace concluded that the factors concerned in species formation would indeed be adequate for the formation of genera, families and orders, but that there was practically no evidence to decide whether classes and phyla (sub-kingdoms) had been so determined, though he firmly believed that they too had been derived from pre-existing forms in some way, by some type of evolution.

This problem has continued to defy complete explanation. Many believe that the mechanism of species formation is adequate to explain all evolutionary sequences. Others believe that some other cause must be sought to account for the evolution of phyla (molluscs from segmented worms, for instance, or chordates from one of the invertebrate phyla). It might be creation, or pronounced changes in chromosome structure (Goldschmidt 1940), or some abrupt change in an important gene. There is little experimental evidence on which to decide the issue. Changes in chromosome structure, breaks and additions and multiplication of complete sets, can be the basis of speciation in some organisms, but there is no evidence that in themselves they bring about anything as dramatic as the formation of a new phylum as would be envisaged by the supporters of the sudden jump theory. Whatever theory is advanced it can be little more than an opinion, though some opinions may seem worse than others. One of the opinions which is enjoying popularity at present is the one that advocates great evolutionary jumps by sexual maturation of larval forms, neoteny. Thus vertebrates might arise from larval sea squirts (Garstang 1928, Berrill 1955), insects from larval millipedes (de Beer 1940) and copepods from larval prawns (Gurney 1942). This is certainly a little different from normal species formation, but no new principles are involved; there must still be variability within the population, and natural selection, and it would be reasonable to conclude with the words Wallace used in 1880: "That all have been alike produced by 'descent with modification' from a few primitive types, the whole body of evidence clearly indicates; but while individual variation with natural selection is proved to be adequate for the production of the former [species], we have no proof and hardly any good evidence that it is adequate to initiate those important divergences of type which characterise the latter [classes]" (SSS I 304).

Darwin was delighted with this clear exposition of their favourite subject and wrote: "As this note requires no sort of answer, you must allow me to express my lively admiration of your paper in the *Nineteenth Century*. You certainly are a master in the difficult art of clear exposition. It is impossible to urge too often that the selection from a single varying individual or of a single varying organ will not suffice" (M I 304).

These were Wallace's most important scientific papers during the two years up to 1880. But much of his writing during this period had been devoted to social problems. There was his article on free trade in the *Nineteenth Century,* in which he argued that whilst free trade was the ideal arrangement, it was a mistake in a world where every country had different ideas, and different ideas on trade. "These various instances do not support the view that we are especially practical in our politics, but rather that we are essentially conservative. We possess as a nation an enormous *vis inertiae*. A tremendous motive force is required to set us going in any new direction, but when once in motion an equally great force is requisite in order to stop or even to turn us" (SSS II 168). For this he was severely attacked in Parliament, not, as he said, on facts but because of prejudice. "My 'Reciprocity' article seems to have produced a slight effect on the *Spectator,* though it did snub me at first, but it is perfectly sickening to read the stuff spoken and written, in Parliament and in all the newspapers, about the subject, all treating our present practice as something holy and immutable whatever bad effects it may produce . . ." he wrote (M II 153).

Such articles were only side lines, means of making a little money or airing deeply felt ideas. Much more important was the work which went on from 1878 to 1880 on further problems of animal distribution, and which led to the publication of *Island Life*.

Island Life ranks with *Malay Archipelago* as the most generally successful of all Wallace's work, putting forward original biological hypotheses in a style free of jargon. *Malay Archipelago, The*

Geographical Distribution of Animals and *Island Life* must be considered the greatest achievements of Wallace's life for, together, they founded the science of zoogeography.

Whilst the material for *Island Life* was being gathered together, financial worries were still overshadowing Wallace's life. Each year saw a decrease in his investments, the results of his eight years' work and hardship in the Malay Archipelago, and each application for employment proved unsuccessful. At the beginning of 1880 he was considering applying to be Registrar, or Curator, or librarian in the new College of Science at Birmingham. He confided his anxieties to Miss Buckley, who had been Sir Charles Lyell's secretary. Unknown to Wallace, Miss Buckley discussed the problem with Darwin and, with Huxley's help, he drew up a petition to present to Mr Gladstone, requesting a pension for Wallace in recognition of his services to science. Darwin and Huxley were warmly supported by fellow scientists in this appeal. "It was signed by twelve good men, and you would have been gratified if you had seen how strongly they expressed themselves on your claims" (M I 313). To Wallace's joy and surprise and the pleasure of all his friends, Darwin, Huxley, Hooker, Balfour and the Duke of Argyll amongst them, the Queen was "pleased to confer a pension of 200l. upon Mr Alfred Russel Wallace". £200 was very much more than he had ever hoped for and so, at the age of 58, Wallace felt he had some security at last.

Alfred Russel Wallace, aged 82

Island Life

Darwin owed many of his early thoughts on the mutability of species to his observations of the fauna of the Galpagos Islands. The fauna was remarkable, and its composition unexpectedly haphazard. There were no mammals and no amphibians, but there were some curious finches and equally curious large reptiles. The observations that Darwin had made during his comparatively short stay provided him with material to support two important scientific principles. In the first place this island fauna provided evidence for evolution by natural selection. The variation of the finches and the turtles from island to island provided evidence of close adaptation to environment, by deviation from a common ancestor. The absence of mammals and amphibians could also only be satisfactorily explained by natural causes. If animals depended for their existence on creation, it seemed extraordinary to Darwin that they should not have been created wherever conditions were suitable for them. And yet this was manifestly not so on the Galapagos nor on other islands. Animals introduced to a new country by man had often been so successful in their new home that they had become a nuisance, like the rabbits of Australia or, Darwin's example, the frogs of the Azores. "He who admits the doctrine of creation of each separate species, will have to admit, that a sufficient number of the best adapted plants and animals have not been created on oceanic islands; for man has unintentionally stocked them from various sources far more fully and perfectly than has nature." (Darwin 1859).

The second scientific principle that emerged from Darwin's study of the Galapagos fauna was that there were two types of island faunas in the world, those which occurred on oceanic islands, and those which occurred on continental islands. Oceanic islands are of either volcanic or coral origin and have never had any physical connexion with neighbouring land, whilst continental islands are usually separated from a neighbouring land mass by only shallow sea and have, until more or less recently, been joined to this land. By reason of their volcanic origin, oceanic islands would receive their fauna only by chance immigration from across the sea. This would account for the absence of mammals and amphibians on the oceanic Galapagos Islands. In contrast, continental islands could be presumed to have acquired at least some of their fauna by direct access from a neighbouring continent. In recognizing two fundamentally different types of island fauna, Darwin was directly opposing the views of Forbes and his followers, who believed that all islands had once had land connexions with continents.

Meanwhile Wallace was also studying island faunas and finding in the variations in the parrots, pigeons and papilios of the Malay Archipelago the same support for the theory of descent and natural selection as Darwin had observed in the finches and turtles of the Galapagos. Later, Wallace developed the subject of island faunas in its own right, as a special case in the geographical distribution of animals.

Apart from the islands of the Malay Archipelago, which he knew from personal experience, he had already studied from books and specimens the details of the land fauna of Madagascar and the insects of Madeira, both of which had formed the subjects for articles and lectures. Islands had been included in *The Geographical Distribution of Animals,* but they were not treated in detail.

Island Life: or, the phenomena and causes of insular faunas and floras, including revision and attempted solution of the problem of geological climates was published in 1880. *Island Life* described the characteristics, the classification and the colonization of some of the main islands of the world. Where *Geographical Distribution* had dealt with the broad principles of distribution of great groups of animals, *Island Life* described the detailed problems of animal dispersal, and speciation. In *Island Life,* Wallace considered in some detail, for the first time, the distribution of plants, an undertaking which had been made possible by the work of Hooker (1867) from whom he received invaluable help in the task. Hooker had treated the flora of islands in much the same way as Wallace was treating the fauna. *Island Life* also gave a considered account of the importance of the ice ages in distribution and reviewed the possible causes of the phenomena. In all these ways it differed markedly from his earlier works.

The reactions to the book were enthusiastic. Darwin wrote: "I have now read your book and it has interested me deeply. It is quite excellent and seems to me the best book which you have ever published" (M I 307). Hooker praised the book in a letter to Darwin: "I am only two-thirds through Wallace and it is splendid. What a number of cobwebs he has swept away" (Huxley 1918).

Wallace followed Darwin in his classification of island faunas into oceanic and continental, surveying a large number of the world's islands in the light of this classification. He was the first to point out that there were great differences in the faunas of ancient continental islands and those of more recent origin, the ancient ones forming an intermediate condition between the recent continental ones and the oceanic islands. For example, the fauna of the British Isles could be classified as of recent continental origin, Madagascar was, according to Wallace, an ancient continental island, and St Helena an oceanic island. There were inevitably some islands which did not fall readily into one of these groups; these were the anomalous islands like New Zealand and Celebes whose origin made difficult guessing.

Before a characteristic land fauna could differentiate on an oceanic island, representative animals had to arrive on the island. Whereas continental islands could become inhabited according to the principles formulated for the stocking of continents, it was obvious that other methods of dispersal would become important for oceanic islands. Wallace, therefore, considered the means of transoceanic dispersal available to various groups of land animals. He believed that birds came to oceanic islands either because they had deviated from their normal migration routes, or because they had been blown there by exceptionally violent storms.

Terrestrial mammals, except bats, would presumably be less likely to arrive on an isolated island. Some, like pigs and deer, might be able to swim short distances, but on the whole it would seem that mammals as a class would have to rely on floating rafts to carry them across the seas (Barber and others 1959). In this pursuit, rats have shown themselves to be expert, colonizing almost every part of the world. Other mammals would seem to have been carried around successfully in this way only on rare occasions. "Such smal' animals as squirrels and mice might have been carried away on the trees which formed part of such a raft, and might thus colonise a new island; though, as it would require a pair of the same species to be carried together, such accidents would no doubt be rare" (IL 72). But perhaps this last condition is not as important as it seemed to Wallace. Recent work on members of several different orders of mammals, notably including bats (Matthews 1952), has confirmed the long suspected phenomenon called delayed implantation. A female is fertilized normally by a male, perhaps in the autumn, as in the case of some species of bats, but the resulting zygote does not become implanted in the wall of the uterus in the usual way and does not, therefore, start its embryonic development. The zygote remains dormant in the uterus until some stimulus, dependent perhaps on the coming of spring, causes it to become implanted and develop. In this way even a small female mammal may be "pregnant" for some seven or eight months, though the actual gestation period may be only a few weeks. This long delay between fertilization and birth might well mean that a female mammal could make an ocean voyage and arrive equipped to found a colony. At least some such consideration might account for the remarkably successful spread across the ocean of bats.

Wallace considered that land reptiles could probably survive a voyage on a raft quite successfully. To this can be added the conjecture that freshwater and land turtles may be able to float for considerable lengths of time in sea water without damage (Simpson 1943b) and some snakes and lizards are competent swimmers (Tercafs 1961).

The means that can lead to the dispersal of amphibians across the sea are less obvious. Amphibia are very susceptible to exposure to sea water. Many authorities have maintained that, as they are so unlikely to achieve a sea crossing for this reason, their presence on, or absence from, any given island should be regarded as a crucial test of the past history of that island and should determine whether it is faunistically an oceanic or a continental island. Wallace was not so extreme. He believed that amphibians might cross short distances of sea water and, further, that in the northern hemisphere they, or their eggs, might have been carried across the sea on blocks of ice. This would account for their wide range in the north.

Of insect dispersal Wallace said, and few would disagree with him: "In the enormous group of insects the means of dispersal among land animals reach their maximum. Many of them have great powers of flight, and from their extreme lightness they can be carried immense distances by gales of wind" (IL 75 and see Taylor 1960).

But terrestrial and freshwater molluscs were a different problem. Wallace found the explanation of their common occurrence on islands and their great range round the world the most difficult of all the problems of dispersal. The means of dispersal of such molluscs was one of the points of disagreement between him and Darwin. Darwin saw no difficulty in supposing that these land shells had been able to survive, on occasion, long periods of immersion in salt water or that, on other occasions, they had survived in mud on the feet of migrating birds and had in some such way colonized the islands of the world. Wallace considered that such happenings must have been very rare and that the explanation of mollusc distribution should be sought mainly in their great antiquity. Wallace visualized the molluscs spreading widely when the land of the world had had other connexions than have been manifest since the end of the mesozoic ages. After their widespread slow dispersal they might have become extinct in some parts of their range, to give the cases of discontinuous distribution known today. Their discontinuity was not usually the result of haphazard dispersal. "Land shells have therefore survived all the revolutions the earth has undergone since Paleozoic times. They have been able to spread slowly but surely into every land that has ever been connected with a continent, while the rare chances of transfer across the ocean, to which we have referred as possible, have again and again occurred during the almost unimaginable ages of their existence. The remotest and most solitary of the islands of the mid-ocean have thus become stocked with them, though the variety of species and genera bears a direct relation to the facilities of transfer, and the shell fauna is never very rich and varied, except in countries which have at one time or other been united to some continental land." But this was a modified view, and a considerable concession to Darwin, whose earlier comment had been : "I think you will have to modify your belief about the difficulty of dispersal of land molluscs" (M I 287).

Other groups of animals, except freshwater fish, he did not consider.

Whilst active dispersal of animals to islands must be considered of great importance, climatic changes in past ages had, of course, a direct bearing on the fauna of islands, of continental islands as well as of oceanic islands.

Wallace had been the first to point out the important effects that a cold northern climate could have on the distribution of animals. He was also the first to utilize the new knowledge of pleistocene ice ages to explain certain phenomena of animal distribution. "Before 1840, when Agassiz accompanied Buckland to Scotland . . . no geologist had conceived the possibility of a recent glacial epoch in the temperate portion of the northern hemisphere" (SSS I 59). Wallace visualized the glaciations as causing some northern animals to migrate gradually southwards, eliminating others completely, wiping out whole faunas of some countries, and bringing into being some species which would be adapted to a very cold climate, in fact, effecting spectacular changes in the fauna of the world, particularly of the north temperate zone.

There seems no reason to doubt this general thesis which was so new to the nineteenth century. Today, very much more is known of the actual extent of the glaciations. Their retreats and advances and their zoological effects can be traced more easily. But with this increase in knowledge has come the realization that the pleistocene ice ages were not the only important climatic events in the distribution of animals during cenozoic days. In fact, it is much more likely that they were merely the culmination, though a spectacular one, of a general cooling of the climate of the northern hemisphere from early cenozoic days onwards. A cooling which might have been responsible for a gradual change in the composition of the northern faunas and their gradual differentiation from those of the warmer south.

As the discovery of former ice ages was a comparatively recent event, Wallace devoted considerable space in *Island Life* to discussing their causes. It was one thing to find actual evidence of glaciation in the north and quite another to find physical causes for it. Several attempted explanations had been advanced during the forty years between the discovery that Scotland had been covered in ice and the publication of *Island Life,* and Wallace discussed the most important of them, and drew his own conclusions.

The most favoured theories depended either on fluctuations in the obliquity of the ecliptic (the angle between the equatorial plane of the earth and the plane of the orbit) or on the precession of the equinoxes caused by the conical movement of the earth's axis, or on the eccentricity of the orbit, though others argued that the actual amount of radiation from the sun had altered, that the earth itself had cooled from inside, that the temperature of outer space had dropped or that there had been a change in the distribution of land and water. On the whole the astronomical theories were those which were the most popular.

The obliquity of the ecliptic produces the seasons, intensifying the seasonal differences with increase in obliquity. The obliquity fluctuates with a period of approximately 40,000 years. The recession of the equinoxes, resulting in a slow shifting of the points which delimit the seasons, has a period of about 26,000 years. The eccentricity of the earth's orbit round the sun provides that there is a time of year when the earth is nearer to the sun than during the rest of the year. More radiation is received by that part of the earth which is enjoying summer when the earth is in this position than does the part which is in winter. The eccentricity fluctuates with periods of 92,000 years.

Of these theories, Wallace followed Croll (1875) in favouring a combination of the precession of the equinoxes and changes in the eccentricity of the orbit as the cause of the pleistocene glaciations. But he went further than Croll, for he realized, as so few did in the nineteenth century, that these astronomical variations must have been going on regularly in the past, and yet there was no evidence of frequently recurring periods of ice ages. Wallace, therefore, added to astronomical causes, changes in the northern land mass. He envisaged the lands becoming elevated at a suitable moment and, therefore, much of the north becoming land locked. If this coincided with a period of high eccentricity, Wallace believed that conditions for an ice age had been achieved.

It is interesting that Wallace should have been one of the few to realize that the suggested causes were not in themselves adequate to explain the onset of ice ages. It was generally accepted that one or other of these theories would prove sufficient explanation. Croll's theory had the merit of combining two causes, but it was left to the twentieth century to combine all three astronomical variables mathematically and obtain a fairly accurate estimate of the fluctuations in the amount of solar heat received by different parts of the earth at different periods.

Even the combination of the three variables is no more satisfactory as an explanation of the actual onset of the ice ages than was Croll's theory. As Wallace had realized, these variables only explain fluctuations in amounts of solar radiation in general. These fluctuations could lead to alternations of warmer and colder times within a general glacial epoch. "But although the evidence of *some* alterations of climate seems indisputable, and no suggestion of any adequate cause for them than the alternating phases of precession during high eccentricity has been made, it by no means follows that these changes were always very great—that is to say, that the ice completely disappeared and a warm climate prevailed throughout the whole year" (IL 148). Here Wallace had almost hit on the theory of successive retreats and extensions of the ice, which have come to be commonly accepted and have some confirmation in geological evidence (Zeuner 1945).

Astronomical changes may be the reason, therefore, for the fluctuations in the extension of the pleistocene ice ages, but the problem of the onset of glaciation remains. Some like Wilson (1957) would support Wallace in his claim that land-locked polar regions are important, whilst Umbgrove (1947) has postulated the rotation of the galactic system as an important causative agent. The period of rotation is estimated at 250 million years, and ice ages have been reported from the cambrian, the permian and the pleistocene, geological epochs separated from one another by roughly 250 million years. This is suggestive, but no more.

The ultimate causes of glaciations have not yet been established.

From a consideration of the ice ages, Wallace went on to discuss the age of the earth. It was relevant to animal distribution, because estimates of the duration of the earth as a habitable planet based on physical calculations appeared to him to be far too small to permit either the slow evolution of animals, which naturalists required, or the slow changes in the continents which many geologists required. Further, Wallace's own principles of geographical distribution of animals required considerable lengths of time.

Bishop Ussher in 1665 reckoned precisely that the Beginning occurred at 9 a.m. 23rd October 4004 B.C. Lyell, using paleontological data, estimated the length of time from the beginning of the paleozoic era (beginning of the cambrian) to the present day as 240 million years. However, W. Thomson, Lord Kelvin, calculated, from the then unexceptionable premisses, the time that had elapsed since the earth was in a molten state, and he obtained a figure lying between 400 million and 20 million years, but favoured the lower of these extremes. From a consideration of the time necessary for evolution of animals, deduced from what was known of the dates of fossil forms, Wallace made a guess at 500 million years since the beginning of life.

Wallace felt that animals could not have evolved in so short a time as Kelvin allowed them, but he was unwilling to doubt the calculations of so eminent a physicist. He resolved the dilemma by compromise. The evolution of animals might have been faster in past epochs than in those for which there was measurable evidence.

Modern work has shown that Wallace's compromise was unnecessary, and that even his longest estimate was too small. The estimate of the age of the earth has increased so much since the nineteenth century that there is more time available for the evolution of animals and plants than even Wallace considered necessary.

The discovery of radioactivity at the end of the last century revolutionized the methods of earth dating and the hypotheses on which earlier calculations had been based. Today, the rates of disintegration of radioactive minerals, the rates of sedimentation and denudation, the analysis of varves (laminations of clay deposits formed at the edge of glaciers) and the analysis of tree rings all contribute to estimations of geological time (Zeuner 1950). Where more than one method is suitable for the time scale, their correlation usually makes precise dating possible. Tree rings and varve analysis are used for periods since the ice ages, and other methods are used for the earlier epochs. Certain pleistocene fossils can now be dated accurately by estimating the amount of radioactive carbon they contain because the amount of carbon 14 diminishes after the death of the organism from being in equilibrium with the atmospheric content during life.

The result of modern estimates has been to give the age of the earth as about 4,500 million years, some 4,000 million years or more older than Kelvin's larger estimate. The first organisms may have been in existence as long ago as 2,000 million years, and the earliest cambrian rocks, which are the oldest in which fossils are abundant and easy to recognize, may be at least 600 million years old (Holmes 1960).

Following this general discussion of the principles underlying animal distribution, means of dispersal, climate and the time scale, Wallace turned his attention to the specific problems of the colonization of the main islands of the world. The second half of *Island Life* is devoted to a survey of these islands, their history and the history of their flora and fauna. He described the oceanic islands of the Azores and Bermuda, the Galapagos, St Helena and the Sandwich Islands. Then he turned to "continental islands of recent origin": Great Britain, Borneo and Java, Japan and Formosa. These were followed by ancient continental islands: the Madagascar group, and finally there were the "anomalous" islands: Celebes and New Zealand.

St Helena lies in the South Atlantic, over 1,000 miles from Africa and considerably more from South America. It is a rocky volcanic island some ten miles long by eight miles wide. Although it lies close to the Atlantic ridge it seemed to Wallace unlikely that it had ever had any continental connexions, a view which its volcanic nature supports.

Wallace described St Helena as, with the Sandwich Islands, combining "in a higher degree than any other spots upon the globe, extreme isolation from all more extensive lands, with a tolerably rich fauna and flora whose peculiarities are of surpassing interest."

He observed that St Helena, like the Galapagos Islands, was without native land mammals and amphibians. Furthermore, there were no terrestrial reptiles, no freshwater fish, and only one land bird, an endemic species of plover *Charadrius* (*Aegialitis*) *sanctae-helenae*. In spite of the ravages caused by goats introduced by the Portuguese in 1513, and the later wholesale stripping of the bark of the trees for commercial uses, so that a once luxuriant vegetation was reduced to barenness and rock, a considerable number of insects and molluscs survived. Many of them were of genera or of species peculiar to the island (twenty species of mollusc and twenty-five of beetle).

From his survey of the animals of St Helena, Wallace concluded that the paucity of the fauna and the presence of indigenous species was characteristic of an oceanic island of considerable antiquity. This being so, it remained to determine where the fauna had come from and by what means. The plover is closely related to a South African species, but the affinities of the beetles and the molluscs is less obvious. The beetles are "... so isolated in their characters as to show no close affinities with any existing insects; while a small number (about one-third of the whole) have some relations, though often very remote, with species now inhabiting Europe, Madeira, or South Africa. These facts clearly point to the very great antiquity of the insect fauna of St Helena, which has allowed time for the modifications of the originally introduced species, and their special adaptation to the conditions prevailing on this remote island."

Of the terrestrial molluscs on St Helena, several species seemed to Wallace, following Wollaston (1878), to be of recent introduction, while the others appeared to be more nearly related to European forms than to any others.

But taking into account all the faunal characteristics of the island, Wallace concluded that the greater part of the fauna had come from South Africa by chance sea-crossings. This view was supported by a consideration of the prevailing winds and ocean currents. The south east trade winds blow almost constantly, and the ocean currents flow in roughly the same direction, that is, from the west coast of Africa. A northerly branch of the Benguela current is known to bring driftwood from South Africa, and modern research has shown this to be responsible for the sporadic occurrence on St Helena of South African shore molluscs (Ekman 1953). There is every reason to suppose that it has been just such driftwood which brought to St Helena many of its beetles and molluscs. Others are not so easily accounted for. Wallace suggested that what seemed to him the European element in this fauna might have arrived by some less obvious utilization of winds or water currents, or alternatively that it might be representative of a fauna which had once existed in South Africa but which had since died out, or even that it had come to the island as the result of southward pressure on animals during the pleistocene glaciations. In considering the St Helena fauna to be characteristic of an oceanic island with African affinities, Wallace was in agreement with Hooker's (1876) interpretation of the flora.

This was not a generally acceptable point of view and many preferred to think of St Helena as the remnant of a South Atlantic continent, a point of view which is sometimes still held, mainly on account of some difficult features of the plant population.

Von Ihering (1907) insisted on a South Atlantic bridge because he did not see how else St Helena could have the South American element which it seems to have. He did not consider that available methods of dispersal were sufficient to produce the flora of the island. And in this view he was later supported by Scharff (1911).

However, the flora is mainly of African origin, like the fauna, and it seems possible that seeds have crossed the sea by the same means as animals, floating with currents, carried by the winds or by animals. Moreover, modern work has shown that, in fact, far more of the St Helena plants are of African origin than von Ihering had thought. For instance, Turrill (1948) names sixty-six indigenous species of which twenty-eight are seed-bearing plants. Twenty-two of the seed-bearers are represented by allied species in the South African flora, only three are allied to South American forms. The compositae, or daisy family, alone are of dubious affinities. Thus, modern studies of both the plant and animal populations mainly reinforce Wallace's contention that St Helena is an ancient island and an oceanic island. Its volcanic origin confirms its status as an oceanic island.

In contrast to St Helena there are the continental islands, geologically complex and stratigraphically related to a neighbouring land mass. Their fauna and flora can arrive along two routes, overland during a period of continental connexion, by sea after separation into an island. Depending on the remoteness in time of their separation, their fauna will be more or less like that of their continental parent.

Of recent continental islands the British Isles form a good example. Almost all the land animals of the islands belong to continental species, and they do not differ from them except in very small points. Only one species of bird, the red grouse *Lagopus scoticus,* is peculiar to Great Britain. Wallace added both the coal tit *Parus britannicus* and the long-tailed tit *P. rosea*, although they differ only slightly, in colour, from their continental relatives. Later ornithologists have reduced them to only subspecific level. Although there are no mammal, reptile or amphibian species peculiar to the British Isles, there are several freshwater fish.

Wallace named twelve different species of char, *Salvelinus* (*Salmo*), from lakes in the British Isles and three species of white-fish, *Coregonus,* and he remarked on their surprisingly limited distribution, sometimes being restricted to one lake. Thus the vendace *C. vandesius* inhabits a lake in Dumfriesshire, the pollan *C. pollan* two lakes in Ireland, the powan *C. clupeoides* Loch Lomond and lakes in the west of Great Britain. Later authorities have subdivided the genera into fourteen species of char and eight whitefish, each more or less confined to its own lake.

Wallace listed a large number of insect species peculiar to the British Isles, making the reservation that when continental faunas became as well known as the British these so-called endemic species might be found on the continent also. In fact, this has been borne out, so that amongst the best known groups of invertebrates no peculiarly British species remains in the lists.

Whereas a century ago many species of moths were known only from the British Isles, only a very few (like the meadow brown *Maniola*) today rank even as subspecies. It must be remembered that this is not necessarily due entirely to increase in knowledge, but in some cases to the use of different criteria for species determination. Whatever the criteria the conclusion remains very much the same, that the fauna of the British Isles resembles closely that of continental Europe (Beirne 1952).

As Wallace pointed out, this lack of differentiation in a fauna is typical of a recent island, and its close similarity to the nearest continent, typical of a continental island. There is, however, one other outstanding characteristic of the British fauna, and that is its comparative poverty in number of species. There are, for instance, only about fifty species of land mammal, Wallace estimated forty, compared with nearly a hundred in Germany, Wallace estimated ninety, and about seventy in Scandinavia, Wallace estimated sixty, and only six species of amphibians compared with twelve in France and the Low Countries. This suggested to Wallace that the duration of the colonizing period was short.

He knew from fossil evidence that the pliocene fauna of Great Britain had been similar to that of the pliocene continent, but that the present day fauna was of more recent origin than this. He supposed, therefore, that the British Isles had been submerged under the Atlantic ocean during a considerable part of the pleistocene, probably because the weight of the ice during that period had caused a lowering of the land. Most of the fauna would be annihilated at this time, except perhaps for a few relicts on the tops of mountains which might have survived on what would have been small islands during this flood. He based his supposition on the presence of boulder clay deposits in this country.

The fauna of the British Isles then had arrived from the continent at a time between the rising of the land at the end of the pleistocene and the time when the channel was cut and Doggerland sank again below the North Sea. "When England became continental, these continental species entered our country; but sufficient time does not seem to have elapsed for the migration to have been completed before subsidence again occurred, cutting off the further influx of purely terrestrial animals, and leaving us without the number of species which our favourable climate and varied surface entitle us to" (IL 319). This account, of 1880, gives a remarkably good interpretation of the origin of the fauna. The principles are entirely acceptable, though the details have undergone considerable revaluation.

One of the most striking changes that has occurred in the story of the British fauna is that which replaces Wallace's pleistocene submergence theory by one of glaciation (Scharff 1907). The boulder clay which he interpreted as evidence of submersion is now considered to be evidence of former glaciation. Ice and not water was responsible for the elimination of practically the whole of the pliocene British fauna, with the possible exception of hares, some voles and bees and the distinctive fish (Beirne 1952).

It is odd that the man who first realized the importance of the ice ages as factors in animal distribution should not have known that they were the determining factor in the constitution of the fauna of his own country.

Recent work has made more precise Wallace's assumption that only a short time was available for migration from the continent at the end of the pleistocene. The last ice age probably left Scotland at about the same time as England lost her connexion with Europe, about 8,000 to 9,000 years ago (Zeuner 1945, Movius 1942, Arnold and Libby 1951). Thus, invasions could take place only during the few thousand years (possibly two thousand) that the ice was retreating from southern England. Where did the fauna come from at this time?

Forbes (1846) distinguished five elements in the British flora, each of which he considered had come into the island across a distinct land bridge. In this way, the Lusitanian element had colonized southern Ireland by means of a bridge from Spain, two separate French elements meant two separate land connexions with France, the mountain flora came from Scandinavia, and the bulk of the flora from Germany. Similar derivations can be suggested for the fauna.

Wallace did not accept all five of Forbes's land bridges, believing that one from Germany and one from France was sufficient to account for the faunal characteristics of the British Isles. These two routes, Doggerland from Germany and Channel Land from France, have never been disputed (Wills 1951), but there still remains considerable doubt as to the existence of the others. Those who postulate the extra bridges do so for biological rather than geological considerations.

The Lusitanian bridge is required by some to account for the restriction of the spotted slug *Geomalacus maculosus* to south west Ireland and north west Spain. It is equally likely that the slug came to inhabit these two areas during a phase of wide distribution, later becoming extinct everywhere else. If this is a correct interpretation, the Lusitanian bridge is unnecessary. There is no geological evidence in favour of it.

Similar arguments can be used to dispel the other two Forbesian land bridges and to arrive at the same conclusion as Wallace. The British fauna is of recent origin, derived from Germany in the east and France in the south east. To these simple components need be added only a few relict species of earlier epochs (Beirne 1952).

Wallace was puzzled by the endemic fish. He could think of no satisfactory explanation of their origin and restriction to separate lakes. Eventually he decided their eggs must have been transported across country from one lake to another by chance, by birds or wind. This was a Darwinian explanation of erratic spread, uncharacteristic of Wallace. Wallace usually preferred theories of continuous distribution, followed by differential extinction to account for discontinuity.

A recent hypothesis comes nearer to a Wallace interpretation than his own did. It has been suggested that the char, whose nearest relatives are inhabitants of arctic seas, became resident in the British Isles during the last glaciation. They migrated up the rivers. When the climate became warmer the main marine population went north, but the river forms were cut off in the cold upper reaches of the rivers or in the depths of cold lakes. Cut off from immigrants from the sea, the isolated populations would become fully adapted to freshwater life (or die out) and become differentiated sooner or later from the original population and from one another (Beirne 1952).

Britain has all the characteristics of a recent continental island. In contrast, Madagascar was classified as an ancient continental island.

Wallace argued, from the fauna, that Madagascar had been connected with Africa until some time in the early cenozoic, losing this connexion in the late eocene. The fauna of Madagascar is highly differentiated, with four endemic families of mammals, as well as endemic birds, reptiles and amphibia. There are no strictly freshwater fish.

All the lemurs of the world, comprising three families, are confined to Madagascar, together with the tenrecs, a family of specialized insectivores. A subfamily of cricetid mice and many genera of civets are also characteristic of the island. There are a few modern African mammals such as shrews, murid mice, the bush pig and the river hog, hardly differentiated from their continental relatives.

A substantial part of the bird fauna is equally distinctive; the rest shows either Oriental or Ethiopian affinities, with a bias towards the Ethiopian. Even so, like the mammals, many common African birds are absent. There are no ostriches, secretary birds or mousebirds (Rand 1936).

Malagasy reptiles and amphibia are mainly common Old World derivatives, with close African affinities although a few are allied to Oriental forms. Again, common African forms are absent; agamids for example. But the reptile fauna is enriched by iguanid lizards and side-neck turtles typical of the New World.

To account for this highly individual vertebrate fauna, Wallace proposed that there had been a land connexion with Africa, followed by a break and subsequent isolation. During the early days of continental continuity, representatives of the insectivores, primates and civets, some birds, reptiles, and amphibia made their way to Madagascar. This, according to Wallace, would be happening during the eocene, when insectivores, lemuroid primates and iguanid lizards, for example, were widespread throughout the world.

Late in the eocene Madagascar became an island. The isolated fauna evolved along its own special lines, reinforced occasionally by migrants from across the sea, either from Africa or, less commonly, from the east. Thus, the river hog *Potamochoerus* and the fossil pygmy hippo *Choeropsis* could be considered comparatively recent arrivals across the Mozambique Channel from Africa, and the magpie robin *Copsychus* and a few other birds, recent arrivals from the Oriental region, by way of the islands of the Indian Ocean. The shrews, murid mice and the bush pig are probably even more recent human introductions.

This was a novel solution of the Madagascar problem. The alternative in the nineteenth century was Lemuria.

In *Island Life* Wallace dismissed all possibility of Lemuria, on the grounds that the endemic fauna of Madagascar was derived from once widespread forms, while forms with close African or Oriental affinities were too recently arrived to have been served by a land bridge of continental extent.

Later workers have questioned the age of Malagasy isolation. A few would put the breakaway from Africa at a more recent date than the eocene, but many would push it back at least to the jurassic.

According to Matthew (1915) and Simpson (1940, 1952), Madagascar has been isolated from Africa during the whole of mammalian history. The number of mammal orders represented on the island is too small, according to Simpson, to be evidence of anything but chance sea crossings. He estimates that twelve or fewer mammalian colonizations in 75 million years account for the whole mammalian fauna of the island. Such a long period of isolation, perhaps since the jurassic, could account for the curious assortment of animals on Madagascar. It could account, in particular, for the absence from it of ancient African forms, such as agamid and varanid lizards. Evidence for the interpretation of earlier events is meagre, but there is a suggestion from dinosaur distribution that Madagascar had some land connexions until the jurassic (Huene and Matley 1933, Darlington 1957).

Only further paleontological and geological evidence will date the separation of Madagascar into an island.

The island of New Zealand, one of Wallace's anomalous islands, is less easily classified. There are no endemic mammals, except for insectivorous bats, one genus allied to an Australian form and a relict family restricted to New Zealand. On the whole, the birds are unlike Australian birds, and in many respects they are very peculiar. The kea parrots, *Nestor,* form an aberrant endemic genus of two living and two extinct species. A flightless goose *Cnemiornis* is known from pleistocene deposits of the island. There are flightless kiwis and extinct flightless moas. Of other vertebrates, *Sphenodon,* a primitive reptile, survives only in New Zealand, whilst fossil relatives very similar to it have been found from the triassic to the eocene in North America and Europe. The only endemic amphibian is a remarkable genus *Liopelma* of great antiquity, whose only living relative *Ascaphus* is found in North America. A freshwater fish *Galaxias* is related to forms from Tierra del Fuego.

The geological structure of New Zealand and the presence of

so many flightless birds, convinced Wallace that New Zealand must have had a continental land connexion at some time. But on this assumption he was at a loss to account for the absence of mammals. The connexion must have been a very long time ago. Furthermore, he was not entirely sure with which continent New Zealand was most likely to have been connected. Originally he thought there had been no connexion with Australia but that it was possible that an Antarctic bridge had once existed, as Hutton (1873) had supposed. Wallace considered that there was insufficient evidence to show that New Zealand had actually been connected to such a southern land mass, but that it was possible that there had been islands extensive enough to serve as stepping stones for a few animals to make their way from South America to New Zealand and, indeed, even into Australia. Later, he modified this view on the grounds that the flora of New Zealand had certain resemblances to that of eastern Australia. He then pictured New Zealand joined to eastern Australia in the cretaceous, with western Australia as a separate entity. New Zealand and Australia could share an archaic fauna at this time, a fauna that New Zealand retained when the connexion was subsequently lost. This same archaic fauna in eastern Australia was then overrun by its western more Asiatic fauna.

Modern views on New Zealand are still as conflicting as those of the nineteenth century. It seems likely that New Zealand received most of its vertebrates from Australia, but whether the mesozoic forms, *Sphenodon* and *Liopelma*, arrived by land, or whether all New Zealand vertebrates should be regarded as chance immigrants from across the sea at various times (Darlington 1957) is still a matter for conjecture. Even the fish *Galaxias* is tolerant of sea water and could be a casual immigrant, and most ornithologists would agree that flying birds often evolve into ground living, flightless forms on isolated islands (Matthew 1915, Stresemann 1927-34).

Since Wallace's time, more has become known of the invertebrates of New Zealand. Mutelid mussels and parastacid crayfishes are typical of New Zealand, Australia and New Guinea. No parastacid fossils are known, and the other living representatives occur in South America and Madagascar. Mutelid mussels are found in South America and Africa, and yet some of the old-established freshwater mussels, unionids, are not found in New Zealand, although they occur in Australia. There has been a revival, therefore, of the Antarctic bridge theory in some circles. For if the Antarctic bridge is not accepted it must be admitted that the distribution of the mussels and the crayfish is difficult to account for in the present state of knowledge, although some (Rick 1959) support a theory of separate freshwater derivatives from common marine ancestry. Wallace's refusal to erect a bridge to account for any particularly difficult problem of distribution was always justified by later work. However, the recent work on paleomagnetism might be thought to lend support to a more southerly position for New Zealand in earlier days and therefore a closer approximation, if not an actual junction, with the southern continents.

From the study of islands in general, Wallace concluded that those that had been isolated from land the longest had more endemic species than those whose separation from other land was recent. From this he argued back that islands that have many endemic species are older than those that do not. In other words, isolation gives rise to new species, and a long time is essential. "Under the different conditions of existence in various portions of its area, different variations from the type would be selected, and, were they completely isolated, would soon become distinctly modified forms" (NS 143). He also considered that there is frequently less competition for a particular place in the community on an island. Chance immigrants, therefore, may have all sorts of evolutionary possibilities opened up to them, possibilities not available in the area of their origin. This would account not only for the colour variations he had observed, but also for such phenomena as the huge land tortoises of the Galapagos and the flightless dodo of Mauritius.

However, island faunas do not always show successful adaptive radiation of their colonists. This may be due, as some believe, to the general difficulties of life which outweigh any possible gains from the absence of predators (Buxton 1938). In other cases, it can be related directly to the size of the population on any particular island. Species tend to become extinct if the population is small. Of seventy-six endemic land birds of Hawaii, eighteen are now extinct, while eleven forms have become extinct in the New Zealand group in historical times (Mayr 1942). According to calculations made by Wright (1931), a very small population does not evolve rapidly because all the individuals soon become the same as one another as the result of intense inbreeding, and it is likely that in such cases the species very soon becomes extinct, although extinction is not inevitable. In large populations individual characteristics cannot spread fast enough for rapid evolution. The ideal place, then, is an island that is not too big and not too small: this provides isolation, and room for an adequate sized population.

The peculiarities of island faunas could only be accounted for by the interaction of complex physical and biological factors, and Wallace concluded *Island Life*: "I trust that the reader ... will be imbued with the conviction ... of the complete interdependence of organic and inorganic nature. Not only does the marvellous structure of each organised being involve the whole past history of the earth, but such apparently unimportant facts as the presence of certain types of plants and animals in one island rather than in another, are now shown to be dependent on the long series of past geological changes—on those marvellous astronomical revolutions which cause periodic variation of terrestrial climates—on the apparently fortuitous action of storms and currents in the conveyance of germs—and on the endlessly varied actions and reactions of organised beings on each other" (IL 511).

Mimicry and other Protective Resemblances

From his days as a professional naturalist in South America, Wallace had been impressed, as all naturalists must be, by the range of colour variation in animals. At an early period he had noticed that quite closely related species could differ strikingly from one another in their colours and patterns. Experience in the Malay Archipelago had roused his curiosity even more, making him anxious to find the explanation of apparently meaningless colour variations. To his own satisfaction he had accounted for the colours of the parrots and the pigeons by the absence of mammalian predators in the eastern islands of the Archipelago. But more detailed problems of colour differences required his attention. He wanted to know the meaning of all animal colour, and out of his search for this grew his contributions to the theory of mimicry and polymorphism, warning colours, sexual colours and concealing colours. His ideas grew slowly, and they developed through a series of papers into finally more extensive discussions in *Tropical Nature* (1878) and *Darwinism* (1889). The general attitude to animal and plant colours before the middle of the nineteenth century was expressed by A. Tylor in 1886 writing *Colouration in Animals and Plants*:

"Before Darwin published his remarkable and memorable work on the Origin of Species, the decoration of animals and plants was a mystery as much hidden to the majority as the beauty of the rainbow before Newton analysed light. That the world teemed with beauty in form and colour was all we knew, and the only guess that could be made as to its uses was the vague and unsatisfactory suggestion that it was appointed for the delight of man."

It was not strictly true to say that no one had thought about the meanings of animal colours other than for the delight of man, before 1858. Erasmus Darwin had drawn attention to the function of colour as a protective device in 1788, and he wrote in 1790: "The colours of insects and many smaller animals contribute to conceal them from the larger ones which prey upon them. Caterpillars which feed on leaves are generally green; earthworms the colour of the earth which they inhabit; butterflies, which frequent flowers are coloured like them, small birds which frequent hedges have greenish backs like the leaves, and bright coloured bellies like the sky, and are hence less visible to the hawk, who passes under them or over them." But it is true to say that no one had seen how the colour could become established. Erasmus Darwin thought that the environment must directly evoke colours, or if it did not, then the reason for colour in the animal kingdom was one of "design". "Hence there is apparent design in the colours of animals, whilst those of vegetables seem consequent to the other properties of the materials which possess them."

The theory of natural selection was more precise. From 1858 onwards the problem was no longer whether the colour of living organisms was created for man's enjoyment or whether it had happened by natural means; the problem was to discover what use colour was to any particular animal or group of animals in the struggle for existence.

Both Darwin and Wallace had given only cursory consideration to the problem of animal and plant colour in 1858, Darwin then was already attributing colour divergence to sexual selection. "Besides this natural means of selection, . . . there is a second agency at work in most unisexual animals . . . namely, the struggle of males for females." Wallace tended to regard colour as just one of the many changes which would take place under the influence of natural selection. "Even a change of colour might, by rendering them more or less distinguishable, affect their safety. . . . Even the peculiar colours of many animals, more especially of insects, so closely resembling the soil or leaves or bark on which they habitually reside, are explained on the same principle; for though in the course of ages varieties of many tints may have occurred, *yet those races having colours best adapted to concealment from their enemies would inevitably survive the longest*" (NS 42).

In 1859 Darwin wrote briefly of the possible direct effects of environment on colour. "Some little influence may be attributed to climate, food, etc.: thus, E. Forbes speaks confidently that shells at their southern limit, and when living in shallow water, are more brightly coloured than those of the same species further north or from greater depths."

Wallace was becoming convinced that colour was subject to the same laws of nature as any other characteristics of an animal or plant. The colour of an animal was somehow the result of natural selection. But it was not until 1867 that he was prepared to make any considered general statement on the matter, although he had cleared up several small problems in earlier papers.

It was eventually H. W. Bates who gave the lead to the interpretation of colour by the elucidation of one of the more obscure of the colour problems. Bates had been an immediate convert to the theory of natural selection, and on the basis of this he attempted to explain the phenomenon of colour variation amongst the butterflies of the Amazon valley. Bates had noticed particularly that the heliconiid butterflies (tropical American forms) which are almost always gaily coloured in crimson, white or yellow on black, were not only some of the most numerous of all the Amazonian butterflies, but also varied in colour pattern from place to place. Further, he observed that the local variations were paralleled by other, unrelated butterflies, inhabiting the same localities. *Dismorphia* (*Leptalis*), a butterfly related to the common whites and not to the Heliconiidae, was found in some cases to be red, yellow and black, instead of the white or yellow of its relatives. Not only *Dismorphia*; several other butterflies seemed to copy the Heliconiidae in both colour and pattern. The heliconiid butterflies excrete strong smelling substances which make them unpalatable to insectivorous animals. The other butterflies, therefore which do not have this protective device, acquire protection by looking like the heliconiids. A palatable butterfly mimics an unpalatable one and so derives protection and survival value. "The principle can be no other than natural selection," Bates wrote in 1862, "the selecting agents being insectivorous animals, which gradually destroy those sports or varieties that are not sufficiently like *Ithomiae* [a heliconiid] to deceive them." The resemblance may be remarkably exact in some cases, but it may be confined to some striking characteristic of the general colour pattern in others.

Bates disentangled one of the most complex problems of colour relationships when he formulated his theory of mimicry in 1862, and in reaching a solution of the problem of butterfly colours he had sought the advice of Wallace.

Both Darwin and Wallace warmly approved of Bates's mimicry theory. Wallace referred to it in *Malay Archipelago*, "and this is what has been happily termed 'mimicry' by Mr Bates, who first discovered the object of these curious external imitations of one insect by another . . ." (MA II 150). Bates's paper provided Wallace with the start he needed to solve the more general problems of animal colour.

In 1864 Wallace read to the Linnean Society a paper on the Malay Papilionidae. It was published in the *Transactions* of that society in 1866 and republished in *Contributions to the Theory of Natural Selection* in 1870. This paper considered not only the status of the butterflies, their remarkable diversity of form and their distributional peculiarities, but also the meanings of some of their colours and, in particular, the phenomenon of polymorphism and mimicry.

Polymorphism is the concurrence in the same locality of two or more distinct forms of the one species. Wallace had noticed in Sumatra that the females of the blue powdered black, *Papilio memnon* could exist in several different colour varieties and shapes. Some of the females were blue powdered black like the male, others were nearly white with red and yellow markings, whilst others were buff striped, with long spoon tails to their wings and resembled an entirely different species, *P. coön*. "These distinct forms generally occur in the female sex only, and their offspring, instead of being hybrids, or like the two parents, appear to reproduce all the distinct forms in varying proportions. I believe it will be found that a considerable number of what have been classed as *varieties* are really cases of polymorphism" (NS 145).

It was Wallace's observations of alternative colour patterns for females of the same species that added the concept polymorphism to biology. From a practical point of view Wallace was able to show that *Papilio aegeus onesimus* from the Aru islands was really a second form of the female of the more widespread *Papilio aegeus ormenus*.

From a theoretical point of view, he searched for a reason for this female polymorphism, and concluded that both forms of female had become adapted to their environment by natural selection. By becoming adapted to two or more aspects of that environment, they would spread the loss incurred through the selective agents and, therefore, the polymorphic state itself would be favoured. Since it is the females who are most in need of protection, owing to the necessity of egg-laying, it is they who are usually polymorphic.

What could be the factors that ensured the persistence of two or more female types? Why was one not replaced by the other? Wallace assumed that the common female form, the one like the male, had some possibly physiological advantage which was balanced against some other advantage in the second form: the advantage of protective colouration. This is known today as balanced polymorphism (Ford 1945). It is presumed, for instance, to account for the existence in some moth populations of a few black forms amongst the peppered varieties long before industrialization changed the countryside. To persist in the population at all, against the strong selective elimination by birds, the black forms must have had some hidden advantage, which could only be fully exploited when the environment changed. What this advantage is, has not been fully established yet, and on this particular aspect of polymorphism, the subject is only beginning to advance beyond Wallace's conception of it in 1864 (Kettlewell 1955, 1956).

Like Bates, Wallace's first written observations on colour were used mainly to provide proof of the theory of natural selection. They were not primarily interpretations of the meaning of colour as such. But by 1867 Wallace was prepared to expand his ideas on mimicry and other protective resemblances among animals. He extended Bates's theory of mimicry to cover cases outside the insects, and ordered the facts into three laws of mimicry. (i) that animals that resemble one another in this way inhabit the same locality, (ii) that such resemblances are limited to abundant groups which have some special protection and (iii) the mimics themselves are often very rare. He collected together many examples of mimics, from other groups of insects, and of insects mimicking other animals. "In the island of Celebes I found one of this group [Longicorn beetle], having the whole body and elytra of a rich deep blue colour, with the head only orange; and in company with it an insect of a totally different family (Eucnemidae) with identically the same coloration, and of so nearly the same size and form as to completely puzzle the collector on every fresh occasion of capturing them" (NS 93).

Wallace also described his own special contribution to the theory of mimicry; that of birds mimicking one another. On Bouru in the Moluccas, he had constantly mixed up two only distantly related birds, an Australian friar bird *Philemon* (*Tropidorhynchus*) and a golden oriole *Oriolus* (*Mimeta*). The friar birds were gregarious, pugnacious birds, whilst the orioles were much weaker and more solitary. On Bouru the oriole had lost the gay colours of its relatives and come to resemble the browner friar bird in remarkable detail. This case was strengthened by similar examples of resemblances between the two genera on other Moluccan islands.

Wallace's example of bird mimicry does not seem to have been either denied or confirmed, although several other examples of birds mimicking one another have been suggested in recent years (Sheppard 1958).

Having surveyed the field of mimetic resemblances, Wallace considered the objections that had been raised to Bates's 1862 paper. Some maintained that mimics had been created, others argued that the environment had directly produced the resemblances, and still others contended that mimicry should be considered a case of reversion to ancestral types of form and coloration. Wallace dismissed these objections, and supported Bates's interpretation that mimicry is a protective device for an otherwise unprotected species, brought about automatically by the operation of natural selection, in this case predators.

To Wallace, colour was above all a protective characteristic for the animal, protective in this case for the female that mimicked an unpleasantly tasting model. The protective colour had been established and perpetuated by the predators, natural selection. Those animals that happened to possess a sufficiently deceptive or protective colour pattern escaped being eaten, those that did not were eaten. To support the argument he described an edible Malayan butterfly *Hypolimnas* (*Diadema*) in which the male, contrary to the usual arrangement, was dull brown and the female bright metallic blue. The female resembled closely a different genus of butterfly *Euploea batunensis* (*nidamus*) and must have come to resemble it by the "preservation of favourable variations in the struggle for life" (1864). She gained protection from resembling more closely an unpalatable species than the edible male of her own species.

Eleven years later in *Tropical Nature* (1878), Wallace added instances of plants mimicking other plants and developed his views further. He realized that a mimic, even at first, would need to resemble its model if it were to be preserved by natural selection. He wondered whether sufficient resemblance could be achieved in one step. If this were not possible, then he suggested there might have been simultaneous evolution of mimic and model to account for the detailed resemblance that often exists. "So soon as the nauseous butterfly varied in form or colour to such an extent that the corresponding eatable butterfly no longer resembled it, the latter would be exposed to attacks, and only those variations would be preserved which kept up the resemblance. At the same time we may well suppose the enemies to become more accurate and able to detect smaller differences than at first. This would lead to the destruction of all adverse variations and thus keep up in continually increasing complexity the outward mimicry which now so amazes us" (TN 191-92).

There were no further developments in the theory of mimetic resemblances until 1879 when the German, Müller, pointed out that many unpalatable species resembled one another. By this communal resemblance all the species would gain, the predator needing to associate only the one pattern with distastefulness.

Wallace immediately accepted Müllerian mimicry. This similarity of two or more unpalatable forms had been noticed by both Bates and Wallace, but neither had been able to give a satisfactory explanation of the phenomenon. "Then came the extension of the principle, by Dr F. Müller, to the case of species of distinct genera of the inedible butterflies resembling each other quite as closely as in the former cases, and like them always found in the same localities. They derive mutual benefit from becoming, in appearance, one species, from which a certain toll is taken annually to teach the young insectivorous birds that they are uneatable" (D 256).

In *Darwinism* (1889) Wallace added a third expansion of the original theory, the "grouping of allied species of the same genera of inedible butterflies into sets, each having a distinct type of colouration, and each consisting of a number of species which can hardly be distinguished on the wing. This must be useful exactly in the same way as in the last case, since it divides the inevitable toll to insectivorous birds and other animals among a number of species. It also explains the fact of the great similarity of many species of inedible insects in the same locality—a similarity which does not obtain to anything like the same extent among the edible species. The explanation of the various phenomena of resemblance and mimicry, presented by the distasteful butterflies, may now be considered tolerably complete" (D 256-57). The completeness was to be gradually supplemented and extended.

Poulton in *The Colours of Animals* (1890) extended Wallace's overall description of mimetic resemblances and called the colours of Batesian mimics false warning colours, pseudaposematic, and those of the Müllerian group, common warning colours, aposematic. Fisher (1930) pointed out that the resemblances in Batesian mimicry must generally be as detailed as possible, to perfect the disguise, whilst Müllerian resemblances need only suggest similarities.

The efficacy of mimicry has been confirmed, in a few cases, in experimental conditions. Darlington (1938) offered edible beetles as food to lizards, and observed that the lizards refused to take the beetles that mimicked a distasteful species, although they fed readily on the others. Scrub jays learnt in captivity not to eat mimetic papilios and danaids (Brower 1960). Starlings could be trained to reject artificially devised mimics (Brower 1960).

Ford (1938) confirmed what both Bates and Wallace suspected. Mimics do not necessarily achieve their resemblances to the model by the same means as the model. The yellow pigment colouring the wings of some papilio species belongs to a group of chemical compounds called pterins, derived from the excretory product uric acid; whereas the yellow pigment of the mimic, although appearing to the eye to be the same, may be formed from a flavone, derived from the larval food. The red pigment of the wings of *P. hector* is chemically distinct from that of its mimic *P. polytes romulus*. Experiment has thus confirmed several points in the mimicry theory which Wallace could only guess from field observation.

But the greatest advances in the twentieth century have been in the genetics of mimicry. It has been shown that most mimics differ from the common species type by only one gene, and intermediate forms between the alternatives are rare, as Wallace and Bates had observed. A female is either like the male or she is like the model, and these alternatives are inherited in a comparatively simple way. Parallel mutations to give similarities of pattern or direct environmental effects on wing pattern have been ruled out as causes of polymorphism.

Following Wallace and Bates: from a general resemblance between mimic and model, acquired presumably by chance in the first place, natural selection draws out a closer and closer resemblance of mimic to model. And, as Wallace thought, whereas a general resemblance to the model might deceive at first, increasing awareness on the part of the predator would be expected to select for closer and closer similarity (Sheppard 1959).

The theory of mimetic resemblance does not owe its origin to Wallace, but to Bates and to Müller. Wallace elaborated their basic hypotheses, in particular speculating on the evolution of mimicry and formulating as a result of it the theory of polymorphism. However, his statements on polymorphism, the existence in the same locality of two or more alternative forms in balanced equilibrium, made little impact at the time, and today he is not remembered as a contributor to this particular branch of evolutionary theory. In fact, workers in the subject would probably be surprised to know that its history went further back than some twenty years, and that it originated before the beginning of modern genetics.

Mimicry is only a special case of adaptive coloration in the animal kingdom and, although it gained such prominence during the middle years of the nineteenth century, it was not the only line of thought on colour that was developing. Certainly mimicry was rivalled by Darwin's theory of sexual selection. But both these theories set out to explain initially why males and females of the same species might differ from one another in colour and ornamentation. At first, the less spectacular features of colour in animals received a rather more superficial attention, although it was Wallace who was the first to lay stress on their importance as protective devices, and Wallace who first recognized the particular use of some types of colour and patterning. Already in 1852 he had pondered over the behaviour of a butterfly of the Amazon valley "... and for what reason should *Charis* always expose itself on the upper surfaces of leaves, while hundreds of its more modest or more timid allies invariably take advantage of the friendly shelter afforded them and rest upon the underside?"

Again, it was his paper on the Malay papilionidae that first brought forward an interpretation of a phenomenon about which he had been thinking for years. This paper contains his first direct reference to warning colours as such. Of course, the theory of mimicry was implicity based on the supposition that unpalatable insects might be brightly coloured, but Wallace extended this assumption to the explicit statement that animals could be garishly coloured actually to advertise their unpleasantness (as in the later understood Müllerian mimicry) and not only in cases of mimicry. The beginnings of this theory came when Wallace tried to explain why papilionid caterpillars shoot out a coloured Y-shaped tentacle when they are touched. "When we consider this singular apparatus, which in some species is nearly half an inch long, the arrangement of muscles for its protrusion and retraction, its perfect concealment during repose, its blood-red colour, and the suddenness with which it can be thrown out, we must, I think, be led to the conclusion that it serves as a protection to the larva, by startling and frightening away some enemy when about to seize it" (NS 135), to which might be added the fact that the tentacle has a sharp stinging taste.

The general application of such an exhibition, however, escaped Wallace at this time, and it was not until he received a letter from Darwin at the beginning of 1867 that the extensive use of warning colours was borne in on him. Darwin wrote from Down: "On Monday evening I called on Bates and put a difficulty before him, which he could not answer, and, as on some former similar occasion, his first suggestion was, 'You had better ask Wallace'. My difficulty is, why are caterpillars sometimes so beautifully and artistically coloured? Seeing that many are coloured to escape danger, I can hardly attribute their bright colour in other cases to mere physical conditions. Bates says the most gaudy caterpillar he ever saw in Amazonia (of a Sphinx) was conspicuous at the distance of yards from its black and red colouring whilst feeding on large green leaves. If anyone objected to male butterflies having been made beautiful by sexual selection, and asked why should they not have been made beautiful as well as their caterpillars, what would you answer? I could not answer but should maintain my ground. Will you think over this and some time, either by letter or when we meet, tell me what you think?" (M I 178).

When Wallace received Darwin's letter he was working on his paper on mimicry and other protective resemblances, and he at once saw the possibility of a correlation between bright colours and distastefulness in other instances than mimicry. He suggested that soft-bodied caterpillars are so vulnerable that a device which would prevent even attempted pecks or bites would be of the utmost survival value. Bright colour, coupled with unpalatability, would provide just such a protective device.

Wallace's reply to this letter is missing except in so far as what seem to be two quotations from it appear in *The Descent of Man* (1871): "Most caterpillars require protection, as may be inferred from some kinds being furnished with spines or irritating hairs, and from many being coloured green like the leaves on which they feed, or being curiously like the twigs of the trees on which they live" and "distastefulness alone would be insufficient to protect a caterpillar unless some outward sign indicated to its would-be destroyer that its prey was a disgusting morsel".

Darwin was delighted with the interpretation, and wrote: "My dear Wallace—Bates was quite right, you are the man to apply to in a difficulty. I never heard anything more ingenious than your suggestion, and I hope you may be able to prove it true" (M I 179).

To try to prove it true, Wallace at once brought the problem to the notice of the Entomological Society, and he appealed in a letter to the *Field* for any information or for anyone to undertake experiments to find out whether insectivorous animals were in fact put off by these colours. Apparently it did not occur to Wallace to undertake a series of experiments of this kind himself. His inclinations were not towards the experimental, even though he realized that this was the only means by which a theory could be verified. He was the theoretical biologist; others could prove his theories false or true. It was two years before there was any response to his appeal, and only comparatively recently have further experiments been undertaken (Poulton 1929, Cott 1940, Goodwin 1951).

Meanwhile, warning colours were incorporated in the 1867 survey of mimicry and other protective resemblances. "It is among the groups that possess some of these varied kinds of protection in a high degree [disgusting smell and taste], that we find the greatest amount of conspicuous colour, or at least the most complete absence of protective imitation. . . . The lady-birds (Coccinellidae) and their allies the Eumorphidae, are often brightly spotted, as if to attract attention; but they can both emit fluids of a very disagreeable nature, they are certainly rejected by some birds, and are probably never eaten by any" (NS 71-71).

Two years after this was written, Butler (1869) showed by experiment that some insects are unpalatable to lizards and frogs, though he did not specify their colours; and Jenner Weir (1869) reported the results of experiments which had been undertaken expressly at Wallace's suggestion, which seemed to prove the correctness of the hypothesis. Weir reported that insectivorous birds refused to eat hairy, spinous and gay-coloured larvae, but did eat smooth, green or dull-coloured ones.

The theory of warning colours was accepted. Darwin wrote in 1871: "This view will, it is probable, be hereafter extended to many animals, which are coloured in a conspicuous manner."

In 1947 Cott extended the theory to birds. He found there was an inverse correlation between palatability and conspicuousness tested by hornets and cats, and he concluded that warning colours were important among birds. He found, for instance, that sparrows and flycatchers were palatable but that kingfishers, orioles and shrikes were unpalatable.

Only Beddard (1892) seems not to have accepted the theory of warning colours. He maintained that "brilliant colours (i.e., the abundant secretion of pigment) have caused the inedibility of the species, rather than that the inedibility has necessitated the production of bright colours as an advertisement" and anyway, he said, some dull-coloured caterpillars are inedible.

By 1878 Wallace had extended the theory of warning colours to cover fruits as well as animals. His theory of warning colours was completed.

Mimicry and warning were not the only uses to which colours could be put in the animal kingdom, though curiously these had been the two that had received Wallace's earliest attention. In the brief statement in 1867 on the uses of colour in general in the animal world he had made passing references to other uses of colour. He attributed all colours to the need for protection in one way or another. To Wallace, protection was the clue to all colour. Besides protection by mimicry and protection by warning, he recognized the existence of protection by concealment.

There were various ways in which colour could be used for this. There was concealment by general resemblance to the background, like the polar bear of arctic snows, the green birds of tropical forests and the sombre-coloured female birds of temperate regions. There was concealment by detailed resemblance, like the fantastic disguises of insects which resemble leaves or sticks. "It varies in degree, from the mere absence of conspicuous colour or a general harmony with the prevailing tints of nature, up to such a minute and detailed resemblance to inorganic or vegetable structures as to realise the talisman of the fairy tale and to give its possessor the power of rendering itself invisible" (NS 65).

Wallace drew attention for the first time to the concealing function of apparently crude likenesses to the background and to the use of disruptive patterns in concealment. The stripes of the tiger would tend to conceal him, as a predator, amongst the grass of the jungle, just as the ocellated skins of other large cats would provide the dappling effect of an arboreal habitat. In fact, many colour patterns which appear startling or unadaptive out of their native surroundings are very effective concealing devices.

In *Malay Archipelago* Wallace wrote of the Argus pheasant "its sober colours and rich eye-like spots, which are so ornamental when seen in a museum, must harmonize well with the dead leaves among which it dwells, and render it very inconspicuous" (I 51-52).

This attempt to organize the multitudinous aspects of animal colour formed a basis for all further discussion, although it did not by any means meet with universal approval. To many, protection was not the whole story.

In *The Descent of Man* Darwin passed over concealing colour rapidly. He accepted warning colours and mimicry, but very much doubted the uses of disruptive colours. "Mr Wallace believes (1867) that the striped coat of the tiger 'so assimilates with the vertical stems of the bamboo, as to assist greatly in concealing him from his approaching prey'. But this view does not appear to me satisfactory. We have some slight evidence that his beauty may be due to sexual selection. . . . The zebra is conspicuously striped, and stripes cannot afford any protection on the open plains of South Africa."

In spite of this criticism, Wallace followed his own line of thought on the protective aspect of colour, and in 1878 in *Tropical Nature* he added to his earlier classification and considered briefly the causes of colour. He argued that colour was not produced by the direct effect of the environment, as many believed, but was the outcome of the physiological processes within the animal, which were then subjected to the pressure of natural selection. He now classified colours into protective (concealing) colours, warning colours (including mimicry), sexual colours, and all those for which no obvious reason could be given, typical colours.

Within concealing colours he recognized the principle of countershading, as indeed Erasmus Darwin had done. He came near to the modern theory of concealment by disruptive colouring when, in disagreement with Charles Darwin, he maintained that the stripes of the zebra could conceal protectively when the zebra was at rest in its natural habitat. Not committing himself to this theory, however, he suggested as an alternative that the stripes might serve as a means of recognition to enable stragglers to regain the herd. Disruptive colouring has been generally accepted. Stripes or spots break up the outline of an animal and make it less visible than a solid block of one colour (Thayer 1903), but there seems to be no evidence that the contrasting stripes are particularly a means of herd recognition.

Finally in *Tropical Nature,* Wallace pointed to the use of deflexion markings. Deflexion markings are, for example, eye-like spots on a comparatively expendable part of an animal which deflect the attack of a predator from the true eye and vital organs. Deflexion was later thought also to be the purpose of the spots on some butterflies' wings and the tussocks on some caterpillars (Poulton 1888) and was incorporated into the general theory of colour by Poulton (1890). Recent work, however, makes it seem likely that the eye spots may be important as warning devices rather than as deflexion marks : the more like a vertebrate eye, the more efficient as a terrorizer (Blest 1957).

Wallace's theories of animal colour and the classification of colour had appeared then on several occasions in brief form (see 1864, 1867, 1878). But brief as they were, they represented the only theoretical statements on colour in general with the exception of those in *The Descent of Man* (1871). Once more Wallace and Darwin were the first in the field, though neither of them had devoted a whole book to the subject since each had used the subject of colour as a subsidiary to some other general thesis.

The first important complete book on colour appeared in 1886. In *Coloration of Animals and Plants* Tylor classified colour in a similar way to Wallace's 1878 classification, discussed the rival theories of Darwin and Wallace towards the meaning of colour, came down on Darwin's side and reduced the bite of his book by attributing to animals the ability to decorate themselves. There was a curious confusion of strict selection and conscious modification.

Three years later, Wallace made his final statement on colour, in four chapters of *Darwinism*. It differed little from his previous writings except that he added to his list alluring colours. "Besides those numerous insects which obtain protection through their resemblance to the natural objects among which they live, there are some whose disguise is not used for concealment, but as a direct means of securing their prey by attracting them within the enemy's reach" (D 210-11). Again colour had formed only part of a more general collection of articles. If Wallace had expanded and stated his views in a book devoted entirely to colour, probably he would have left his name on this branch of biology as indelibly as he has on natural selection and geographical distribution.

Bulk and an overwhelming number of examples were needed to carry conviction. But whether it was this comparative slightness of his contribution or whether it was that he disagreed with Darwin over sexual selection, it is Poulton's name that is associated with the treatment of colour and not Wallace's. Poulton's work *The Colours of Animals* (1890) was based directly on that of Wallace and, in so far as sexual selection was concerned, on Darwin. Poulton extended Wallace's ideas and applied a much more rigid classification to the groups and subgroups of colours. He made a distinct advance on both Darwin and Wallace. The different categories of colour were made more precise by the invention of special names which eliminated the subjective associations of the previous words of common usage.

In almost every chapter of *The Colours of Animals* Poulton refers to Wallace's work, to examples provided by Wallace or to an original contribution by Wallace. If Wallace did not write the first post-Darwinian treatise on colour, he certainly provided a great deal of the material for it. For all modern theories of colour are based on Poulton's work. Examples have been added, particular cases have been reclassified, and Poulton's groupings have been both sub-divided and enlarged in *Adaptive Coloration in Animals* (1940) by H. B. Cott, but the general principles laid down by Poulton, based on Wallace, are still recognized to be valid interpretations of the phenomena of colour variation in animals.

Wallace invented warning colours, deflexion colours, alluring colours, disruptive colours and recognition colours, all of which have been confirmed and amplified. Cott has extended warning colours to birds, deflective eye spots have been widely reported, alluring colours and devices are known to be common amongst fish and other lower vertebrates as well as amongst insects and spiders, disruptive colours have been shown to be widespread and applicable to the zebra, and recognition colours are yearly seen to be more important.

There was still, however, another aspect of the colour problem to be considered, the problem of why in non-mimetic animals also, the males and females often differed in colour.

The Theory of Sexual Selection

In the papers read to the Linnean Society in 1858 both Darwin and Wallace had made passing reference to colour as an example of the modification of a characteristic under natural selection, but, whereas Wallace was concerned with showing how colour would evolve as a protective device, Darwin had already stressed sexual differences in colour.

Then, in 1859, Darwin recognized two aspects of sexual colour dimorphism.

The first maintains that there is a continual struggle for mates, and even for existence, between males at the breeding season. They fight, and the winner succeeds in getting a female and, therefore, passes on his winner's attributes to the next generation. As a result of this, there are the antlers of the male deer, the spurs of male birds. "Sexual selection by always allowing the victor to breed might surely give indomitable courage, length to the spur, and strength to the wing to strike in the spurred leg, as well as the brutal cockfighter, who knows well that he can improve his breed by careful selection of the best cocks," Darwin wrote. Sexual selection does not necessarily lead to the death of the unsuccessful as does rigorous natural selection, and it does not necessarily mean that the unsuccessful leaves no offspring, but he leaves fewer offspring, for he mates with fewer females than his successful rival. Sexual selection is, therefore, less rigorous and of less importance than natural selection.

The second aspect of Darwin's theory was that of female choice. He believed that gaily coloured male birds displayed their plumage to the females who selected as a mate the male that was the most beautiful. And so gradually, by inheritance, the males became more and more beautiful. "Thus it is, as I believe, that when the males and females of any animal have the same general habits of life, but differ in structure, colour or ornament, such differences have been mainly caused by sexual selection. . . ." (Darwin 1859).

When they first postulated their theory of evolution by natural selection, the two men had stressed different aspects of the evolution of colour in animals. Each elaborated his attitude. Darwin extended his theory of sexual selection, and Wallace recognized various types of protective colour. Essentially, they started off laying different stresses on the use of colour. Later work and further thought only accentuated these differences.

At first, however, it did not seem as though these small differences of stress would lead to fundamental disagreement. It appears that in the course of their correspondence over the next few years, Wallace was urging on Darwin certain instances of protective coloration and Darwin was considering extending to man his theory of sexual selection. "I fully admit the probability of 'protective adaptation' having come into play with female butterflies as well as with female birds. I have a good many facts which make me believe in sexual selection as applied to man, but whether I shall convince anyone else is very doubtful," Darwin wrote to Wallace in 1860. Unfortunately, Wallace's part of this early correspondence is missing; there is no mention of the evolution of colour in their letters until 1864, when the problem of sexual selection in relation to man occupied more of their attention. Wallace was not convinced that selection by women had led to the establishment of racial differences in man as Darwin believed, although he did at this time believe with Darwin that natural selection had been responsible for the evolution of man. Darwin, however, was becoming convinced of the reality of sexual selection: "My belief in it, however, is contingent on my general beliefs in sexual selection. It is an awful stretcher to believe that a peacock's tail was thus formed; but, believing it, I believe in the same principle somewhat modified applied to man," he wrote to Wallace in 1864 (M I 159).

But in spite of reservations in private, Wallace's first publication which considered the problem of colour in animals after the publication of the *Origin,* accepted both parts of Darwin's theory of sexual selection as well as considering the role of colour in protection.

By 1867 Wallace and Darwin were beginning to get into difficulties over one another's theories, although they still accepted both concealment and sexual selection as being instrumental in the production of colour differences. Wallace was laying more and more stress on the protective function of colour and Darwin was becoming more and more unwilling to accept this point of view. In that year Wallace wrote: "Hence there is a wide difference in the need for protection in the two sexes, and we should, therefore, expect to find that in some cases the special protection given to the female was in the male less in amount or altogether wanting" (NS 112). Just as the female butterfly gained protection in some cases by mimicry, so female birds, equally in need of more protection than the males, gained protection by concealing colours. In cases where hen birds incubated their eggs in open nests, the overriding need would be effective concealment during the vulnerable period. Selection would be strong in keeping such female birds dull-coloured. "The facts presented by the sexual differences of colour and their mode of nesting, are on the whole in perfect harmony with that law of protective adaptation of colour and form, which appears to have checked to some extent the powerful action of sexual selection, and to have materially influenced the colouring of female birds, as it has undoubtedly done that of female insects" (NS 117).

In the same year Wallace enlarged on his theory of the correlation between the colours of birds and their nesting habits, and he read an article *Birds' Nests and Plumage* to the British Association meeting in Dundee. A fuller version was published the following year under the title *A Theory of Birds' Nests*. Darwin's sexual selection had not yet been abandoned, and indeed male rivalry and fighting never was abandoned by Wallace, but female choice had become much modified and female protection had become of paramount importance. "The sexual differences of colour and plumage in birds are very remarkable, and have attracted much attention; and, in the case of polygamous birds, have been well explained by Mr Darwin's principle of sexual selection. We can, to a great extent, understand how male Pheasants and Grouse have acquired their more brilliant plumage and greater size, by the continual rivalry of the males both in strength and beauty; but this theory does not throw any light on the causes which have made the female Toucan, Bee-eater, Parroquet, Macaw and Tit, in almost every case as gay and brilliant as the male, while the gorgeous Chatterers, Manakins, Tanagers and Birds of Paradise, as well as our own Blackbird, have mates so dull and inconspicuous that they can hardly be recognised as belonging to the same species" (NS 239).

Wallace proposed that it is the females which have been modified towards dullness at least equally with the modification of the males towards brightness. And the reason for this is found in the nesting habits of the birds. Those birds which nest in holes or in roofed nests are more often than not brightly coloured in both sexes. On the other hand, birds which build open nests often show colour dimorphism or are dull-coloured in both sexes. The paramount selective necessity is the protection of the incubating female, otherwise of course neither she nor her mate would leave offspring to further the cause of the species. To support this view Wallace pointed out for the first time the curious situation where the female is brighter than the male, and he showed that in such cases, the phalarope for instance, it is the male which does the incubating of the eggs. Furthermore he argued in 1868 that it was more likely that the type of nest determined the colour of the incubating bird than that the colour of the bird determined the type of nest it would build. Although this proposition was challenged by Darwin in 1871, who maintained that the opposite was more likely, and although it is obviously almost impossible ever to decide which was cause and which effect in such a case, Wallace kept to this early opinion for the reason that he considered colour to be a very easily modified characteristic in living organisms. "The fact that all classes of nests occur with dull coloured birds in both sexes, merely shows, as I have strongly maintained, that in most cases the character of the nest determines the coloration of the female, and not *vice versa*" (257).

Finally, in contrast to Darwin, Wallace believed that there was no reason to impute choice to a female rather than to a male bird. Why should the male not choose the female? There is some evidence that both males and females take individual likes and dislikes to potential mates (Lorenz 1931).

Darwin was impressed by this theory of birds' nests, as he himself had never gone so far as this in imputing dull colours in some birds to the natural selection of concealing colours, although he had considered that young birds were often protectively coloured. But after the first enthusiasm for the birds' nest theory, Darwin became more and more wedded to his theory of sexual selection.

"Mr Tegetmeier is convinced that a game cock, though disfigured by being dubbed with his hackles trimmed, would be acceptable as readily as a male retaining all his natural ornaments. Nevertheless I am still inclined from many facts strongly to believe that the beauty of the male bird determines the choice of the female with wild birds, however it may be under domestication," he wrote to Bates in 1867 (Darwin 1903). In February of the same year he wrote to Wallace: "I am fearfully puzzled how far to extend your protective views with respect to the females in various classes. The more I work, the more important sexual selection comes out" (M I 194).

Darwin did not agree with Wallace that males might be equally selective, but maintained that they seize the first female they see. Moreover, Darwin had started to extend his theory of female choice to butterflies, a view which Wallace was quite unable to accept.

The division of opinion was widening. "In truth, it has vexed me much to find that the further I get on, the more I differ from you about the females being dull-coloured for protection. I can now hardly express myself as strongly even as in the 'Origin'. This has *much decreased* the pleasure of my work" wrote Darwin in 1868 (M I 220).

But Wallace stuck to his point and replied: "I am certainly surprised that you should find so much evidence against protection having checked the acquirement of bright colour in females; but I console myself by presumptuously hoping that I can explain your facts, unless they are derived from the very groups on which I chiefly rest—birds and insects. There is nothing *necessarily* requiring protection in females, it is rather a matter of habits. There are groups in which both sexes require protection in an exactly equal degree, and others (I think) in which the male requires most protection, and I feel the greatest confidence that these will ultimately support my view, although I do *not* yet know the facts they may afford" (M I 221). To which Darwin replied: "You will be pleased to hear that I am undergoing severe distress about protection and sexual selection: this morning I oscillated with joy towards you; this evening I have swung back to the old position, out of which I fear I shall never get" (M I 223).

The problem of the inheritance of the colours came up next. Why are the bright colours only transmitted to the males? To what extent are they passed through the females? The problem was baffling in the days before anything was known of the mechanism of inheritance. Darwin conceded, "I am quite willing to admit that the female may have been modified, either at the same time or subsequently, for *protection,* by the accumulation of variations limited in their transmission to the female sex. I owe to your writings the consideration of this latter part. But I cannot yet persuade myself that females *alone* have often been modified for protection" (M I 226).

"To answer your first question is most difficult, if not impossible," Wallace replied, "because we have no sufficient evidence in *individual cases of slight sexual difference*, to determine whether the male alone has acquired his superior brightness by sexual selection, or the female has been made duller by need of protection, or whether the two causes have acted. Many of the sexual differences of existing species may be inherited differences from parent forms who existed under different conditions and had greater or less need of protection. . . . Now, supposing on your view, that the colours of a male bird become more and more brilliant by sexual selection, and a good deal of that colour is transmitted to the female till it becomes positively injurious to her during incubation and the race is in danger of extinction, do you not think that all the females who had acquired less of the male's bright colours or who themselves varied in a protective direction would be preserved, and that thus a good protective colouring would be acquired? If you admit that this could occur, and can show no good reason why it should not often occur, then we no longer differ, for this is the main point of my view" (M I 228).

Later Wallace wrote: "I am sorry to find that our difference of opinion on this point is a source of anxiety to you. Pray do not let it be so. The truth will come out at last, and our difference may be the means of setting others to work who may set us both right."

By this time Darwin was well on with putting together his material for *The Descent of Man,* which was to be devoted for half of its length to the problem of sexual selection amongst animals in general, and at the end of 1870 he wrote to Wallace: "I have finished the first volume, and am half-way through the first proof of the second volume, of my confounded book, which half kills me by fatigue, and which I much fear will quite kill me in your good estimation" (M I 254).

With the publication of *The Descent of Man* in 1871 Darwin came down firmly on the side of male rivalry and female choice and extended it from man to cover the greater part of the animal kingdom. "... for the males have acquired their present structure, not from being better fitted to survive in the struggle for existence but from having gained an advantage over other males, and from having transmitted this advantage to their male offspring alone. It was the importance of this distinction which led me to designate this form of selection as sexual selection."

Furthermore, *The Descent of Man* argued in favour of unilateral transmission of colour characteristics, in contrast to Wallace's expressed views that colours were passed on equally to the two sexes but sorted out selectively.

"After mature reflection on all facts which I have been able to collect, I am now inclined to believe that when the sexes differ, the successive variations have generally been from the first limited in their transmission to the same sex in which they first appeared....

"Since my remarks appeared, the subject of sexual coloration has been discussed in some very interesting papers by Mr Wallace, who believes that in almost all cases the successive variations tended at first to be transmitted equally to both sexes; but that the female was saved, through natural selection, from acquiring the conspicuous colours of the male, owing to the danger which she would thus have incurred during incubation. . . . It seems to me, on the contrary, far more probable that it is the males which have been chiefly modified through sexual selection, the females having been comparatively little changed."

The Descent of Man extended the theory of sexual selection to butterflies: "From the foregoing statements it is impossible to admit that the brilliant colours of butterflies and of some few moths, have commonly been acquired for the sake of protection.... Hence I am led to believe that the females prefer or are most excited by the more brilliant males."

Darwin had stated his case for colour dimorphism and there was very little room in it for the use of colour as a concealing device. Protection had not exactly been ruled out, but it was of far less interest to Darwin than sexual selection. "The absence of bright tints or other ornaments may be the result of variations of the right kind never having occurred, or of the animals themselves having preferred plain black or white. Obscure tints have often been developed through natural selection for the sake of protection, and the acquirement through sexual selection of conspicuous colours, appears to have been sometimes checked from the danger thus incurred" (Darwin 1874).

The time at which characters appear in the life of an animal were important to Darwin for explaining transmission of characters to the male alone, in contrast to Wallace's contention of their being passed to both sexes but only showing up in the male. "When variations occur late in life in one sex, and are transmitted to the same sex at the same age, the other sex and the young are left unmodified."

Darwin had given his views to the world. They were the result of years of work, years of thought. His conclusions he never saw need to alter. Wallace was still not convinced. "On the subject of sexual selection and protection," he wrote, "you do not yet convince me that I am wrong. . . . But my view is, and I thought I had made it clear, that the female has (in most cases) been simply prevented from acquiring the gay tints of the male (even where there is a tendency for her to inherit it) because it was hurtful; and that when protection is not needed, gay colours are so generally acquired by both sexes as to show that inheritance by both sexes of colour variations is the most usual, when *not prevented* from acting by Natural Selection" (M I 256).

Although Wallace had written several articles and many letters on the subject of colour, he had not yet been able to account for the bright colours of some males. According to his theory, females would become protectively coloured; according to Darwin males would become brightly coloured. Neither theory seemed to cover both sexes completely. Wallace was well aware of the gap in his own theory, although in some cases he was able to fill this gap by the alternative theories of mimicry and warning colours. But on the face of it these arguments did not apply to birds. What then could be the reasons for the tendency to bright colours which was almost a necessity of his theories? "I am almost afraid to tell you that in going over the subject of the colours of animals, etc., etc., for a small volume of essays, etc. I am preparing, I have come to conclusions directly opposed to voluntary sexual selection, and I believe that I can explain (in a general way) all the phenomena of sexual ornaments and colours by laws of development aided by simple Natural Selection" (M I 298).

By 1876 Wallace had given up the whole of the female choice aspect of Darwin's sexual selection and in 1877 he published his revised opinions in *The Colours of Animals and Plants.* These new ideas were elaborated into a larger essay which appeared in *Tropical Nature*. In this he suggested that all animals which were vigorous and in good health would tend to be coloured rather than dull; also that, as the males were more active and more vigorous than females in the breeding season, they would have a tendency to be brighter than the females. Given this tendency for bright colours, natural selection then either suppresses or elaborates them according to the habits and habitats of the particular animals, and their elaboration is more often than not for protection against predators. To female choice he gave no importance now, pointing out that, for instance, if a female loses her mate she takes the next unmated male who comes along, and pointing out also that females frequently show little interest in the antics of the males.

Wallace agreed that probably some males were more able than others to stimulate a female physiologically to accept them as a mate. This they did by courtship display rather than brightness of colour for, as he pointed out, dull birds, too, may have differential mating success. However, he argued, if there were no overriding need for dull colours, bright colours might be an additional stimulant and, therefore, of some selective advantage. But bright colours would tend to be manifest to the greatest extent in the most virile and most successful males anyway. The colours, therefore, would be perpetuated.

Adornments associated with male rivalry and fighting were acceptable on Darwin's theory. Although dull-coloured males display and threaten other males, Wallace considered it likely that colour and ornaments would enhance a rivalry display.

By this time Wallace had a further contribution to make. This was the theory of recognition colours. Colour could be an important recognition mark, and it might well be the main positive reason for the general tendency to intricate colour patterns. Such recognition marks would be important between the sexes. ". . . colour, which continually tends to appear, is utilised for purposes of identification and distinction when not required to be modified or suppressed for the purpose of protection" (TN 203). Recognition marks are also important for the young. "But this very conspicuousness while running away, may be useful as a signal and guide to the young" (TN 197).

Wallace had begun to realize that the difficulties of generalizing about animal colour were great. A theory which might account for the colour of one group of animals might not be a satisfactory explanation of the colours of another. The hunt for an all-embracing theory was probably the main reason for the divergence in the views of Wallace and Darwin.

Wallace believed in the effectiveness of natural selection as against sexual selection in the fixing of colours, but he was gradually building up several different subsidiary theories to account for particular instances of coloration. In different animals and in different places, different selective agencies might be at work on the colour of animals and the difficulties of generalizing were very great. "If this explanation is correct . . . it may serve as a warning of how impossible it is, without exact knowledge of the habits of an animal and a full consideration of all the circumstances, to decide that any particular coloration cannot be protective or in any way useful" (TN 197).

In 1877 Darwin and Wallace gave up trying to convince each other of their own points of view. Their differences were in print for all to see. "You will not be surprised that I differ altogether from you about sexual colours. . . . I cannot help doubting about recognition through colour," Darwin wrote to him.

Wallace replied : "Of course I did not expect my paper to have any effect on your opinions. You have looked at all the facts so long from your special point of view that it would require conclusive arguments to influence you, and these, from the complex nature of the question, are probably not to be had" (M I 300).

Here the correspondence on the causes of animal colours more or less closed. They had realized that they looked at the subject from different standpoints and, as Wallace had said, neither of them could yet be proved right or wrong, so there was nothing to be gained by continuing the discussion.

Wallace's final statement on colour came in essays in *Darwinism*. He went over the opposing views of Darwin and himself on the theory of sexual selection and, not unexpectedly, he dismissed all possibility of female choice as an explanation of colour dimorphism in animals. He repeated his own views that protection was all important. He believed that the general tendency towards colour, which seemed to exist in some animals, was due to differing reasons; but, in so far as a generalization could be made, he believed it was to be found in the theory of recognition colouring.

In *Darwinism* he now extended this theory. To those recognition colours that he had already defined, colours for recognition between the sexes and of parents by the young, he added social recognition and species recognition. "Recognition marks during flight are very important for all birds which congregate in flocks or which migrate together; and it is essential that, while being as conspicuous as possible, the marks should not interfere with the general protective tints of the species when at rest" (D 222).

Recognition colours might be important in keeping apart closely allied species living in the same area, so that any attempt at intercrossing between the two would be prevented. "At the same time, the need for recognition must be satisfied; and this seems to have led to diversities of colour in allied species . . . which have, therefore, in all probability been acquired in the process of differentiation for the purpose of checking the intercrossing of closely allied forms" (D 227, 273).

Finally, Wallace assigned bird song to the category of a recognition or advertising characteristic, as distinct from the more generally held view that it was a seductive characteristic chosen for its beauty by the female. "These songs may well have originated merely as a means of recognition between the two sexes of a species, and as an invitation from the male to the female bird" (D 284).

Darwin and Wallace had made up their minds about animal colours and others were about to take up the story.

At first it seemed that Darwin's theory of sexual selection was unlikely to receive the support of naturalists in general. Darwin wrote to the German naturalist Müller (brother of the mimicry Müller) in 1872: "The reading of your essay has given me great confidence in the efficacy of sexual selection, and I wanted some encouragement, as extremely few naturalists in England seem inclined to believe in it. I am, however, glad to find that Prof Wiesmann [his spelling] has some faith in the principle" (Darwin 1903).

Yet, in spite of this apparently poor start, Darwin's theory caught the general attention. Wallace's name eventually dropped out of discussions on the subject, and it is doubtful whether today anyone would associate it with theories of sexual selection any more than with any of the other problems of animal colour.

How do the rival theories of sexual selection appear in the light of modern research?

Darwin's theory quickly became acceptable. When Lankester

reviewed *Darwinism* in 1889, he wrote: "Mr Wallace seems scarcely to have succeeded in showing that Darwin's theory of sexual selection is inapplicable to the explanation of special developments of colour and ornament, although he has suggested additional causes which influence the primary distribution and development of colour." In the same article Lankester suggested another reason for the comparative lack of influence of Wallace's views. "Mr Wallace's book necessarily suffers, in comparison with works of Darwin himself, by the limitation of space. It is in consequence of this compression that we miss in the new statement by Mr Wallace that extraordinary cogency or power of convincing which so distinguished the writings of Darwin."

Wallace's facility for compression and making subjects readily understandable seems to have been to some extent his undoing on the subject of colour. He made it sound so easy. Could it be true when there was, so far, no actual proof either for or against sexual selection and, in a sense, it was a question of who could name the most examples in support of his theory?

Poulton (1890) accepted many of Wallace's interpretations of the meaning of animal colours even to the extent of recognition colours (episematic), which Wallace had been the first to stress, and he gave full acknowledgement to Wallace's contribution to the subject. But Poulton would not go as far as Wallace in attributing cases of colour dimorphism to the need for recognition on the one hand and concealment on the other. And he did not accept recognition colours as applicable to insects. In any case, Poulton came down heavily in support of Darwin's theory of sexual selection. He was hardly prepared to concede a point to Wallace for an alternative interpretation.

One of the main reasons for Poulton's wholehearted support of Darwin was his strong belief in the sense of the aesthetic in animals. Poulton believed, as many did, that birds and insects appreciate beauty so as to be critically capable of choosing it for themselves. Unless they exercise this choice when choosing a mate, the colours would not be beautiful but only conspicuous, and he wrote, "For the purposes of recognition, beauty is entirely superfluous and indeed undesirable; strongly marked and conspicuous differences are alone necessary."

This was the most favoured way of looking at much of the colouring in the animal kingdom. The theory of sexual selection introduced not only choice but also beauty. It provided delight for those who thought of the awfulness, blindness and cruelty of natural selection.

Wallace did not regard natural selection as in any way awful or unpleasant. The conferment of an aesthetic sense on female animals was to him an unjustified assumption. Wallace maintained that it was not possible to prove a sense of beauty, of appreciation of patterns for their artistic merits, in birds and insects. It was not even likely that insects would see in the same way that man does, considering the differences in structure of their eyes and brain (WL). "It appears to me, in imputing to insects and birds the same love of colour for its own sake and the same aesthetic tastes as we ourselves possess we may be as far from the truth as were the writers who held that the bee was a good mathematician, and that the honeycomb was constructed throughout to satisfy its refined mathematical instincts" (D 336).

Poulton also rejected Wallace's interpretation of bird song as a recognition feature. If it were only a means of advertisement or recognition it would not be beautiful.

Reviewing Poulton's work in *Nature* (1890), Wallace stressed its importance to the theory of animal colours, and then took up Poulton on the question of animals' aesthetic sense. Wallace argued that there is no reason to suppose that a female spider, for instance, rejects a red in favour of a black male for a mate because of his colour, but rather because he fails to stimulate her by reason of "a deficiency in activity, or in size, or in some exciting odour, or in the excitability of the female at the moment". Others, too, were not entirely convinced by sexual selection. Beddard (1892) more or less rejected the theory of female choice; but in its place he suggested only that colour dimorphism was dependent on the differences in the germ cells of the two sexes. This was perceptive but did not go far enough. It left out of account all selective agencies which would be at work on the colour so produced.

Cunningham (1892) agreed with Wallace that there was no proof that a female actively chooses her mate; but he disagreed with the alternative, that only the most vital males stimulate females. This, in his view, was contrary to natural selection, for successful males were not being favoured for themselves but only for the number of offspring they would leave. This drew a sharp retort from Wallace, who pointed out that the selection of the species as a whole, through the individual, was just what natural selection was about.

Romanes (1892), and with him the majority of biologists, accepted Darwin's sexual selection theory unconditionally, and by the end of the century it was firmly established. It lacked proof, but it was more satisfying to the majority than any of the alternatives. It had the great merit of general application. All cases of colour dimorphism could be ordered into one hypothesis, whereas Wallace had to break down the cases into separate categories. One sweeping generalization is nearly always more acceptable than several more specific theories. The matter rested without fundamental change of attitude: either an author accepted Darwin with the majority, or he did not.

Today, few biologists accept female choice as an explanation of all the bright colours of male animals, but they accept the first part of Darwin's theory of sexual selection which attributed male adornments to fighting and rivalry between males. This part of the theory has, in fact, never been seriously disputed since it was first propounded. What can be put in place of female choice? Do Wallace's alternative theories look better or worse in the light of increasing knowledge of animal behaviour?

Close observation of the behaviour of birds during courtship displays has shown that in almost all cases there is no question of choice by the female. The peahens are said to take no notice of the display of the peacock, the females of territorial birds have no choice by the time "courtship" is reached, as they have already accepted a mate who has advertised himself by his song. There is no case on record where the female of an established pair has rejected the male because he turned out not to be beautiful enough when the time came for coition. "I cannot call to mind a single instance in which I have, even for a brief moment, seen the female looking at the male while assuming these positions" (Howard 1907-14).

Even though the female does not exert a choice, it may still be possible to interpret the divergence in colour between males and females as a modified form of sexual selection. According to Huxley (1938) the courtship display of a male bird stimulates the female so that she becomes both physiologically and psychologically ready for coition. During such courtship, a coloured male displays his bright colours and his special adornments as Stonor (1938 and 1940) has shown in the case of the birds of paradise and many pheasants. Whether this can be considered a modified form of sexual selection depends on the reaction of the female to more and to less brightly coloured males. The more brightly coloured males should succeed in achieving coition more often than the less brightly coloured ones.

Does the more "vital" male of Wallace achieve a mate, and is he more brightly coloured than his fellows? There seems little direct evidence, although Allen (1934) observed that successful displays in grouse promote sexual vigour, and pre-sexual displays often have a very deleterious psychological and subsequent physiological effect on the loser. If several sticklebacks are kept together, the male that is successful in combat stays bright and the others lose their brilliance. Against this can be set the observations on the robin made by Lack (1946). In one area occupied by robins Lack found that in any one breeding season about one fifth of the cock robins failed to get mates. Here was a situation where sexual selection might be thought to come into play. But, in fact, it was observed that a cock robin deserted by his mate often found and kept another, and one that had no mate in one season had one the next and *vice versa*.

To quote such instances is to do no more than Darwin and Wallace did, quoting as many examples as can be found to support a particular hypothesis. If a theory has a vestige of truth in it some examples can always be found to support it. As Wallace wrote to Darwin in 1868: "I do not, however, at all think the question can be settled by individual cases, but only by large masses of facts. The colours of the mass of female birds seem to me strictly analagous to the colours of both sexes of snipes, woodcocks, plovers, etc., which are undoubtedly protective" (M I 228). Both Darwin and Wallace made use of as many facts as they could, and each constantly urged people to undertake experiments to test their hypotheses. But the necessary mass of facts was not available, and is still not available, even for birds. If details of the behaviour of a large sample of birds were available, modern statistical methods might be expected to provide some sort of answer to these questions.

Do all, or almost all, male birds display during courtship if they are coloured? Do most coloured birds nest in holes? A general hypothesis to cover all birds, and other animals as well, must be true in more cases than it is untrue. A decision to this effect can only be given as a result of the answer to the question, how many? And there is no answer to this question in the case of mating or other behaviour of birds, or insects or mammals, because the behaviour of all animals, or even of the majority, is not known in any detail. For instance, among birds of the temperate British climate as well as those of tropical Malaysia only some twenty-three to twenty-nine per cent show striking dissimilarities between the colours of the sexes. The colour dimorphism problem may not be quite as large as it seems. In those birds whose behaviour is known roughly, the male bird is more often than not the active one of the pair during courtship displays, though by no means always, but he is equally likely to be so whether he is the same colour as his mate or not. Amongst those birds then, it might seem that there was not very much support for a theory of sexual selection, nor very much reason to suppose that colour was primarily associated with sexual activities. But it is dangerous even to make this generalization until more is known about the activities of birds from other parts of the world.

Display for stimulatory purposes is obviously important in bird behaviour, but the use of colour in this display seems to be subsidiary. If a bird is coloured, he uses his colours to enhance the display, but the figures suggest that courtship display has not been the chief selective agency in establishing the colours. It is probably wise to reject Darwin's female choice theory on the grounds that "female birds may be charmed or excited by the fine display of plumage of the males, but there is no proof whatsoever that slight differences in the display have any effect in determining their choice of partner" (D 287). For the same reasons Wallace's theory of male vitality leading both to the acquisition of mates and colour must go. It may sometimes be important, just as some females may sometimes exert a choice, but it does not seem to be a prime cause of colour differences.

But what of the other side? How far is concealment important to birds, and how far does that lead to colour dimorphism? Was Wallace nearer to the correct answer in saying that "when both sexes are of strikingly gay and conspicuous colours, the nest is . . . such as to conceal the sitting bird; while, wherever there is striking contrast of colours, the male being gay and conspicuous, the female dull and obscure, the nest is open and the sitting bird exposed to view" (NS 187). For both British and Malaysian birds, a count of their behaviour during incubation and their colours, shows that there is indeed a correlation between colour and type of nest. The bird or birds which do the incubating are more often than not dull when the nest is open and coloured when the nest is closed, except in the case of social birds. Social birds seem to rely on numbers for their safety, and may even be advertising their presence by warning colours. To this extent Wallace would seem to have been correct in his theory of birds' nests, although as Darwin said, such a correlation does not prove whether selection pressure has kept birds dull when they sit on open nests or whether dull coloured birds have been able to utilize open nests with comparative immunity and have, therefore, never learnt to build closed nests. Although there is this mathematical correlation between the colour of the sitting bird and the type of nest among these non-social birds, Skutch (1957) came to the conclusion from personal observations, but no counts or statistical appreciation, that there was no such correlation to be found amongst the birds of South America. Further, although nesting habits may explain lack of colour, they do not explain why some birds are brightly coloured.

In place of sexual selection as a cause of bright male colouring, Wallace had suggested the need for recognition colours. It is even more difficult to assess this theory numerically, but more and more evidence is accumulating to support it. Huxley (1938) suggested that colour might be of importance in the recognition of males by females, but it is not clear whether colour is usually a dominant feature in this type of recognition.

No general method of sex recognition has emerged from recent field observations. The female of the flicker *Colaptes ornatus* recognizes a male by his moustache (Noble 1936). It has been reported that sexual colour dimorphism is important for rapid sex recognition amongst some North American species of warblers and orioles (Hamilton 1961). In contrast, male yellow wagtails mate with blueish headed females apparently as readily as with the yellow variety (Tucker 1949).

The male robin distinguishes an unmated female by her behaviour towards him. Most territorial birds advertise their maleness, and singleness, to prospective mates by song, as Wallace suggested and Eliot Howard corroborated (1907-14). Once a pair is established the two partners recognize each other by individual details (Lorenz 1931).

In social birds, however, there seems little doubt that colour often serves an important function in recognition. Tinbergen (1948) has confirmed that the conspicuous wing patterns of the ducks and geese act as signs to members of the flock and elicit the appropriate behaviour from a stray so that it will rejoin the flock.

The importance of recognition marks among insects has received less attention. At first, Wallace believed that insects, as well as birds, used colour as a recognition device between the sexes. "In the more gaily coloured Pieridae of which our orange-tip butterfly may be taken as a type, we see in the female the plain ancestral colours of the group, while the male has acquired the brilliant orange tip to its wings, probably as a recognition mark" (D 272). Wallace later doubted the value of colour for sexual recognition amongst butterflies (as Poulton had already done), substituting for it recognition by odour, and putting the responsibility for butterflies' colours on to their predators (WL).

It must be admitted that the evidence is meagre, but there seems to be some foundation for accepting colour as a recognition mark between social animals, between the young and their parents, and in some cases between the sexes.

But Wallace had come to stress more and more the importance of recognition marks in keeping allied species apart. Although at the time there was practically no evidence to support this theory, a little more has accumulated over the years; and there has been an increasing tendency for a few biologists to accept it, with the modification that whilst Wallace regarded barriers to species crossing (such as colour) as arising during the formation of the species, most modern authorities would consider that such a barrier to mating would only be formed or enhanced after the initial formation of two or more species. It could not become effective, nor have any selective advantage, until two physically separated species came once more to have overlapping ranges. But this is a modification to the theory of species formation rather than to the question of the effectiveness of colour as an isolating mechanism. In 1938 Huxley suggested that the differences in colour between male blackbirds and thrushes might be important, since it permitted the hen birds to distinguish between the two males from a distance; to which might be added the importance of the males distinguishing one another. Others have considered that the colours of allied species of birds of paradise, humming birds and grouse may be important in this respect (Mayr 1942).

Wallace had noticed that birds living on isolated small islands were often dull-coloured compared with their closest relatives. This suggested that, where closely allied species or members of one species are not competing immediately with one another, there is little advantage to be gained from advertisement. Thus, three species of New Guinea papilios are very pale, and the rich dark *Euploea* of Malaya have pale species on the small islands of Kei, Banda and Matabello (1876). Furthermore, sexual dimorphism itself tends to deteriorate on small islands where only one species of a genus is represented (Mayr 1934).

In at least one case, colour has been suggested to act as an isolating mechanism between fish species (Haskins and Haskins 1949) and evidence is accumulating for its importance in separating butterfly species. Recently Brower (1959) for example, has shown that males of the yellow *Papilio rutulus* court indiscriminately the females of their own species and those of the similarly yellow *P. multicaudatus* when given the opportunity, whilst showing less tendency to court the closely allied whiteish species *P. eurymedon*.

Finally, to return to Darwin's original hypothesis of male rivalry with which Wallace agreed. Is it possible that it is this side of the sexual selection theory which should be elaborated rather than the female choice aspect? Threat displays in birds usually take place between members of the same sex, serving as advertisements of maleness to other males. Lack (1946) came to the conclusion that the coloured breasts of robins are recognition marks that elicit threat reactions or displays towards territorial intruders. Threat display between two males involves the puffing out of the breast, and showing off its red colour. Although robins chase non-red-breasted birds, and attack anything the shape of a robin, they do not display unless red feathers are present. Colour in this case, and others (Noble 1936), seems to be primarily for recognition or advertisement between birds of the same species. It acts according to Lorenz (1937) as a sign or "releaser" which elicits behaviour proper to intimidation. It is only comparatively recently that threat displays have been found to be common amongst birds, many which were thought to be associated with courtship now being considered to be threatening activity between members of the same sex (Huxley and Montague 1925). Such displays do not normally end in fights and were not included, therefore, in Darwin's theory of male rivalry. In fact, they seem to be mainly important in preventing fighting. Display of maleness permits an intruding male to recognize in his opponent aggressive maleness. This is usually enough. These are only odd examples of the association of colour with threat display and, again, it is not possible to decide whether this association is widespread amongst birds: almost nothing is known of such activities in other animals.

Where then does the theory of sexual selection stand today? How do modern biologists interpret sexual colour dimorphism? There seems to be no single answer to these questions, and to some extent different biologists give different answers just as they did in the nineteenth century. There is still too little experimental evidence to be sure of any of the suggested generalizations. But, summing up, it would seem that female choice has been abandoned, but colour if present is often used in courtship displays and can elicit sexual behaviour (Lorenz 1937). In addition there is some evidence for some sort of selective breeding amongst insects (Maynard Smith 1956), but it is a considerable way from female choice and much nearer to Wallace's own observations that in some cases in a variable population of insects, like tends to breed with like. The need for concealment during incubation in birds, and of female butterflies laden with eggs or seeking a place to lay them, is obviously of very great importance, but it provides only a reason for some animals *not* being brilliantly coloured; it does not give a selective reason for the tendency to bright colours. Male vitality is also not adequate.

The best single theory to account for colour dimorphism seems to be a combination of Darwin's male rivalry and Wallace's theory of recognition and warning colours. Colour seems, where it is not for some sort of obvious protection, to have been evolved as a means of recognition; recognition between young and old, recognition sometimes between opposite sexes, recognition between members of a social group and, perhaps most important, recognition between members of different species to prevent hybridization, and recognition of maleness by other males of the same species. This last, threat display is, of course, only a special case of recognition as Wallace realized when in 1910 he concluded that the horns of antelopes were recognition marks (WL 161).

The present attitude to colour should be attributed to both Darwin and Wallace, therefore, even though Wallace's name has dropped out of the controversy. Recognition colours seem to be of far greater importance than most nineteenth-century naturalists believed and, although many biologists would find it difficult to believe for the lack of reference to him, the first realization of the importance of recognition colours is due entirely to A. R. Wallace.

Social Problems

During the period between the publication of *Island Life* in 1880 and what were to be almost his final statements on biological problems, *Darwinism* (1889), Wallace contributed little more than the occasional lecture, short article or book review on scientific subjects. The greater part of his writings at this time was concentrated on social problems, notably on the then much discussed subject of land reform.

After his return from the Amazon in 1853 Wallace had been influenced by Herbert Spencer's advocacy of land reform in *Social Statics* and had reinforced his convictions of the barbarism of private ownership of the land by his experiences of other forms of land tenure in the east. At the end of *Malay Archipelago,* in a last note, he criticized European land tenure: "we permit absolute possession of the soil of our country, with no legal rights of existence on the soil, to the vast majority who do not possess it. A great landholder may legally convert his whole property into a forest or a hunting ground, and expel every human being who has hitherto lived upon it. In a thickly-populated country like England, where every acre has its owner and its occupier, this is a power of legally destroying his fellow-creatures; and that such a power should exist, and be exercised by individuals, in however small a degree, indicates that, as regards true social science, we are still in a state of barbarism" (MA II 464).

As a result of this statement he became acquainted with John Stuart Mill, who persuaded him to join the Land Tenure Reform Association. The object of this Association was to claim the future unearned increment of land from the state "by fixing the present market value of all lands and appropriating to the state future increases in value" (George 1879) not due to the improvements made by the proprietor. Wallace agreed to join and suggested that, in addition to Mill's proposals, the state should be empowered to buy back land for itself; it should also be made the owner of historic monuments and buildings. Mill approved of Wallace's additions to the programme. Wallace attended one or two meetings, but a year later the Association came to an end when Mill died and Wallace gave up any positive advocacy of reforms. At this time, he was mainly influenced by the individualist philosophies of both Spencer and Mill and, therefore, although he believed in land reform and was angered by the injustices of private ownership, he was not prepared to support any particularly revolutionary changes. And in spite of their own strong feelings on the abuses of land ownership, on evictions and enclosure, neither Spencer nor Mill had been prepared to go so far as to demand state ownership of the land. Their dislike of extending state influence prevented their seeking this solution to their problem.

During the years 1879-80 the subject of Irish landlordism became such a burning issue in the country that Wallace's interest was again aroused, and this time he was gradually forced to the conclusion that some form of state ownership was the only way out of the difficulties. This was, of course, no new idea; it had been advocated as long ago as 1775 by Thomas Spence, but it had been suppressed until this revival of interest in the problem nearly 100 years later. To reform Irish land tenure and to reduce the number of evictions and of exploitations, the Irish Land League had suggested that the Government should buy out the Irish landlords, and that the tenants should then redeem their holdings from the Government over a period of thirty-five years. To Wallace this seemed the wrong way to go about the problem, as it solved nothing in the long run. Those who were tenants today would become the owners of the future, so that in thirty-five years' time the situation would be much the same, but with a new set of landlords. Wallace believed that everyone should have the opportunity of owning a piece of land and of having access to open country. To him the land was a common heritage of the nation and should be available to all. The activities of the Irish landlords provided him with the stimulus to find a means by which such an ideal situation could be brought about. He was angered by the injustices of the system. Land was not a new subject to Wallace. His years of surveying had provided him with a thorough understanding of enclosures and of rights of tenure and of the attitudes of both tenants and owners to their land. His disgust at many of the activities of landowners, of their business methods, had been the final provocation to leave surveying and become a naturalist.

In 1880 Wallace published an article in the *Contemporary Review* entitled *How to Nationalize the Land: a radical solution of the Irish Land Problem.* His solution, new to the supporters of land nationalization, was that the state should become the ground landlord of the land it acquired from private owners. Wallace seemed to have found a middle way between the outright confiscation of all landed property advocated by Spence and the do-almost-nothing of Mill and Spencer. Thus, the buildings and other fittings on the land should remain the saleable property of the tenants. There would be no sub-letting, except in specified cases of owners of flats and lodging houses. The state would acquire the land gradually through inheritance. In cases of intestacy where there was no direct heir, or in other cases after three generations of inheritance, the land would pass to the state.

This article attracted a good deal of attention and brought him the acquaintance of many who were worried over the land problem. As a result of it, the Land Nationalization Society was founded in 1881 and, Wallace, reluctantly consenting, was elected the first president.

The Society issued a pamphlet containing three propositions, based on Wallace's 1880 article, but considerably modified in respect of the means by which the state should come into possession. Proposition I stated that *Unrestricted private property in land is inherently wrong, and leads to grievous and wide-spread ills.* It gave seven reasons for the statement, including the evils of eviction, enclosure, rack rents and exploitation of the natural resources of the country. Proposition II was: *In order that the land of the country may be free for the enjoyment of all its citizens to the fullest extent compatible with the well-being of the community the following principles should be embodied in law.* The proposals for the state to act as ground landlord only followed, and they suggested that everyone should be allowed to choose a piece of land for his own occupation *once* in his lifetime. Proposition III was: *In order that the community may reap the full benefit of the proposed system of land-tenure as soon as possible, it is essential that the entire interest in the land of the country* (*as distinguished from the tenant-right*), *should pass to the State by means of a general law, securing to all existing landowners and their heirs revenues equal to the annual value of the land, apart from the tenant-right.*

The society, unlike its president, was not prepared to wait for the acquisition of land by inheritance; it proposed that only some five or ten years should elapse before the state should compulsorily buy out all landlords. It was assumed that the rents accruing from tenants, and the profits acquired from the mines and other natural resources would be very much more than enough to provide the money for buying.

Herbert Spencer was even less inclined than Wallace to support such a proposition, and in 1881 he wrote to Wallace: "Argument aside, however, I should be disinclined to commit myself to any scheme of immediate action, which, as I have indicated to you, I believe at present premature. For myself I feel that I have to consider not only what I may do on special questions, but also how the action I take on special questions may affect my general influence; and I am disinclined to give more handles against me than are needful" (M II 155).

But Wallace, with his usual thoroughness and enthusiasm, had no sooner been caught up in the activities of the Society, than he delved into the history of land tenure, from the nineteenth century to Domesday, comparing the various customs of the British Isles and investigating systems of land tenure in other European countries. The outcome of this was *Land Nationalization: its Necessity and its Aims,* a book published in March 1882.

In it he reviewed the whole subject of land tenure, considered the evils of private ownership, the advantages of nationalization, and drew for his arguments on sources of the most diverse kind, from agricultural reports and the history of the Irish famine, to reports on Highland crofters and treatises on the land systems of Europe.

Among the points he made for solving the land problem in Britain, most of which had already been made in the syllabus of the Land Nationalization Society, were the necessity of acquiring ancient monuments to prevent their destruction, a plea he had already made as long ago as 1871 (I 10), and the importance of state or municipal planning.

Wallace tentatively suggested planning for green belts near large towns. "Other checks might be applied by local authorities, which would tend greatly to the healthiness and enjoyability of our larger towns, such as the interposition of belts of park and garden at certain intervals around dense centres of population—

a class of improvement which the ruinous competition prices of land held by private owners now renders impossible" (L N 126).

Although Wallace would not at this time call himself a socialist because land reform was the only equalizing measure which seemed to him necessary, he was in fact propounding the principal item on the programme of British socialism. Land nationalization was a widely discussed subject at this period. By 1889 *Fabian Essays in Socialism* was making a case for the acquisition of the land by the state, by gradual purchase, and in the same year both Spencer and Huxley, on the other side, were corresponding in *The Times* against land nationalization.

Huxley believed neither in Fabian socialism nor the laissez-faire policies of Mill; he based his beliefs for social progress, like Matthew Arnold, on the improvement and extension to all of elementary education. Spencer no longer believed that an equitable distribution of land could be effected.

Wallace was annoyed by what he considered Spencer's defection, and he wrote: "When the great philosopher who first taught us how enormous was this wrong, goes back on his own words, declares that he sees no way out of the difficulty, and that the huge injustice to the living and to the unborn must go on indefinitely, then we refuse to accept the teachings of such a helpless guide, who sets before us this most important conclusion under the holy name of JUSTICE" (SSS II 340).

Gradually the seemingly urgent problem of land nationalization died away and was lost from the socialist programmes of the twentieth century. Although the acquisition of agricultural land by the state for its more rational development has been advocated from time to time, for example by Tawney (1931) and by Orwin and Peel (1926), and the mining interests have been nationalized, even the postwar Labour Governments were not prepared to advocate land nationalization. Private ownership of land is in less danger than it was in the nineteenth century but, in contrast, many of Wallace's nineteenth-century proposals have been implemented by planning control of private property (Town & Country Planning Act 1947).

Perhaps Wallace had no direct part in bringing about such things, but historic monuments have become public property, the green belts and national parks he desired have been established as open spaces with free access, and many tenants had between 1943 and 1957 the security of tenure and protection from exploitation which would probably have satisfied Wallace's sense of justice. In 1881 Wallace was ahead of his time in land reform, as in so many other things. It took two world wars to provide the stimulus to some degree of land reform which Wallace optimistically believed could be provided by the pronouncement of the Land Nationalization Society.

In spite of its apparent lack of influence, Wallace continued to support the Society. He gave it an address as late as 1895, and all his life he retained an active interest in land reform, devoting most of a chapter of *My Life* to it, with quotations from his addresses. Curiously, the last letter Darwin wrote to Wallace was not devoted to a scientific event or a biological problem but had as its main topic *Progress and Poverty* and land nationalization. Wallace had urged Darwin to read Henry George's book and Darwin replied that he would, but "I read many years ago some books on political economy, and they produced a disastrous effect on my mind, viz. utterly to distrust my own judgment on the subject and to doubt much everyone else's judgment. . . . I see that you are going to write on the most difficult political question, the land. Something ought to be done—but what is to rule? I hope that you will [not] turn renegade to natural history; but I suppose that politics are very tempting."

Wallace's social and economic ideas continued to develop, and in 1884 he wrote an article on *The Morality of Interest—the Tyranny of Capital* in reply to a discussion that had been going on for some time in the *Christian Socialist*. Wallace maintained that there was nothing immoral about lending money and earning interest on money. Capital and interest were not a matter of morality but ways of running an economy but, to his way of thinking, they were not the best ways of running the economy for the benefit of the majority. To banish the tyranny of capital he therefore advocated a programme of nationalization.

In addition to land, the railways should be acquired by the state and the Limited Liability Act repealed "because it has served only to foster the worst and most iniquitous speculations, and has deluded the public into the idea that they could safely share in the profits of commercial enterprises of the nature and management of which they are profoundly ignorant. There would remain no safe investments for money, except in some branch of agriculture, manufactures, or commerce in which either the investor or some relation or friend was personally interested, and thus would be brought about the diminution and practical abolition of usury as a system, and of whole classes living idle lives on the interest of money derived from the accumulations of previous generations" (II 247).

Wallace considered this article to be such an important stage in the development of his ideas that he had the whole of it printed in the first edition of *My Life*.

At this time he was in correspondence with several eminent men who were interested in problems of welfare and of redistribution of wealth. At the instigation of a Mr Miller of Edinburgh, a conference was called to consider such problems. The conference lasted three days and was attended by 150 delegates from labour associations and representatives of political and social science, including Frederic Harrison.

How to Cause Wealth to be more Equably Distributed, concerned almost entirely with the redistribution of land, was Wallace's contribution to the conference. The redistribution of wealth was a painful question during the depression of the late nineteenth century. The stage was being set for the renewed interest in socialism and Trade Unionism, which had been momentarily popular during Robert Owen's life but had become dormant during the unprecedented prosperity of the middle years of the century. Neither the conference nor Wallace's contribution had any material effect on this awakening.

Wallace fast became involved in the intellectual swing to socialism. He abandoned Herbert Spencer to return to Robert Owen. But in 1884 Wallace was not yet ready to proclaim himself a socialist.

Wallace's next literary adventure into political economy was to produce an essay on *The Depression of Trade* for a £100 competition. He did not win the competition, but the judges considered his essay interesting enough to ask him to let part of it, the factual analysis stripped of policy, be printed with the other essays. Wallace refused to print the facts without the conclusion.

The complete essay was published in 1885 under the title *Bad Times*. Wallace reviewed the causes of the depression, and he concluded that they were to be found in the increase in production of the instruments of war, industrial speculation, the migration from the land. He proposed as remedies the limitations of such activities. The book attracted mainly adverse criticism and did not sell well.

North America

At the end of 1885 Wallace received an offer from the Lowell Institute of Boston for an American lecture tour, and he accepted it because of financial pressure.

Wallace prepared his lectures, writing and rewriting, making for them a set of new diagrams and maps as well as coloured lantern slides. He enlarged and perfected some lectures he had already given in England, on island faunas and other problems of geographical distribution, and he added four new subjects, three on various aspects of colour in both plants and animals, and one entitled *The Darwinian Theory*.

Wallace was particularly pleased with *The Darwinian Theory* because he felt that it disposed of many of the obstacles to a full understanding of the original theory of natural selection. It was typical of him that he should emphasize by the title Darwin's part in the formulation of the theory to the exclusion of his own.

On 9th October 1886 he left London on a slow steamer, arriving in New York fourteen days later after a "cold and disagreeable passage". He spent a few days in New York, renewing his acquaintance with Henry George, whom he had met in England as a result of his *Land Nationalization* book. Because of this, the first words Wallace addressed to an American audience were not on the subject of Darwinism but on social conditions and, presumably, land reform. On this first occasion of public speaking in America, he "could see that I did not impress them much" (II 108).

Wallace's first official lecture, *The Darwinian Theory,* was given in Boston on 1st November. Like those that followed, it was a great success. *The Transcript* wrote : "The first Darwinian, Wallace, did not leave a leg for anti-Darwinism to stand on when he had got through his first Lowell lecture last evening. It was a masterpiece of condensed statement—as clear and simple as compact—a most beautiful specimen of scientific work. Mr Wallace, though not an orator, is likely to become a favourite as a lecturer, his manner is so genuinely modest and straightforward" (II 109).

One of the first eminent biologists with whom Wallace became acquainted in Boston was Professor Asa Gray, the botanist, who had done so much to spread Darwinism in America and who had been the recipient of the letter from Darwin, which was read as part of Darwin's contribution to the Linnean Society meeting of 1st July 1858. Asa Gray introduced Wallace to the biologists of Boston and Harvard. Wallace was a frequent visitor at his house, and he attended meetings of the National Academy of Sciences, naturalists' clubs and university functions with Gray and other biologists. At one meeting of the National Academy of Sciences when the discussion turned on geographical distribution, Professor Gray called on Wallace to speak.

"I was rather taken aback, and could think of nothing else but the phenomenon of seed dispersal by the wind, as shown by the varying proportion of endemic species in oceanic islands, and by the total absence in the Azores of all those genera whose seeds could not be air-borne (either by winds or birds), thus throwing light upon some curious facts of plant-distribution. I think the subject, as I put it, was new to most of the naturalists present" (II 110). This particular problem of distribution had a bearing on one of the differences of opinion between Wallace and Darwin.

Darwin maintained that the presence of arctic plants in the southern hemisphere and isolated on mountain tops in the tropics was the result, even evidence, of the cooling of the whole earth during the ice ages. During the cool period arctic plants spread over almost all the world. When the temperature rose again the arctic plants in the lowlands and tropics died out. Only the few isolated communities survived where the temperature remained suitable.

Wallace agreed that the glaciations might explain the spread and subsequent retreat of the arctic plants round the northern hemisphere, but he was not convinced that they could explain the discontinuous distribution of arctic forms in the southern hemisphere and in the tropics. He therefore advocated aerial dispersal of seeds as the explanation. Wallace supposed that cold-adapted plants could be carried across unsuitable warm habitats along mountain tops. "The study of the floras of oceanic islands having led me to the conclusion that the greater part of their flora was derived by aerial transmission of seeds either by birds or by gales and storms, I extended this view to the transmission along mountain-ranges, and from mountain-top to mountain-top, as being most accordant with the facts at our disposal" (II 20).

Wallace put forward the theory of aerial dispersal in *Island Life,* and he wrote to Darwin a few weeks after its publication: "No doubt, direct evidence of seeds being carried great distances through the air is wanted, but, I am afraid, can hardly be obtained. Yet I feel the greatest confidence that they *are* so carried. Take for instance the two peculiar orchids of the Azores (Habenaria species): what other mode of transit is conceivable?" (M I 311).

Darwin replied: "But I remain as great a heretic as ever. Any supposition seems to me more probable than that seeds of plants should have been blown from the mountains of Abyssinia, or other central mountains of Africa to the mountains of Madagascar" (312).

When it had been molluscs, Darwin had been anxious to establish their haphazard dispersal, through the sea or by birds, and Wallace, because such animals were of great antiquity, had preferred a theory of once continuous distribution with subsequent differential extinction. But by 1876 Wallace came round to the idea that some molluscs could be dispersed in much the same way as he advocated for the seeds of plants. In *Island Life* he suggested the dispersal of freshwater fishes' eggs by similar means. By 1893 he could write: "It is owing to such trifling occurrences as the occasional attachment of a living shell to a beetle's leg, or the conveyance of seeds in the mud adhering to a bird's foot, that many remote islands have become stocked with life, and the range of species extended or modified over the earth; while through changes of the organic environment thus effected even the origination or the extinction of species may have been brought about" (Kew 1893).

The aerial dispersal of seeds was novel enough at the time to interest the members of the National Academy of Sciences. Today, there is still little direct evidence to support Wallace's theory, although recordings taken from aircraft have shown at least that spores and pollen grains are airborne over unlikely places, for example the Canadian arctic, and to heights of at least 5,000 ft. (Polunin 1951).

Wallace was praised by the Americans for clarifying the theory of natural selection by his lectures, and for the same reasons he praised American museums. At Harvard he visited the Museum of Comparative Zoology which had been constructed according to the plans of Louis Agassiz and was run by Agassiz' son Alexander. The Harvard biological museum had not been built on the cathedral plan, but it had plain light rooms for exhibition and rooms for students and curators. It did not show everything it had in confusion but had a plan of exhibition. He contrasted it with "the vast paleontological gallery at South Kensington", where "the crowded heaps of detached bones and jaws and teeth of fossil elephants and other animals, [are] all set up in costly mahogany and glass cases for the public to stare at . . . but all crowded together in one vast confusing series from which no clear ideas can possibly be obtained" (SSS II).

The Harvard museum, too, fulfilled other requirements Wallace had advocated when he applied for the directorship of the Bethnal Green Museum in 1869. Zoology was shown as a study of animal types, as a succession of fossils and as a study in geographical distribution, and " . . . the specimens are comparatively few in number, not crowded together, and so arranged and grouped as to show at the same time the wonderfully varied forms of animal life, as well as the unity of type that prevails in each of the great primary groups under very different external forms."

When Wallace visited the museums in Washington and Yale he found the same clear exposition, all incomparably better than anything in Europe. But no museum accorded so closely with his own specifications as the Agassiz museum, and he commented: "It is surely an anomaly that the naturalist who was most opposed to the theory of evolution should be the first to arrange his museum in such a way as best to illustrate that theory, while in the land of Darwin no step has been taken to escape from the monotonous routine of one great systematic series of crowded specimens, arranged in lofty halls and palatial galleries, which may excite wonder, but which are calculated to teach no definite lesson."

Once Wallace had given his lectures at the Lowell Institute he was permitted to give them again, in the same or modified form, at other places. Soon, therefore, he travelled round New England, mainly by train. He admired the almost complete series of fossil horses, from the eocene *Hyracotherium* (*Eohippus*) to the modern *Equus,* preserved in the Peabody Museum at Yale. And among others, he met Professor Dana, the geologist, who had been writing on speciation by creation when Wallace's ideas had already developed towards evolution (1857).

After wintering in Washington, Wallace determined to see as much of the country as possible. The journey through the United States would be very different from previous travels to distant lands. He came as a distinguished scientist, lecturing on the results of earlier expeditions, not as an unknown collector seeking the meaning of speciation. He came, too, as the pioneer of zoogeography, to acquaint himself at first hand with the fifth of the six regions of the world. Only the Ethiopian region and the continent of Australia itself were to remain unvisited.

In contrast to his earlier visits to the Neotropical, Oriental and Australian regions, he came to the Nearctic with a considerable knowledge of the flora and fauna. His aim was not to discover but to observe what he already knew. His first opportunities were during long walks round Washington with Lester Ward, professor of botany, who introduced him to the typical flowers of a New England spring.

From Washington in March Wallace made a ten day visit to Canada to lecture at Kingston and Toronto, and on the way back he spent four days at Niagara. "The small Luna Island dividing the American falls was a lovely sight; the arborvitae trees (*Thuja Americana*), with which it is covered, young and old, some torn and jagged, but all to the smallest twigs coated with glistening ice from the frozen spray, looked like groves of gigantic tree corals —the most magnificent and fairy-like scene I have ever beheld. All the islands are rocky and picturesque, the trees draped with wild vines and Virginia creepers, and afford a sample of the original American forest vegetation of very great interest. During these four days I was almost entirely alone, and I was glad to be so. I was never tired of the ever-changing aspects of this grand illustration of natural forces engaged in modelling the earth's surface" (II 127).

Evidence of the natural forces that had modelled the earth's surface in former days became one of his chief preoccupations during his travels through North America. Evidence for glaciation, with which he had first become acquainted in Wales and

Switzerland, was of particular interest to him. It was one of the few scientific subjects on which he had still much to write (SSS I).

South of Cincinnati, the origin of a group of conglomerate boulders had been traced to the north of Lake Huron, 600 miles away. Presumably they had been shifted by the extension of the ice in pleistocene days. To hear American geologists ascribe phenomena such as this to the occurrence of vast sheets of ice over much of the North American continent in pleistocene days was particularly satisfactory to Wallace. He had been one of the first to accept Agassiz' interpretation of glacial phenomena in Europe. He had been the first to relate Palearctic glacial epochs to the distribution of animals. But until now he had been hesitant to pronounce on Nearctic ice ages and their effects on the fauna and flora of that part of the world.

As Wallace travelled through the United States more examples of former ice ages and other geological events came to his notice. There were thick beds of loess round Sioux City and canyons and peaks in the Sierra Nevada "... a region of extinct (Pliocene?) volcanoes, but at and near the summit these rocks have been denuded down to the gneiss and granite, which there exhibits the grinding power of ice as in the mountains of Europe. In this region we have the results of fire, water, and ice action well illustrating their respective shares in modelling the earth's surface" (II 175).

By this time Wallace had become more interested in the observation and collection of plants than of animals. In any case, plant collecting was more suitable to the present type of restricted journey than even insect collecting could have been. It was, therefore, the blue cowslip of Virginia and the profusion of butterfly tulips, godetias, mimuluses, nemophilas and lupins of California that caught his imagination and determined an expedition into the Rockies for the express purpose of studying the alpine flora of the Nearctic.

Travelling by train was not perhaps the ideal way of studying a flora. By jumping out whenever the train stopped at a station, however, or when it stopped for the night or for the passengers to have a meal, or when as frequently happened it stopped because the line was being repaired, Wallace was able to observe a wide section of the Nearctic flora through the sandstone rocks and the Soda Springs to the prairie lands beyond Denver.

The most showy and widespread flowers of the Nearctic Rockies were columbines, castilleras, pentstemons and purple and yellow compositaes, in marked contrast to the anemones, gentians, campanulas and primulas of the Palearctic Alps. Nevertheless, Wallace was struck by the number of species which the two regions had in common, many in the mountainous areas, fewer in the lower warmer parts of the two continents. Common yarrow, silver weed and cinquefoil occurred and, in all, Wallace estimated that of some 125 species ninety-five were either identical with, or very closely related to, European alpine species. The similarity required an explanation, and the explanation was found in Wallace's glaciation theory.

Wallace argued that as the ice advanced southwards so did the arctic and alpine plants. With the subsequent retreat of the ice the cold climate flora was left only on mountain tops. The once homogeneous widespread flora had been broken up into isolated populations by extinction in the intervening lowlands where the temperature had risen too high.

Wallace's explanation for these northern similarities of alpine flora was in accordance with the views Darwin had extended to the southern hemisphere. But what for Wallace satisfactorily explained similarities between the Rockies and the Swiss Alps would not necessarily explain similarities between Abyssinian mountains and Madagascar. He did not regard as permissible the extension of the theory of glaciation to the southern hemisphere.

In spite of a desire for unification within a general theory, Wallace thought the pleistocene glaciation theory, like the theory of sexual selection, had been extended by Darwin beyond its legitimate boundaries.

It was not only extensions of his biological philosophy that emerged from the Nearctic travels. He also added to biological facts as in former days. This time it was not to the fauna that he added but the heath plant *Phyllodoce* (*Bryanthus*) *empetriformis* to the flora of Colorado.

"... but if I were asked what most powerfully impressed me, as at once the grandest and most interesting of the many wonders of the western world, I should answer, without hesitation that it was the two majestic trees ... together with the magnificent and beautiful forests in the heart of which they are found. Neither the thundering waters of Niagara, nor the sublime precipices and cascades of Yosemite, nor the vast expanse of the prairies, nor the exquisite delight of the alpine flora of the Rocky Mountains—none of these seem to me so unique in their grandeur, so impressive in their display of the organic forces of nature, as the two magnificent 'big trees' of California" (SSS I 234).

The big trees, giant sequoias *Sequoiadendron gigantea,* and the redwoods *Sequoia sempivirens* are typical of the original forests of California. These once covered the whole of the coastal ranges, but they are confined now to the northern part of the state and to a few mountain slopes near San Francisco. It was one of these isolated groves at Santa Cruz that Wallace visited with his brother John, who had left England to settle in California whilst Wallace was exploring the Amazon. Although this was their first meeting for forty years, John had provided his younger brother with descriptions of the Nearctic flora and fauna and, whenever possible, with specimens of it. He had once sent him a live *Phrynosoma* lizard, the horned toad, which had lived for months in the study at Grays.

In the arid prairie country between Sioux City and Denver Wallace first saw *Phrynosoma* in its native surroundings, also another animal typical of Nearctic deserts, the prairie dog *Cynomys.* At Denver he was amused to meet chipmunks for the first time and to find them as friendly as robins in England. On the whole, however, he was disappointed to have seen so little of the North American fauna, and he wrote: "... I never once saw a humming bird or a rattlesnake, or even any living snake of any kind. In many places I was told that humming-birds were usually common in their gardens, but they hadn't seen any this year!" (II 191).

The human fauna was more in evidence. "Near me in the train was a lady chewing gum; I saw her at intervals for an hour, her jaws going regularly all the time, just like those of a cow when ruminating. *Not* a pleasant sight, or conducive to beauty of expression. It must be tiring for beginners" (II 156).

His impressions of American society were decidedly mixed. The pride with which his host at Sioux City showed him the new pork curing factory, in which pigs went in at one end and bacon and sausages came out at the other, nauseated him. Other modern developments he found interesting and worth imitating.

When he lectured at a university in Indiana he became aware for the first time that men and women could be admitted on terms of complete equality. Everywhere in the west he found co-educational colleges and even women professors. To his surprise he met nothing but praise for the arrangement. In fact, he himself came to regard the American educational system with favour, and he commented: "They are comparatively free from those old-world establishments and customs whose destructiveness so often paralyses the efforts of the educational reformer, and their originality of thought and action has thus freer scope; they are not afraid of experiments, and do not hastily condemn a thing because it is new; while, in all they undertake they are determined to have the best or the biggest attainable. Hence it is that colleges and universities for women, schools where the two sexes study together, institutes for the most complete instruction in technology and in all branches of experimental science, and the combination of manual with mental training as part of the regular school course, are to be found in successful operation in various parts of America, though, with rare exceptions, only talked about by us; while in most of the higher schools and colleges science and modern literature take equal rank with those classical and mathematical studies which still hold the first places in Great Britain" (SSS II 16).

It was not only educationists, professors and biologists, whom Wallace met during his stay in the States. He continued his first adventure in speaking to an American audience, by accepting several invitations to speak on political subjects. In Boston he spoke on economic and social justice to the New England Women's Club, giving his views on land reform, tax reform, the evils of inherited property and the general incompetence of government. "Can a state of society which leads to this result be called civilisation? Can a government which, after a century of continuous reforms and gigantic labours and struggles, is unable to organise society so that every willing worker may earn a decent living, be called a successful government?" (SSS II 439).

A similar lecture in Washington brought a sharp attack from the press. *The Washington Post* wrote: "It is astounding that a man who really possesses the power of induction and ratiocination, and who, in physical synthesis has been a leader of his generation, should express notions of political economy, which belong only or mainly to savage tribes" (II 129).

His theories may have seemed more suitable to savage tribes than to the urban civilization of the United States of America, but his observations on that civilization did not compare favourably with his observations on the organization of the so-called savage tribes. "Here is a country . . . which has yet, in little more than a century, destroyed nearly all its forests, is rapidly exhausting its marvellous stores of natural oil and gas, as well as those of the precious metals; and as the result of all this reckless exploitation of nature's accumulated treasures has brought about overcrowded cities reeking with diseases and vice, and a population which, though only one-half greater than our own, exhibits all the pitiable phenomena of women and children working long hours in factories and workshops, garrets and cellars for a wage which will not give them the essentials of mere healthy animal existence" (II 196).

These were sidelines compared with the biological interest of the visit and with that other interest which meant so much to Wallace. In North America he met the leading spiritualists and indulged in séances and spiritualist talk to an extent which he had never before enjoyed. During his visits to Oliver Wendell Holmes, the *Autocrat of the Breakfast Table,* at the beginning of his stay, the talk would be turned to spiritualism, Holmes being "evidently inclined to accept, though he had little personal knowledge of the phenomena" (II 110).

With Professor Ward, a socialist and agnostic, there were many arguments on politics and spiritualism, between discussions about the botany of North America. "But as I had a basis of spiritualistic experiences of which he was totally ignorant, we looked at the subject from different points of view; and I was limited to urging the inherent and absolute differences of nature between matter and mind, and that though, as a verbal proposition, it may be as easy to assume the eternal and necessary existence of matter and its forces as it is to assume mind as the fundamental cause of matter, yet it is not really so complete an explanation or so truly monistic, since we cannot actually conceive matter as producing mind, whereas we certainly can conceive mind as producing matter" (II 118).

The most profitable lecture Wallace ever gave was on spiritualism to a San Francisco audience. More than a thousand people attended. "The audience was most attentive, and it was not only a better audience, but the net proceeds were more than for any single scientific lecture I gave in America." This lecture introduced Wallace to a wide range of Californian society, both rich and not so rich, who were interested in spirits, and gave him an entrance to any séance he cared to attend.

Among the local rich spiritualists Wallace again saw Stanford whom he had met in Washington. He visited Stanford among his 300 Chinese servants at his summer residence in the millionaire district. "The most remarkable of these [houses] was Mr Flood's —a kind of fairy tale palace built entirely of wood, highly decorated with towers and pinnacles, and painted pure white throughout" (II 166).

Senator Stanford had been guided to commemorate his son, with whom he was in constant touch through several mediums, in the construction of a new university. He had already chosen the eight thousand acre site and had had extensive plans made for the buildings. Wallace visited the site with him, admired it and imagined the projected campus that would rise among the trees and avenues.

Wallace had enjoyed his ten months in North America, but he summed up his impressions of the landscape in an article written in 1891: "What most impresses the nature-loving Englishman while travelling in America is the newness and rawness of the country, and the almost universal absence of that harmonious interblending of wild nature with human cultivation, which is so charming over a large part of England.... Instead of the old hedgerows with tall elms, spreading oaks, and an occasional beech, hornbeam, birch or holly, we see everywhere the ugly snake-fence of split rails, or the still more unsightly boundary of barbed wire" (SSS I 209).

Spiritualism

Until the middle of the eighteenth century little attempt had been made to study the anatomy of the human brain in relation to its functions or to try experimentally to alter human behaviour. In about the year 1770 the Viennese physician, Mesmer, discovered what was called animal magnetism. He discovered that he had the power of inducing a state of trance in many of his patients, and influencing their behaviour. Then, a few years later the German medical Dr Gall announced the results of his investigations into the structure of the human brain. He showed, for instance, the difference between the grey and white matter. The white matter consisted of connecting strands between the cortical patchwork of grey matter. He suggested that particular areas of the cortex were responsible for particular types of behaviour. Gall's attempt was probably the first to localize different faculties in different parts of the brain.

These eighteenth-century discoveries were of outstanding importance and represented a change in outlook towards the study of the mind from two aspects. Mesmer's work seemed to have important practical application as a method of reducing pain during surgical operations. Gall's locatable areas were a challenge to all previous assumptions of the mysterious unity of the working brain. But the line of development from such early contributions to modern psychology and neurophysiology was not direct. The immediate diversions of the nineteenth century were into the scientifically sterile practices of exhibition mesmerism, spiritual trances and phrenology.

Gall was side-tracked into phrenology because he believed he had noticed a correlation between certain types of behaviour and bumps in particular places on the head. He inferred that external bumps located those areas of grey matter he had discovered within the brain. An outside bump would indicate, by muscular analogy, exceptional activity of the faculty within. A study of head bumps, therefore, could reveal something of a subject's mental capacities. It seems likely that Gall believed that head bumps could be read.

Mesmer certainly could induce trances, but he exploited his powers for his own gain and in giving public performances with magnetic wand and iron rods, was probably rightly suspected of charlatanism.

It was the melodramatic aspects of the work of Mesmer and Gall that attracted the widest publicity. Popular demand reached astounding proportions. There was a constant appeal to the medical profession to take more interest. Phrenologists and mesmerists toured the country, and books were written about the subjects.

Scientific opinion however was divided. Mesmer's animal magnetism, the presence of an actual magnetic influence, was generally considered to be suspect. Other aspects of Mesmer's work, such as the influence of suggestion on another mind and the practice of what grew into hypnosis, were considered worthy of investigation, though hypnosis became less attractive to the medical profession with the discovery of the uses of ether in 1846 and chloroform in 1848.

Gall's hypothesis of cortical localization was attractive but difficult to investigate. Scientific opinion, even if it accepted this hypothesis, found it more difficult to pronounce on the correlation between external bumps and internal efficiency. The simple correlation between overall brain size and intellectual ability, which Gall also maintained to exist, could be shown not to be applicable in all cases.

While theologians and mystics generally would not accept morphological localization within the brain, the general public believed that from bumps or depressions of the skull predictions of personality could be made. Phrenology became a parlour game, an alternative to horoscopes.

Wallace first became acquainted with phrenology and mesmerism at a public lecture in Leicester in 1844. He attended a series of lectures and demonstrations with some of the boys from the Collegiate School. Not unnaturally, the boys tried to mesmerize each other afterwards. Wallace was asked to co-operate in the experiment. To his astonishment he found he possessed powers of hypnosis. "I thus established, to my own satisfaction, the fact that a real effect was produced on the actions and speech of a mesmeric patient by the operator touching various parts of the head; and that the effect corresponded with the natural expression of the emotion due to the phrenological organ situated at that part—as combativeness, acquisitiveness, fear, veneration, wonder, tune, and many others; and that it was in no way caused by the will or suggestion of the operator" (I 235).

Wallace became an enthusiast. He attended lectures in London, read books on phrenology and mesmerism and availed himself of every opportunity to watch performances. "Knowing by my own experience that it is quite unnecessary to resort to trickery to produce the phenomena, I was relieved from that haunting idea of imposture which possesses most people who first see them, and which seems to blind most medical and scientific men to such an extent as to render them unable to investigate the subject fairly, or to arrive at any trustworthy conclusions in regard to it" (I 236).

A few years afterwards, Wallace had his head read by two touring phrenologists in Neath. "As the fee for a full delineation was rather high I only received a sketch, and many details were therefore omitted" (WC 174). Wallace was impressed by the result, in spite of the fact that one said he was a mathematical genius and the other that his mathematical abilities were not high.

Phrenology, apart from parlour games, provoked investigation. But, as T. H. Huxley pointed out, investigation proved negative, "Because, owing to the varying thickness of the skull the form of the outside does not correspond to that of the brain itself, and therefore the comparative development of different parts of the brain cannot be determined by the form of the skull."

Modern opinion would agree with Huxley. Attempts to estimate the relative sizes of parts of the brain, the position of the folds and ridges, by study of even the inside of a skull has proved either impossible or misleading.

But that certain areas of the brain are concerned primarily with particular activities is doubted no longer. By the use of weak electrical or other stimulation, the visual, auditory, touch, pressure and motor areas of the mammalian brain have been roughly mapped. Electrical stimulation of a point in the motor area, for instance, brings about a twitch of a specific group of muscles. There is localization within the brain, though it has proved difficult to circumscribe areas with exactness, and almost impossible to identify them by morphological or histological methods. ". . . for even the study of the gross anatomy of the normal human brain itself has so far not demonstrated any feature by which the intellectual abilities of the individual during life can be deduced" (Le Gros Clark 1955). The problem is now further complicated by the realization that the brain has considerable powers of compensation.

Having been swept up in the first general enthusiasm, Wallace made no further effort to practise phrenology or mesmerism; but he continued to believe that they had a part to play in understanding the human mind, and he wrote: "Certain individuals are gifted with unusual powers of perception, sometimes by the ordinary senses leading to the discovery of new forces in nature, sometimes in a manner which no abnormal power of the ordinary senses will account for, but which imply the existence of faculties in the human mind of a nature analogous to those which are generally termed supernatural, and are attributed to the action of unembodied intelligences" (MS 52).

In spite of the belief in mesmerism and the reality of the trance state, when he had to have several teeth extracted in 1874 Wallace asked for a doctor to administer nitrous oxide. The dentist, a mesmerism enthusiast and Wallace's friend, would not hear of an anaesthetic. When Wallace insisted, the dentist flew into a rage and ended the friendship.

The practice of phrenology and mesmerism may have dropped out of Wallace's repertoire, but the idea of the supernatural and unembodied intelligences did not. All reports on spiritualist experiences interested him profoundly.

"During twelve years of tropical wanderings, occupied in the study of natural history, I heard occasionally of the strange phenomena said to be occurring in America and Europe under the general name of 'table-turning' and 'spirit-rapping'; and being aware, from my own knowledge of Mesmerism, that there were mysteries connected with the human mind which modern science ignored because it could not explain, I determined to seize the first opportunity on my return home to examine into these matters. It is true, perhaps, that I ought to state that for twenty-five years I had been an utter sceptic as to the existence of any preter-human or super-human intelligences, and that I never for a moment contemplated the possibility that the marvels related by spiritualists could be literally true. If I have changed my opinion, it is simply by the force of the evidence" (MS 125).

The immediate years after Wallace's return from the east were taken up with biology, however. There was little time for the proposed examination of spiritualistic matters. It has been said that the first indications of the way in which Wallace's thoughts were going occurred in an article on natural selection applied to man, written in 1864. But in the original article Wallace's views on the evolution of man followed strictly Darwinian lines, except that he believed structural changes had occurred early and mental elaboration had followed. The nearest approach to a spiritual line in the article was the new stress on the importance of mind, its shielding influence and the power it gave man over his environment, with the consequent modification of natural selection. It was not until six years later that a new ending was written for this article, relying heavily on the power of spirits.

The year after the first version of this article, however, Wallace did commit himself when he went to his first séances with his sister and subsequently started holding them at his own house. For instance, on 22nd July 1865 he experienced the first of many amateur exhibitions of table turning and spirit rappings. "These experiments have satisfied me that there is an unknown power developed from the bodies of a number of persons placed in connection by sitting round a table with all their hands upon it" (MS 127).

Wallace took to visiting a professional medium where tables rose in the air and moved round the room. "However strange and unreal these few phenomena may seem to readers who have seen nothing of the kind, I positively affirm that they are the facts which really happened just as I have narrated them, and that there was no room for any possible trick or deception."

With his usual thoroughness, Wallace started to read up spiritualism, and soon he accumulated enough material to write a long article which was published in pamphlet form as *The Scientific Aspect of the Supernatural.* In it he discussed the problem of miracles, animal magnetism, clairvoyance and apparitions, the spiritualist experiences of well known men from all walks of life and made a plea for the investigation of inexplicable phenomena, a plea for the investigation of the nature, or supernature, or miracles, of thought transference and suggestibility.

Wallace himself was inclined to think that miracles were not evidence of a supernatural. Miraculous cures, for instance, were psychological jolts for people already cured but unable, because of their disposition, to get better. "Our orthodox medical men are profoundly ignorant of the subtle influences of the human body in health and disease, and can thus do nothing in many cases which Nature would cure if assisted by proper conditions" (M II 192). But in spite of some objectivity, the article gives the general impression that Wallace was so convinced of spirits that he was more willing to give prominence to the work of William Crookes who believed than to the experiments of the physicist Faraday (1853) who did not.

The Scientific Aspect of the Supernatural was used by Wallace as an attempt to persuade his scientific and literary friends to take an interest. He sent copies or wrote to, for example, Huxley, Tyndall and Lewes. His friends were astonished that he should be taking spiritualism so seriously. Lewes, having convinced himself of the trickery of one medium, would not discuss it. Tyndall, who had already rebuked Thackeray for his public advocacy of spiritualism, took a later opportunity to rebuke Wallace. "I see the usual keen powers of your mind displayed in the treatment of this question. But mental power may show itself, whether the material be facts or fictions. It is not lack of logic that I see in your book, but a willingness that I deplore to accept data which are unworthy of your attention" (II 281).

Darwin was grieved, Hooker surprised. "I am only two-thirds through Wallace [*Island Life*] and it is splendid," he wrote. "What a number of cobwebs he has swept away. That such a man should be a spiritualist is more wonderful than all the movements of all the Planets" (Huxley 1918).

Huxley was tolerant towards Wallace himself, but regarded spiritualism as a farce. He wrote: "The only good that I can see in the demonstration of the truth of 'Spiritualism' is to furnish additional argument against suicide. Better live a crossing-sweeper than die and be made to talk twaddle by a 'medium' hired at a guinea a *séance*" (Huxley 1903).

But Robert Chambers was enthusiastic over the pamphlet. "I have for many years *known* that these phenomena are real, as distinguished from impostures, and it is not of yesterday that I concluded they were calculated to explain much that has been doubtful in the past, and when fully accepted, revolutionise the whole frame of human opinion on many important matters" (II 285).

In 1869, four years after the pamphlet, an article appeared showing that spirits had become an important influence in

Wallace's life. Up to this time his interest could have been dismissed as idiosyncratic. It had not been made explicit how far his spirit experiences had influenced his general outlook.

In the *Quarterly Review* for April Wallace reviewed at length the tenth edition of Lyell's *Principles of Geology* in which Lyell first admitted the probability of evolution by natural selection. Wallace took the opportunity not only to congratulate Sir Charles on the youthfulness and integrity of his outlook, but also to outline once more the general principles of natural selection, with a few words on the evolution of man. Wallace stated categorically for the first time his belief that natural selection could not account for the evolution of the mind of man. "But if the researches of geologists and the investigations of anatomists should ever demonstrate that he was derived from the lower animals in the same way that they have been derived from each other, we shall not be thereby debarred from believing, or from proving that his intellectual capacities and his moral nature were not wholly developed by the same process. Neither natural selection nor the more general theory of evolution can give any account whatever of the origin of sensational or conscious life. They may teach us how, by chemical, electrical, or higher natural laws, the organized body can be built up, can grow, can reproduce its like; but those laws and that growth cannot even be conceived as endowing the newly-arranged atoms with consciousness. But the moral and higher intellectual nature of man is as unique a phenomenon as was conscious life on its first appearance in the world, and the one is almost as difficult to conceive as originating by a law of evolution as the other."

Wallace still believed that man had evolved from ape-like ancestors through the agency of natural selection, but he added that a spirit had been put in, through the intervention of a Power. "While admitting to the full extent the agency of the same great laws of organic development in the origin of the human race as in the origin of all organized beings, there yet seems to be evidence of a Power which has guided the action of these laws in definite directions and for special needs."

Darwin praised the review in general. "It is a great triumph that such an article should appear in the 'Quarterly' and will make the Bishop of Oxford etc. . . . gnash their teeth," he wrote to Murray (Darwin 1887). But Darwin realized for the first time that Wallace was not prepared to apply natural selection fully to man. "If you had not told me I should have thought that they [Wallace's remarks on man] had been added by someone else. As you expected, I differ grievously from you, and am very sorry for it. I can see no necessity for calling in an additional and proximate cause in regard to Man. But the subject is too long for a letter," he wrote (M I 243).

Wallace was adamant. He was convinced of the existence of spirits. Wallace experimented. He set traps for the unwary medium, such as extending paper or strings under the table.

There is no evidence that Wallace ever made an experiment in biology. It was not Wallace who investigated the preferences of lizards for different coloured beetles. It was not Wallace who experimented to find out whether molluscs or plant seeds could withstand long periods of immersion in salt water. Wallace was a theoretical scientist, a biological philosopher. He had the ideas, others set up the experiments to test them. Usually he accepted the results of their investigations.

With spiritualism, however, Wallace imagined himself an experimentalist, and he rejected the evidence of non-believers. No one could convince him that séances were a fraud. If a man said he had seen his dead son it was a fact. If a medium said he could raise spirits it was a fact. Transferring to others his own attribute of innocent generosity, he was deceived by them and by himself. All men conformed to his own standards of integrity. Amongst them he never even suspected deception although he had been one of the first to detect deception by edible butterflies taking on the colours of the inedible.

It never seemed to occur to Wallace that mediums making money out of spiritualism were suspect, because Wallace collecting specimens to sell would never have painted a butterfly's wing to get a higher price. "This was one of the ordinary phenomena, and thousands of persons have witnessed it; and when we consider that Home's *séances* almost always took place in private houses at which he was a guest, and with people absolutely above suspicion of collusion with an impostor, and also either in the daytime or in a fully illuminated room, it will be admitted that no form of leger-demain will explain what occurred" (II 287).

Throughout the late sixties and early seventies of the century he was a constant visitor to séances, mostly of the more or less amateur sort, in private houses.

In 1871 Wallace read a paper to the Dialectical Society

called *An answer to the arguments of Hume, Lecky and others against miracles,* a paper in which he concluded: "I must again emphatically point out that the question I have been here discussing is—in no way, whether miracles are true or false, or whether modern spiritualism rests upon a basis of fact or of delusion—but solely, whether the arguments that have hitherto been supposed conclusive against them have any weight or value. . . . It is time that the 'derisive and unexamining incredulity' which has hitherto existed should give way to a less dogmatic and more philosophical spirit, or history will again have to record the melancholy spectacle of man, who should have known better, assuming to limit the discovery of new powers and agencies in the universe, and deciding, *without investigation,* whether other men's observations are true or false" (MS 28).

His theories on the evolution of man were affected by spiritualism. *Contributions to the Theory of Natural Selection* (1870) contained two such articles. The first was almost a reprint of the 1864 article, but instead of the paragraph on the goodness of the human race and the possibilities of social advancement, Wallace had substituted one which ended: "Yet there is undoubtedly an advance—on the whole a steady and permanent one—both in the influence on public opinion of a high morality, and in the general desire for intellectual elevation; and as I cannot impute this in any way to 'survival of the fittest', I am forced to conclude that it is due, to the inherent progressive power of those glorious qualities which raise us so immeasurably above our fellow animals, and at the same time afford us the surest proof that there are other and higher existences than ourselves, from whom these qualities may have been derived, and towards whom we may be ever tending."

The second article *The limits of natural selection as applied to man* detailed the points at which Wallace departed from the Darwinian doctrine. It was an enlarged version of the few sentences on the evolution of man that had appeared in print in 1869. "It will, therefore, probably excite some surprise among my readers, to find that I do not consider that all nature can be explained on the principles of which I am so ardent an advocate; and that I am now myself going to state objections, and to place limits, to the power of 'natural selection'.

"But, if, further, we could see that these very modifications, though hurtful or useless at the time when they first appeared, became in the highest degree useful at a much later period, and are now essential to the full moral and intellectual development of human nature, we should then infer the action of mind, foreseeing the future and preparing for it, just as surely as we do, when we see the breeder set himself to work with the determination to produce a definite improvement in some cultivated plant or domestic animal."

In 1874 Wallace was asked to write an article on spiritualism for the *Fortnightly Review*. There had been a progressive expansion of interest in spirits in that quarter of the nineteenth century, involving men in all walks of life. Literary men like Tennyson, Thackeray and Trollope, numerous barristers and doctors, Robert Owen the economist and Crookes the physicist had become enthusiasts. Crookes had just published the results of his experiments with Home the medium. The Royal Society, tending more towards the views of Huxley and Tyndall, refused to witness these experiments. In this atmosphere of combative excitement Wallace wrote *A Defence of Modern Spiritualism* and, later in the same year, combined his three essays into a book, *Miracles and Modern Spiritualism* which went through three editions in the course of the next twenty years.

Darwin and Huxley corresponded on the subject of spiritualism. "The Lord have mercy on us all, if we have to believe in such rubbish," wrote Darwin. After Huxley had attended a séance, he wrote: "My conclusion is that Mr X is a cheat and an impostor, and I have no more doubt that he got Mr Y to sit on his right hand, knowing from the turn of his conversation that it would be easy to distract his attention, and that he then moved the chair against Mr Y with his leg, and finally coolly lifted [it] on to the table, than that I am writing these lines" (Huxley 1903).

Darwin replied "I am pleased to think that I declaimed to all my family, the day before yesterday, that the more I thought of all that I had heard happened at Queen Anne St, the more convinced I was it was all imposture" (Darwin 1887).

By 1876 the British Association admitted the subject to its discussions. Professor Barrett read a paper in which he claimed to have witnessed undoubted examples of mind reading or what came to be known as telepathy. The paper was not printed in the official records of the British Association, but there was correspondence in *The Times* and several scientists, at Barrett's invitation, witnessed the phenomena. Gurney and Myers agreed with Barrett that the performances were examples of genuine mind reading. Sidgwick was non-commital.

Wallace did not contribute to the controversy. He was more interested in the philosophical problems of the intellectual influence of bodiless spirits on the normal routine of the world and its future development. "The communion of spirit with spirit is said to be by thought-reading and sympathy, and to be perfect between those whose beings are in harmony with each other. Those who differ widely have little or no power of intercommunion, and thus are constituted 'spheres', which are divisions, not merely of space, but of social and moral sympathetic organisation. Spirits of the higher 'spheres' can, and do sometimes communicate at will with those below; but these latter cannot communicate with those above. But there is for all an eternal progress, a progress solely dependent on the power of will in the development of spirit nature" (MS 109).

But Wallace commented on some of Barrett's examples. Cards were used for telepathic identification. Wallace expressed the opinion that cards were not suitable for such experiments, since people have different methods of visualizing objects, in respect of colour, form and arrangement and that, unless the two performers have the same method, the experiments are likely to fail. This comment is interesting because the twentieth-century experiments on extrasensory perception, as it is now called, over which controversy rages from time to time, have been performed with cards (Rhine 1937, Spencer-Brown 1953).

The Society for Psychical Research was formed in 1882. Wallace became a member. He was invited several times to be president, but he refused and took very little active part at any time in the affairs of the society. In fact active participation in spiritualism seems to have waned after 1880, except for the period when he was in America. In America he was caught up in the general enthusiasm.

Wallace experienced slate writing in San Francisco. "From a pile of small slates on a side-table four were taken at a time, cleaned with a damp sponge, and handed to us to examine, then laid in pairs on the table. All our hands were then placed over them till the signal was given, and on ourselves opening them writing was found on both slates."

Variations were practised. On one slate Wallace received a

message from his sister Elizabeth, and "the next was addressed to my brother, referring to me as 'brother Alf', and is signed 'P. Wallace'. This we cannot understand, as we have no relative with that initial, except a cousin, Percy Wilson. It is, I think, not improbable that in transferring the message through the medium, and perhaps through a spirit-scribe (as is often said to be the case), the surname was misunderstood owing to the latter supposing that the communicant was a brother."

The spirit scribe's spelling was as bad as that of Davey, the conjuror's scribe. Davey, having performed a "feat of clairvoyance" on slates, could not persuade his audience he was not a medium. Davey had written the term *books* on a slate to open his next trick. A member of the audience, who had changed his name from Boorzu, declared it was his name not *books* that the "medium" had been guided to discover (Wells, Huxley and Wells 1931).

Maskelyne and Houdini claimed that mediums were all conjurors. Others claimed that mediums were split personalities able to induce in themselves abnormal activity of the normally inhibited subconscious. Whether consciously or subconsciously deceiving, they required the co-operation of what Tyndall called "dupes beyond the reach of proof, who like to believe and do not like to be undeceived" (MS 174).

Wallace himself unconsciously records the diagnostic skill of the medium, as, by hit and miss technique, he gradually sums up his audience. "Those who follow the more scientific method of beginning with observation only—which, strange to say, the scientific men are hardly ever willing to do—almost always find that their early doubts and suspicions are, one by one, shown to be unfounded, through the occurrence of phenomena which seem specially adapted to answer them" (II 302).

The enthusiastic chatter of the American spirit world would seem to have ended all further desire in Wallace for spirit gossip. He confined his spiritualism to letters, three chapters of his autobiography, and a summing up in *The World of Life* (1910). "We conclude, therefore, that there are now in the Universe infinite grades of power, infinite grades of knowledge and wisdom, infinite grades of influence of higher beings upon lower. Holding this opinion, I have suggested that this vast and wonderful universe, with its almost infinite variety of forms, motions, and reactions of part upon part, from suns and systems up to plant life, animal life, and the human living soul, has ever required and still requires the continuous co-ordinated agency of myriads of such intelligences."

This was his religion. It replaced the Christianity he had rejected as a boy. "Although I look upon Christianity as originating in an unusual spiritual influx, I am not disposed to consider [it] as *essentially* different from those which originated other great religious and philanthropic movements. It is probable that in *your* sense of the word I am not a Christian" (M II 209).

Wallace's spiritualism, regarded by his scientific friends with astonished tolerance, was less humanely respected by the scientific world in general, and it resulted in long-lasting damage to his reputation as a biologist. It is suggested that it is the reason why Wallace's scientific contributions are neglected among the works of the great nineteenth-century biologists "... here reference is made to it [spiritualism] as furnishing the explanation why Mr Wallace kept not his 'first estate', and dropped out of the ranks of pioneers of Evolution." ... "But both these pleas prevail when we find the co-formulator of the Darwinian theory among mediums and their dupes. The respectful attention which his words command: the tremendous claims which he makes on behalf of the phenomena at *séances* as proving the existence of soul apart from body after death, and as revealing the conditions under which it lives, have made incumbent the foregoing attempt to indicate what other explanation is given of the phenomena, showing how those fall in with all we know of man's tendencies to imperfect observation and self-deception, and with all that history tells of the persistence of animistic ideas" (Clodd 1897).

Dohrn, of the marine biological station at Naples, accused Wallace of being influenced by clerical and religious prejudice and declared that spiritualism and natural selection were incompatible.

Romanes, angered by a difference of opinion with Wallace over a theory of physiological selection, denigrated Wallace's biological criticism by dragging in spiritualism. Romanes wrote of the last chapter of *Darwinism*: "we encounter the Wallace of spiritualism and astrology, the Wallace of vaccination and the land question, the Wallace of incapacity and absurdity" (II 317).

Wallace, in fact, had only a slight interest in astrology: "I am quite astonished at your wasting your money on an advertising astrologer. In the horoscope sent you there is not a single definite fact that would not apply to you any more than to thousands of other men" (M II 215).

Most nineteenth-century scientists were forced to take notice of spiritualism. But by the end of the century there were few of Wallace's eminence, with the exception of Crookes and Oliver Lodge, who had not dismissed it. "Neither the testimony of all the Fellows of the Royal Society, nor even the evidence of my own senses could lead me to believe in the transmission of thoughts from one person to another, independently of the recognised channels of sensation," declared Helmholtz.

The prevailing feeling of scientific agnosticism was summed up by Carpenter: "With every disposition to accept facts when I could once clearly satisfy myself that they were facts, I have had to come to the conclusion that whenever I have been permitted to employ such tests as I should employ in any scientific investigation, there was either intentional deception on the part of interested persons, or else self-deception on the part of persons who were very sober-minded and rational upon all ordinary affairs of life" (Clodd 1897).

Darwinism

Back in England after his American tour, Wallace was invited to repeat his American scientific lectures on many occasions. They were always a success. Time and again, as in America, members of the audience expressed their gratitude for his straightforward exposition of the Darwinian theory. Wallace made clear what was obscure for them in the *Origin*.

With such encouragement Wallace decided to enlarge the American lectures into a book, since it seemed to him "that a popular exposition of the subject might be useful, not only as enabling the general reader to understand Darwin, but also to serve as an answer to the many articles and books professing to disprove the theory of natural selection" (II 201).

Darwinism was published in 1889 and explained and reviewed the theory of natural selection as it stood after thirty years of praise and abuse. It gave a short history of theories of speciation before Darwin, and it discussed the merits of some of the books published since, such as Cope's *Origin of the Fittest* (1887). Wallace gave space to the problems of colour and the points of difference between Darwin and himself. Mimicry, recognition marks, sexual selection were discussed at length. Zoogeography was included. But perhaps the most interesting innovations in *Darwinism* were the extension of the concept of speciation and the assessment of the work of the German Weismann on the continuity of the germ plasm.

It has been pointed out many times that the *Origin of Species* was not strictly concerned with speciation. It was concerned with establishing natural selection as the directive force in the steady evolution of one species into another over geological time. Little was said about the circumstances in which a population could be divided into two or more groups, each of which would become a species contemporaneously.

Wallace was always more interested than Darwin in this aspect of the problem of the spatial as distinct from the temporal. He argued in 1880 that for spatial speciation to occur, some form of isolation between the parts of the original population was necessary, and in *Darwinism* he brought his theory up to date.

For speciation to occur several requirements had to be satisfied. There must be variability, isolation, natural selection. Variability in the population was an essential prerequisite for selection. Selection implied a choice between differences. Darwin had found his differences exemplified by domestic animals, in particular the various breeds of domestic pigeons. Wallace, in contrast, had found his differences in wild populations, variation in butterflies' wings and wild pigeons.

In *Darwinism* Wallace again stressed the magnitude of variability within wild populations, countering the arguments of the opposition who refused to accept domestic examples as evidence. He added to his previous examples of qualitative variation of, for instance, the colour-markings on the wings of papilios, quantitative assessments of variability in the size of lizards, birds' limbs, mammalian skulls and internal organs.

Variability supplied the raw material for species formation but in itself did not make a species. Variable populations must be isolated from one another before they will become separate species. Wallace reiterated the importance of spatial isolation. Two groups separated physically from one another cannot interbreed and are, therefore, potentially new species. Physical isolation, or geographical isolation as it is often called, is the most important isolating mechanism in species formation, but Wallace added also recognition marks and differences in mating behaviour as important factors in keeping related populations apart.

Given variability and isolation, or break-up of the original population by some means, natural selection was still necessary to effect speciation. Selection by the different environments in which the now separated populations lived could, but not necessarily would, lead to speciation, the incapacity of the populations to interbreed.

"On the whole then, we conclude that, whilst isolation is an important factor in effecting some modification of species, it is so, not on account of any effect produced, or influence exerted by isolation *per se,* but because it is always necessarily accompanied by a change of environment, both physical and biological" (D 150).

And Wallace reached a further interesting conclusion which has never been fully appreciated. He pointed out that organisms are finely balanced systems and that changes effected in them by selection may alter this balance to such an extent that sterility between them and their nearest relatives automatically ensues. Thus, adaptation of populations to new environments would in itself accelerate speciation. ". . . the physiological adjustments producing fertility are so delicate that they are disturbed by almost any variation or change of conditions . . . and in some considerable number of individuals, variations in nature, accompanied by somewhat changed conditions of life, is accompanied by, and probably correlated with, some amount of infertility" (M II 42).

In *Darwinism* Wallace laid considerable stress on the principle of utility. More than Darwin, or any other selectionist, he stressed the importance of the usefulness of variations to their animal possessor. He maintained that unless a variation, a new characteristic, was actually useful to its bearer, it would not be preserved in competition with other members of the population. Wallace maintained, therefore, against Bateson and many others, that all specific characteristics are useful, had been recently useful, or were correlated with a useful characteristic. He pointed out further that useless characters would be variable and unstable in a population because they would not be held stable by the operation of natural selection.

Wallace expanded the principle of utility in a paper read to the Linnean Society in 1896. "The preceding discussion may, I hope, be considered sufficient to show that useless specific characters, if they exist, can only be the result of some comparatively rare and exceptional conditions, and that they certainly are not, as has been alleged, a general characteristic of species."

Again Wallace was involved in a controversy which was to prolong itself beyond the middle of the twentieth century.

Today there are some, Fisher (1930), Fisher and Ford (1947), Cain and Sheppard (1950), for example, who would wholeheartedly endorse Wallace's statement that, "If some useless character appears as a variation in some individuals by exceptional vigour, it may increase by interbreeding, and its repeated production being perhaps favoured by some local conditions, it may come to form a marked local variety. Now, if the conditions become unfavourable to the species in the area occupied by the type, this may in course of time become extinct, and the variety distinguished by the altogether useless character will remain as the only representative of the species. It may be admitted that such a mode of origin of a non-utilitarian specific character is conceivable, but whether it ever actually occurs in nature may be doubted; while if it does occur, it must be owing to so rare a combination of circumstances that it can produce no such general prevalence of useless specific characters as is claimed by the advocates of that theory. (Footnote: If, however, the variation is preserved because it occurs in exceptionally vigorous individuals, it is correlated with a character which is useful.)" (SSS I 396).

Today, there are others, for instance Wright (1931), Diver (1940), Carter (1951), who would lay more stress on the proposition that "such a mode of origin of a non-utilitarian specific character is conceivable". Accepting this proposition, they would then go further and suggest that not only is it conceivable that such characters should come to exist but, also, that in some circumstances they do actually come into being, and become fixed in the population.

This modern stress on the fixation of Wallace's so-called useless characters has given rise to the much disputed theory of evolutionary drift.

The difficulty in reaching a decision between the two alternatives, whether a character is or is not useful, is still the same that faced Wallace and his contemporaries. It is almost impossible to prove non-utility, and it has not turned out to be easy to prove usefulness. Characteristics which may not appear to be useful in themselves may still be only the superficial expression of factors which have an as yet unknown physiological usefulness. Wallace recognized this possibility. It is a possibility which can always be used as an argument against the theory of drift, the spread of neutral characteristics by chance fixation in the population.

Until only recently the problem was in the main a theoretical one. It had developed little since 1896, except in so far as mathematics had been brought in to solve the problems of gene frequency and rate of spread of genes under different conditions of selection. But mathematics had not shed much light on what was actually going on in a wild population. Mathematics had made it seem possible in theory that a neutral character could spread through a population under certain circumstances (Wright 1949, 1955), but it had also made it seem possible to others (Fisher 1930) that such circumstances might never prevail. Mathematics had been unable to prove whether either of these propositions held in practice. So that there were those who expressed the same opinion as Wallace, that characteristics must be useful to be perpetuated, and others like Bateson who maintained that neutral characters could persist. But on whichever side, no one was expressing more than an opinion or reflecting mathematical probabilities. The conflict could only be resolved by experiment or by finding out what actually occurred in wild populations.

Only in the last few years have investigations been made in an attempt to solve the problem of what Wallace called utility. Cain and Sheppard (1950) studied the differences in colour and pattern in populations of snails in different environments, and found that these differences were not fortuitous, as had always been supposed, but were directly related to the environment, and presumably served as a cryptic protection against predators. Thus heavily banded and pinkish shells were more common in beechwoods than elsewhere, unbanded shells in open country. Fisher and Ford (1947) studied the spread of a gene through a colony of moths over nearly 20 years, and they concluded that although the characteristic appeared to have no selective value, the numerical form of its spread was proof that it must have been fixed by positive selection in its favour, and not by random, chance fixation. There are a few more such investigations, and in each case the theory of utility seems to have been confirmed.

But a more precisely controlled experiment was reported in 1957 which again raises doubts. The experiments (Dobzhansky and Pavlovsky 1957) were not undertaken in the field and can, therefore, perhaps be condemned for that reason. But it was found that in twenty experimental populations of the fly *Drosophila pseudoobscura* a known gene combination, which was originally in fifty per cent of the individuals, became fixed in different proportions in the populations after eighteen months of free interbreeding. Furthermore, there was more variation in the frequency of this gene combination in populations which had been small at the outset of the experiment than in those which had numbered thousands of individuals. Dobzhansky and Pavlovsky concluded that both random drift and natural selection were at work to produce the results: randomness fixing the characteristic at first in different proportions in the small, expanding foundation stocks, natural selection then coming in to exert its effect on what were already different populations.

The problem of utility is certainly nearer solution than it was when Wallace propounded it sixty years ago, but what the final solution will be is difficult to estimate. It seems likely, however, that the fixation of neutral characters is comparatively rare, compared with the fixation of useful characters, and only of real significance in small expanding populations. But, as Wright (1955) has pointed out, positive selection within a partially isolated population or on an individual may be of neutral or negative value to the species as a whole, whereas positive selection on the species as a whole may equally be neutral or injurious to the individual or partially isolated population. Whatever the outcome of the dispute, no one is likely to differ from Wallace in his estimate of his own 1896 paper: "my most important scientific essay this year."

Even more fundamental to the species problem was the work of Weismann which Wallace incorporated in *Darwinism*. It seemed to be the culmination of the work on the cell and cell lineages which had been in progress since the beginning of the century. The continuity of cell lineages had a direct bearing on the origin of variation.

In 1838-39 it was recognized that all organisms were composed of similar units, the cells (Schleiden and Schwann). Several years later the cells were shown to be formed from pre-existing cells (Virchow 1855). The next advance was the demonstration that the spermatozoon and the ovum were each single cells (Gegenbauer 1861). In 1884-85 Hertwig and Strasburger showed that it was the nucleus of these cells that was passed from generation to generation and therefore transmitted the physical basis of heredity.

Working on the embryology of coelenterates, Weismann confirmed Virchow's discovery of cell continuity and progressed a stage further. From his observations he concluded that the germ cells arise early in the development of an organism and from that time onwards form a separate cell lineage from the rest of the body cells.

Weismann was lecturing on these lines in Germany in 1881, but it was not until 1885, when he published *Die Continuität des Keimplasmas als Grundlage einer Theorie der Vererbung,* that his contributions were noticed in England. Weismann argued that, once the germ cells had differentiated, the germ cells remained a separate line of descent from the other cells of the body, were unaffected by the rest of the body, were the only cells which were passed on to the next generation. He followed Strasburger in believing in the importance of the nucleus as such as the transmitter of heredity from cell to cell and from one generation to the next. But Weismann, distinguishing between cells, differed from Strasburger in believing that the somatic cell nucleus changed at each division during development, thus causing differentiation into tissues and organs, but the nuclei of the germ cells did not change because they were laid aside very early.

From this theory of the continuity of the germ plasm it followed that characteristics acquired during an organism's lifetime could not be passed on to its offspring. The germ cells, laid aside early, were not infiltrated by cells from other parts of the body. Lamarck's theory of acquired characteristics and Darwin's pangenesis, both of which required alterations in body cells to be reflected in alterations in germ cells, were in doubt (Weismann 1886).

A mechanism for variability had not been found, but the search had been narrowed down to the nucleus of the germ cells. It was Larmarck versus Weismann, variability caused by environment, or variability inherent in the nucleus of the germ cells.

Wallace sided with Weismann, and wrote: "The most remarkable steps yet made in advance are, I think, the theory of Weismann of the continuity of the germ plasm, and its corollary that acquired modifications are never inherited" (M II 41).

Wallace rejected Lamarckism. He finally dismissed pangenesis as explanations of variability in organisms and accepted in their place the theories of Weismann. "*. . . or the new germ-cells arise, as far as their essential and characteristic substance is concerned, and not at all out of the body of the individual but direct from the parent germ-cell.* This latter view Weismann holds to be the correct one, and, on this theory, heredity depends on the fact that a special molecular composition passes over from one generation to another" (D 438).

Wallace further found in Weismann a justification for his own opinion of the importance of sexual reproduction as a source of variability, an opinion he had long held with no other evidence than that of field observation. "Diversity of sex becomes, therefore, of primary importance as the *cause of variation*. . . . But when a complex organism is sexually propagated, there is an ever-present cause of change which, though slight in any one generation, is cumulative, and under the influence of selection is sufficient to keep up the harmony between the organism and its slowly changing environment" (439).

In Weismann Wallace found all he seemed to need to provide an explanation of the variability on which selection could function.

The controversy raged over the choice between the theories of Lamarck and Weismann as the source of variability, and in 1887 the British Association held a discussion on *The Transmission of Acquired Characters,* a discussion introduced by Ray Lankester in the presence of Weismann. Two years later there was a long correspondence in *Nature* entitled *Lamarck versus Weismann.* Whichever theory was preferred it provided for variability amongst organisms on which the Darwinian natural selection could act.

Somehow this clear-cut distinction became blurred. Instead of arguments over the source of variability, the arguments gradually changed in the succeeding years and came to emphasize differences of opinion on the causes of evolution. Sides were taken according to whether selection was thought to be the directive cause in evolution or whether variability itself was thought to be directive. Thus arose the Lamarck—Darwin antithesis.

Wallace dismissed this interpretation of Lamarck in *Darwinism*: "We cannot therefore, accept any arguments against the agency of natural selection which are based upon the opposite and equally unproved theory that acquired characters are inherited, and as this applies to the whole school of what may be termed Neo-Lamarckians, their speculations cease to have any weight" (441).

Herbert Spencer was seriously worried by the new developments in Darwinian theory and was not prepared to accept Weismann's opinions. In the *Contemporary Review* he championed the Lamarckian cause in direct opposition to the views Wallace expressed in *Darwinism*. Wallace replied, denying the validity of any of Spencer's arguments. "I have now fairly met, so far as the space at my disposal will allow, the strongest arguments of the advocates of use-inheritance as a law of nature and as a factor in evolution. I have shown that the effects which it ought to produce in the case of mankind do not appear, and that breeders of animals do not recognise it as a factor to be taken account of. . . . Mr Herbert Spencer's three main arguments to prove the inadequacy of natural selection have been fully discussed, and have, I venture to think, been shown to be entirely inconclusive, since they are either founded on comparatively unimportant and adventitious peculiarities, or on a neglect of some of the most important conditions under which natural selection in its various forms comes into play" (SSS I 341).

Spencer was not persuaded. "Thistleton-Dyer," Wallace wrote to Meldola, "tells me that H. Spencer is dreadfully disturbed on the question. He fears that acquired characters may not be inherited, in which case the foundation of his whole philosophy is undermined!" (M II 56).

But the theory of natural selection was attacked not only by Herbert Spencer and the Lamarckists. It was attacked also by those who, though not believing in the inheritance of acquired characters, believed that intrinsic variability was the directive force in evolution.

Bateson (1894) expressed his opinion that species arose by discontinuous jumps. They did not grade into one another by gradual and continuous variation but tended to be produced in one event. This was not in itself a fundamentally new proposition because Darwin had long ago recognized the existence of "sports" and had considered their significance in the origin of species. But Bateson at this time was stressing the importance of sports in species formation and, although he did not actually deny the operation of selection on sports, he seems to have thought that in some circumstances at least they would provide an evolutionary advance in a way alternative to natural selection.

Wallace believed absolutely in the need for natural selection and any alternative evolutionary mechanism was to him unthinkable.

When de Vries (1895 published 1901) claimed to have shown a cause for discontinuous variation in his theory of mutation, sports, or large-scale heritable changes in characteristics, Wallace was neither convinced that mutations were the cause of evolution nor that they were the source of variation in populations in the field. The main reason for this rejection of the theories of both de Vries and Bateson was field observation of continuous variation, small variations between species. A second reason was the almost certain upset of viability or fertility of the individuals concerned in any big jump from normal which would not be preserved therefore in competition with those which were more viable, more fertile.

Wallace's arguments are unexceptionable and would form the basis of any modern discussion of evolutionary mechanisms. But from 1894 until well on into the twentieth century there was a swing away from strict selection to the discontinuity mutationists, the big jump supporters. Many, particularly in America, believed that mutation caused evolution, that natural selection was therefore unnecessary and that the newly discovered Mendelian laws (1865 but only generally recognized in 1900) supported their case.

There were Mutationists, Mendelists, Lamarckists and Darwinians.

Wallace remained a Darwinian, but probably the majority of biologists had become Mutationists or Mendelists. "What a miserable abortion of a theory is 'Mutation', which the Americans now seem to be taking up in place of Lamarckism, 'superseded'. Anything rather than Darwinism!" he wrote to Poulton in 1904 and in 1907, "I am glad to hear that you have a new book on 'Evolution' nearly ready and that in it you will do something to expose the fallacies of the Mutationists and Mendelians, who pose before the world as having got *all* wisdom, before which we poor Darwinians must hide our diminished heads" (M II 79 and 84).

It was a curious feature of the time that there was so little synthesis of the new hypotheses and the new experimental findings which were being published. To most biologists it was either Mutation or Darwinism, Lamarckism or Darwinism, responsible for evolution. The sudden rapidity of development of the science of heredity and evolution seems to have led to enthusiasm and confusion, in which the issue, Mutation or Mendelism against Lamarckism, was lost sight of.

It was not until the general acceptance of the Mendelian laws as the basis of continuous variability that the real issue emerged. De Vriesian mutation or the production of sports, or Bateson's discontinuous variation were modified to conform to the Mendelian laws and the theory of big jumps in species formation were generally abandoned (although see Goldschmidt 1940), except for special cases (neoteny, polyploidy). They were abandoned for the reasons that Wallace gave for his rejection of them: that they would upset the delicate balance of an organism to such an extent as to make it less viable and less fertile.

It came to be realized that it was possible to accept the particulate theory of inheritance of Mendel and a modified theory of mutation without the necessity of discontinuous variation or jumps in species formation. Discrete particles or genes could be combined and assorted in sexual reproduction in such a way as to give the continuous variation with which field naturalists had become familiar. Discontinuity and continuity were no longer in opposition. Out of discontinuity could come continuity. There was no longer anything irreconcilable about the theories of Bateson, de Vries and Mendel on the one hand and Wallace and Poulton on the other.

With Mendelism as a basis, superseding Lamarckism, selection came back into its own. The inheritance of non-blending Mendelian units and their mutation would provide variability. Natural selection would determine which varieties would survive and which would not. Selection would therefore determine the direction of adaptation. Isolation would break up populations into potentially species forming groups.

By the middle of the twentieth century there was no longer any controversy between Mutationists, Mendelists and Darwinians. Neo-Darwinism embraced them all.

At the beginning of the century, however, when the theories were new and the reconciliation had not taken place there were many who accused Wallace of taking a conservative attitude to the new developments in the theory of heredity, the theories of Mutation and Mendelism. But looking in detail at his statements it seems hardly a fair accusation. He denied them as alternative mechanisms to natural selection which is, after all, what they were being advertised as. Wallace, like almost everyone else at the time, failed only to make the synthesis between them and Darwinism as he had been so quick to do with Weismann's theory of the continuity of the germ plasm.

But Wallace was not too reactionary to come very near to the solution when he wrote, at the age of 85, to Poulton in 1907: " 'Mutation', as a theory, is absolutely nothing new—only the assertion that new species originate *always* in sports, for which the evidence adduced is the most meagre and inconclusive of any ever set forth with such pretentious claims! I hope you will thoroughly expose this absurd claim. Mendelism is something new, and within its very limited range, important, as leading to conceptions as to the cause and laws of heredity, but only misleading when adduced as the true origin of species in nature, as to which it seems to me to have no part" (M II 84).

It is a pity that Wallace did not develop this more fully, but his contributions to biological theory were effectively over by the end of the century. For over forty years he had written a continuous stream of articles and books devoted to the development of pioneer ideas in biological philosophy. His writing life was not over, however. The second phase of book writing was only beginning, but his subjects became more general and of less enduring interest although, even in this last phase, Wallace occasionally touched on problems which are still the centre of lively discussion.

Language

In 1892 Wallace enlarged for the *Fortnightly Review* the lecture he had given in America on the origin of language. The subject had interested him ever since he had learnt the Malay language and studied its variations among the islands of the archipelago. He had listed as an appendix to *Malay Archipelago* the fifty-seven distinct languages he had encountered, together with the distinctive words for certain nouns in the different languages. "I profess to be able," Wallace commented at the time, "to draw very few conclusions from these vocabularies" (MA II 471). He apparently made no further attempt to solve the problem nor to develop it in any way. But the facts were not forgotten, they were readily available in his mind when a suitable occasion offered. After twelve years' storage they proved to be more amenable to treatment.

The occasion that renewed Wallace's interest in language was when he read E. B. Tylor's *Anthropology* in 1881 and reviewed it for *Nature*.

Among other things Tylor discussed the origin and evolution of language among primitive men and expressed doubts that language was primarily imitative in its sounds and formation. On this point Wallace found himself in disagreement with Tylor; therefore, he propounded his own theory of the origin of language.

Wallace suggested that language was not only imitative of sounds but also had a primitive gestural component. Darwin commented on the sympathy of hand and mouth in conveying meaning, but Wallace went further. Wallace maintained that many words had originated out of the attempt to make gestures with the mouth either with or without the aid of the hands. Thus, the words *come* and *go* represented the pulling towards or the pushing away gestures of the lips.

"Now many savages point with the lips as we do with the finger, signifying *there,* by protruding the lips in the direction to be indicated; and any one who has seen this curious gesture must be struck with its close similarity to the protrusion of the lips in pronouncing the word *go*. The same difference of the nearly closed or open lips characterises the words for these two ideas [*come* and *go*] in many other languages."

Such mouth gestures would have been used in preference to hand gestures in times of emergency or from crouching positions when the hands were not free. From this it would be only a step to turn them into noises for communication in the dark.

The theory of mouth gestures was enlarged until it was published in 1895 as *Expressiveness of Speech; on Mouth Gesture a Factor in the Origin of Language* in *The Fortnightly Review* (SSS II 115).

Wallace considered that for primitive man mouth gesture words would have been the earliest. "He had, as it were, to struggle hard to make himself understood, and would, therefore, make use of every possible indication of meaning offered by the positions and motions of mouth, lips, or breath, in pronouncing each word: and he would lay stress upon and exaggerate these indications, not slur them over as we do" (118).

Words would then come to imitate sounds and motions. "Compare, for example, the words *smooth, even, polished* with *rough, rugged, gritty,* and we at once see that these are not merely conventional terms, but that they are as truly and naturally expressive as are the most direct imitations of human or animal cries" (129).

Wallace's stimulating contribution to the problem of the origin of language provoked little attention at the time. Gladstone wrote and confirmed that there were many examples to support the theory in Homer. But no one seemed to want to investigate or comment on the new idea.

Philologists, when Wallace wrote on language, had in the main been more concerned with the origin and evolution of historic languages than with the origin of language itself. There had been little speculation, as for example by modern anthropologists, on its prehistoric derivation.

It was these still unanswered questions that made the problem of the origin of language so attractive to Wallace as a biologist. There is no way of telling when language first came into existence or what were the particular circumstances which led to its use and elaboration but the event itself can be considered one of the biggest single advances made during the evolution of man from ape-like ancestors.

It is over fifty years since Wallace wrote on the subject, but only recently have philologists concerned themselves with it. So far it has been found impossible to decide conclusively between Wallace's gestural theory of the origin of language and any of the alternatives. Philologists have found themselves divided. But on whichever side they take their stand their arguments necessarily stem from the pioneer work of Wallace. It is impossible to discuss the origin of language without at least taking note of the gestural theory of language of 1895.

Jóhannesson (1950) studied the roots of guttural sounds in six apparently unrelated languages. He decided that these sounds fell readily into two groups that meant, on the one hand, to cover, to hide or cut, and on the other to eat or grasp. Similarly, he found consonants having like meanings in Icelandic and Hebrew, and concluded that there was something to be said for the gestural origin of language, although he thought the mouth gestures were the results of unconscious imitation of hand gestures. Of 320 Indo-European roots 85 per cent were explicable as pantomimic mouth-gestures; of seventy-eight Hebrew words 80 per cent were found to be gestural; and of the Sumerian language he said "that the Gesture Theory is evident in this language". The following year Paget, another advocate of the gestural theory of language, wrote: "Dr Wallace did not recognise Dickens' observation of hand and mouth as exemplified by Sam Weller; but he was, I believe, the first to point out that the pantomimic principle may be still active in man's unconscious development of his spoken language, and that modern languages may be just as gestural as the older ones."

The problem of the origin of language has not been solved and the final verdict may go against the Gestural Theory, but, whatever the outcome, Wallace will be recognized as the first to propound a serious theory to account for the earliest origin of language.

As on so many other subjects, Wallace threw out fundamental ideas which had to wait fifty years and more before being taken up for experimental treatment, or reinvented.

The Wonderful Century

In September 1896 Wallace was invited to join a house party in Switzerland. Dr Lunn arranged his parties for instruction as well as for pleasure, and Wallace's contribution was to be a lecture on scientific progress in the nineteenth century.

The subject of the lecture grew to book size. *The Wonderful Century* was published in June 1898. It ran to a further edition six months later. It was translated into all the main European languages and into Japanese.

Wallace regarded the eighteenth century as a period of stagnation in the history of England, a period when so little of importance happened that there was nothing better to do than invent rules, but he thought the nineteenth century was exciting, a time of change, a moment of progress.

Wallace described inventions in historical terms, how they grew out of previous inventions and, in terms of utility, their social use to the community. Thus, he wrote that the bicycle grew to perfection in the nineteenth century by the elaboration and improvement of older methods of locomotion, the sewing machine, the typewriter and the combine harvester also being perfected examples of already known machines.

In contrast, the steam engine was different in principle from anything that had gone before.

The nineteenth century was particularly productive of new methods of communication. It was also remarkably successful in finding new methods of lighting, gas and subsequently electric, and producing fire by the new invention of the phosphorus match.

Another new departure, based on the properties of light, was the invention of photography and spectrum analysis. To improved communications and improved lighting he added, for their social utility, the new inventions of anaesthetics and antiseptics in medicine.

Turning from practical inventions to discoveries, Wallace differentiated between those, like X-rays, the bacterial origin of disease and fermentation, which conferred immediate practical benefits on society and those, like the discovery of new planets and evidence of previous ice ages, which were predominantly of theoretical interest. Of the main advances in theory of the nineteenth century he selected as his choice of the most important the law of conservation of energy, the atomic theory of Dalton, the periodic table of Mendeleeff, Lyell's evolutionary geology, Laplace's evolutionary astronomy, Darwin's evolutionary biology, the cell theory and the recapitulation theory in embryology.

He sketched the development of some of these theories, differentiating between the gradual emergence of the theory of evolution and the sudden new impetus given to it by the new theory of natural selection, the emergence of the atomic theory and the new point of departure given to chemistry by the theory of atomic weights and the periodic table.

No one invention seemed to mark out the nineteenth century from all previous centuries, but rather was it the multiplicity of invention and discovery which seemed to Wallace the most impressive feature. In every field of invention or scientific thought he could find more progress during the nineteenth century than in any preceding century.

Bernal writing *Science and Industry in the Nineteenth Century* (1953) made a similar estimate of the century's progress. Both authors follow a similar method of argument. Bernal, like Wallace, points to the inventions which were the result of the gradual perfecting of processes already known. Where Wallace selected the specific examples of the typewriter and the bicycle, Bernal sees the progress in terms of improved technique with wider applications. In general, there is remarkable agreement in the two books. A year before the close of the century Wallace was able to make almost as objective a survey as Bernal fifty-five years later. Each took an evolutionary standpoint.

The achievements were great, but Wallace was also concerned with the failures. He considered that although his contemporaries had at their disposal all the means that science had given them, they had failed morally to use the knowledge for the equal betterment of man and for the abolition of war.

Wallace accused the age of neglecting phrenology, hypnotism and psychical research. He also denounced his contemporaries for the practice of vaccination.

Wallace had been vaccinated several times, and his children had been vaccinated in infancy. He had assumed it was a beneficial operation. But between 1875 and 1880 he came under the influence of the anti-vaccinators. From them he learnt that vaccination could give rise to a disease which might be not only injurious to health but, in some circumstances, fatal. He had not been able to find a statistical summary of the facts to help him to make a decision on the problem, and so he set to work to collect the figures himself, from the reports of the Registrar-General. He published his findings in 1885 in a pamphlet entitled *Forty-Five Years of Registration Statistics, proving Vaccination to be both Useless and Dangerous.*

Wallace was not alone in his stand against vaccination. The anti-vaccinators became such a force that a Royal Commission was appointed to investigate compulsory vaccination. Wallace refused to be a member of the Commission, but he gave evidence. He argued from statistics that smallpox had not decreased over the past sixty years any more than any other infectious disease had done; therefore, there was no proof that vaccination had played any part in the decline in deaths from smallpox.

In 1896 the Report of the Royal Commission was published, favouring vaccination. In support of the decision there were new statistics on the incidence of smallpox epidemics and on the number of deaths from the disease. Wallace analysed the new material and in January 1898 published another pamphlet, *Vaccination a Delusion: its Penal Enforcement a Crime, proved by the Official Evidence in the Reports of the Royal Commission.* It was this pamphlet that formed the chapter on vaccination in *The Wonderful Century.*

His campaign was mainly remarkable because of the use he made of statistics. His advocacy of numerical assessments for arriving at scientific conclusions was progressive. In principle Wallace was right, but in practice his data were not adequate and his statistics too crude.

Statistical analysis can show that a postulated relationship does not exist, or that it may, but what Wallace did not recognize, is that such methods do not prove that the right cause and effect are being tested.

Most people would probably agree today that vaccination lowered both the incidence and the death rate from smallpox. But it is still not an easy point to prove and there is no doubt that deaths are caused by vaccination itself. At every outbreak conflicting voices are heard.

During the vaccination controversy Wallace became finally convinced of the unscientific attitude of the medical profession. He had thought for some years that the profession was corrupt because it parasitized sickness. After his experience with the Royal Commission on vaccination he attributed all the faults of the profession to inefficiency resulting from the lack of a scientific attitude. Wallace believed that doctors should keep people healthy and not wait to cure them when they were ill. "He believed in a Ministry of Public Health, that doctors should be servants of the State, and that they should be paid according as they kept people well and not ill" (Marchant 1916).

But although the century had given many examples of failure, Wallace was finally optimistic. The hope for the future was the spread of socialism and the consequent reorganization of society.

For many years Wallace had advocated social reform. He had written and spoken against the many abuses of capital and followed the writings of the political economists, but it was not until 1889 that, as he records in his autobiography "my views were changed once for all, and I have ever since been absolutely convinced, not only that socialism is thoroughly practicable, but that it is the only form of society worthy of civilised beings, and that it alone can secure for mankind continuous mental and moral advancement, together with that true happiness which arises from the full exercise of all their faculties for the purpose of satisfying all their rational needs, desires, and aspirations" (II 266).

Wallace's socialism had evolved under the early influences of Owen, through the individualistic theories of Mill and Spencer, to land reform, coal nationalization (1873) and controlled trade (1879, 1886) to agreement with the American writers Henry George and Bellamy.

In 1890 he made what he considered a public declaration of socialism. In doing this he acted with courage and his usual disregard for social conventions.

"It would not do for my reputation," wrote Herbert Spencer to Beatrice Webb in 1892, "that I should be openly connected with an avowed and prominent socialist.

"Many good people today who are almost horror-struck at hearing that anyone they know is a socialist, would be still more amazed if they knew how many of the very salt of the earth belong (or did belong) to this despised and much dreaded body of thinkers" (II 272).

Beatrice Webb classified Wallace with Henry George as one who had come to socialism by the rational historical and explanatory approach.

Wallace's declaration of socialism was contained in an essay for the *Fortnightly Review* of September 1890.

Human Selection (SSS I 509) was hardly practical socialism but rather an idealized view of a happy community. Wallace's main thesis was the need for equality of opportunity. Given this equality, women would have a wholly admirable influence on the development of the human race. They would select only the most "desirable" men for husbands and thus the race would be bettered. In this Wallace approached Darwin's hypothesis for human evolution expressed in the *Descent of Man* and he apparently contradicted his own belief that sexual selection was not effective.

Wallace, always eager in the defence of women's rights, later lent his support to the suffragettes. Equality of opportunity and selection by women would lead to raised standard of living and later age of marriage. This in its turn would reduce the chance of over-population. Thus the human race would progress. "Equality of opportunity is as Herbert Spencer has shown in his 'Justice', the correlative of natural selection in human society, and has thus a broad foundation in the laws of nature. But Spencer himself did not follow out his principles to their logical conclusion as I have done" (II 272).

Between 1892 and 1894 Wallace published articles in which he stressed equality of opportunity as the fundamental precept of socialism.

Wallace argued, against the educational reformers, that education was not enough to improve mankind. It would benefit the generation that received it and influence its culture, but it would not have a permanent heritable effect on the human race as many believed. Education would, however, provide equality of opportunity, so that those who were superior could be selected.

Wallace's arguments followed strict biological lines and are particularly interesting since very few have used this sort of reasoning. "If the theory is a true one, it certainly proves that it is not by the direct road of education, as usually understood, that humanity has advanced and must advance, although education may, in an indirect manner, be an important factor of progress. . . . If it is thought that this non-inheritance of the results of education and training is prejudicial to human progress, we must remember that, on the other hand, it also prevents the continuous degradation of humanity by the inheritance of those vicious practices and degrading habits which the deplorable conditions of our modern social system undoubtedly foster in the bulk of mankind" (SSS II).

But though he thought the effects of education might not be as marvellous as many believed, Wallace nevertheless advocated universal education.

Wallace went further than Mill or Spencer who could hardly be accused of lacking at least some altruistic and progressive leanings. He went further than Benjamin Kidd. He praised Kidd's *Social Evolution* in a review in *Nature,* but at the same time he admonished Kidd for not taking the recommendations to their logical conclusion. Kidd admitted that social equality of opportunity was fundamental. Wallace maintained that once this had been admitted there was no escape from the corollary that in order to achieve that equality of opportunity it was necessary to abolish the inheritance of private wealth.

Wallace's socialism is interesting because of the biological interpretations he brought to it, interpretations which, although they may have led him to some airy hopes, prevented him from making some of the unwarranted assumptions others made.

Biological variability was not confined to plants and the lower animals; it occurred also in man. Therefore all men were not equal in their potentialities. Given this biological fact, Wallace believed that all men deserved equal opportunities in which to develop whatever inherited qualities they had.

Wallace returned to a consideration of this apparent conflict between inherent potentiality and opportunity, between nature and nurture, in 1913 in his two last publications, *Social Environment and Moral Progress* and *The Revolt of Democracy*. They had a remarkable reception and were "hailed as a virile and notable production from a truly great man" (Marchant 1916). Both books were essentially syntheses of the several articles Wallace had written in earlier years on social problems and which had already been published in *Studies Scientific and Social* (1900).

Social Environment and Moral Progress was an essay on the social order. In it Wallace attempted to interpret particular facets of the human race in the light of current biological theory. He discussed the incidence and distribution of certain outstanding characteristics of human beings, and he studied particular aspects of the social environment. From this he attempted to determine which peculiarities of man could be assigned to hereditary causes and which to environment.

Wallace concluded that at least some part of what he called intellect and intelligence were inherited, but that even the most outstandingly beneficial inherited faculties could not be expected to thrive or even to establish themselves in the social environment that he observed all around him. Only a combination of good heredity and good environment could produce the first class human being.

Thus sixty-five years after his first contact with Owenites, Wallace went back to the teachings of Robert Owen, although his arguments had become more sophisticated and less a simple appeal to sense of justice. "We are obliged to conclude, therefore, that what is commonly termed morality is not wholly due to any inherent perception of what is right or wrong conduct, but that it is to some extent and often very largely a matter of convention, varying at different times and places in accordance with the degree and kind of social development which has been attained often under different and even divergent conditions of existence. The actual morality of a community is largely a product of environment, but it is local and temporary, not permanently affecting the character" (SEMP 3).

The Revolt of Democracy, published a few months after *Social Environment,* was less concerned with the application of biological theory to the problems of the human race than with discussing some of the specific components of the environment, facets of the environment Wallace considered to be of surpassing importance in their influence on the development of each human individual or the most amenable to quick alteration. From that point of view Wallace discussed problems of unemployment, trade, living conditions and competition. "The principle of competition—a life and death struggle for bare existence—has had more than a century's unbroken trial under conditions created by its upholders, *and it has absolutely failed*" (77).

Wallace was disgusted by the slow rate of social progress, in such marked contrast to the rapid progress of science during the nineteenth century.

Life on other Worlds

The twentieth century saw the publication of nine new books and further editions of several of Wallace's most popular scientific works including *Darwinism* and *Island Life,* but there was only the occasional original contribution to a scientific journal.

To make up for the decrease in number of new articles from his pen, Wallace published in 1900 a collection of some of his earlier ones on diverse subjects as *Studies Scientific and Social.* The first volume consists of twenty-three articles on biological and geological problems, first published between 1867 and 1896. The second volume consists of twenty-nine articles on social problems covering a period between 1865 and 1899.

A new book was not delayed for long, however, because Wallace was persuaded by the New York *Independent* to write an article on any scientific subject he chose for any fee he liked to name. When writing *The Wonderful Century* he had necessarily become acquainted with nineteenth-century astronomy. Wallace chose to write on *Man's Place in the Universe,* therefore. But even before the article was published in the *Independent* and the *Fortnightly Review,* Wallace had been persuaded to expand the article into book form. *Man's Place in the Universe* (1903) was a great success, but it roused a considerable amount of antagonism.

In the middle of the century there had been an outburst of speculation, particularly amongst geologists, on the possibility of life on other planets. *Man's Place in the Universe* took up this problem once again.

From his far reaching study Wallace concluded that the universe was finite and that the solar system was situated in the plane of the Milky Way not far removed from the centre of the plane, that is, from the centre of the stellar universe. Further, he concluded that the universe consisted throughout of the same kinds of matter so that, this being so, there could be only one sort of life made up of the same component parts, the same chemical constituents, as made up the living organisms known on earth. Combining these arguments from stellar physics and biology, he decided that only a planet in a so-called optimum position and of an optimum size could provide conditions suitable for living organisms. The optimum position, near the centre of the universe, and the optimum size were achieved by the earth alone of all the heavenly bodies. Wallace concluded, therefore, that no other planet in the solar system, nor any other planet in any other solar system, was likely to provide as successfully as the earth those conditions favourable for life. "There is absolutely no evidence which shows even a probability of there being other inhabited worlds" (M II 175).

Man's Place in the Universe illustrates Wallace's remarkable grasp and understanding of a wide range of subjects and his talents for synthesis. When it was first published most of his hypotheses were generally acceptable. Since 1903 astronomy and microbiology have made spectacular advances. Kelvin's theories of heat production by the sun, which were for long the best approximations to the observed conditions, have been superseded. Wallace's universe now ranks only as a galaxy, one galaxy among many which together comprise the universe, and the position of the solar system within this galaxy is almost certainly not central. Similarly, Wallace's requirements for the start of organic life are not at present favoured. His oxidizing atmosphere, for example, has been replaced by a reducing atmosphere (Bernal 1951, Oparin 1957).

Although wrong in detail, there is so far no conclusive evidence to contradict his main thesis that organic life, as known on this earth, exists only on this earth.

Interested by his work for *Man's Place in the Universe* in the structure and climatic conditions of other planets, Wallace was critical when he read a book on Mars by the astronomer Lowell.

Mars and its Canals (1906) described in detail the surface and atmosphere of the planet. Lowell prepared more accurate maps of Mars than had been attempted before and revealed in more startling outline the famous canals. The canals, or channels, straight lines on the surface of the planet crossing at various angles and often extending to a thousand or more miles in length, had been discovered in 1877 by the Italian, Schiaparelli.

Before this, Mars had attracted interest because of the yearly change in what appeared to be snow caps at the two poles. Then, in 1892, green patches were observed on the surface of the planet coincident with the melting of the polar snows. From the supposition that the waxing and waning of blue-green patches on the surface was the seasonal growth and decline of vegetation equivalent to earth's vegetation it was only a step to suppose that the canals were not natural phenomena but the constructions of Martians.

In his book on Mars, Lowell argued for the artificiality of the canals. He concluded that they could not be accounted for by any inorganic laws, "no natural phenomena within our knowledge show such regularity on such a scale," and they must therefore be the work of intelligent beings.

Wallace had already decided, to his own satisfaction, that no planet other than the earth could support life. Lowell's book therefore incited him to make a reply. He started to write a review, but he found that to answer Lowell adequately a detailed discussion of Mars was necessary. And so, in 1907, instead of a review, Wallace published a book called *Is Mars Habitable?*

From his researches into the literature, Wallace decided that Mars was characterized by scarcity of atmospheric water vapour and surface water. The polar caps, therefore, might be frozen carbon dioxide but not frozen water. The average surface temperature of Mars appeared to be very low, but the fluctuations round this average appeared to be great.

Taking these facts into consideration, it seemed impossible that earthly life, and particularly animal life, could exist on Mars. The green patches should be interpreted as areas of heavily dustladen atmosphere rather than as the chlorophyll of plants. Therefore, he concluded that the canals were not designed by intelligent beings, but were the result of some natural phenomenon such as the cracking of basaltic rocks, giving an appearance of artificiality such as is given by the Giant's Causeway. "His [Lowell's] observations, drawings, photographs, etc., are all quite right, and I believe true to nature, but his interpretation of what he sees is wrong—often even to absurdity. He began by thinking the straight lines are works of art, and as he finds more and more of these straight lines, he thinks that proves more completely that they are works of art, and then he twists all other evidence to suit that. The book is not very well written, but no doubt the newspaper men think that as he is such a great astronomer he must know what it all means!

"I am more than ever convinced that Mars is totally uninhabitable" (M II 176).

Wallace assumed both in the book on Mars and in the earlier *Man's Place in the Universe* that no other form of life was possible other than the sort known on this earth. This followed from the opinion that was becoming general at the time, that the inorganic elements were the same throughout the universe and that the same physical laws applied. He did not consider the possibility that other forms of living material might have evolved, organisms which did not rely on water or constant temperature, and whose chemical composition might be different.

Since 1907 surprisingly little has been added to the knowledge of Martian structure.

There is general agreement that the surface is subject to a wide range of temperature, and that the predominating gases of the planet's atmosphere are carbon dioxide and nitrogen. There is little water on the surface or water vapour in the atmosphere. In spite of the scarcity, the polar caps are thought to be composed of frozen water, not of carbon dioxide snow as Wallace had suggested (Kuiper 1949).

Similarly it is generally agreed that the Schiaparelli canals are natural phenomena, though their precise nature has not yet been determined.

There is much less agreement over the structure of the seasonal green patches. No one seems inclined to accept Lowell's intelligent animal life, constructors of canals, but some scientists believe they have confirmed the presence of plant life (Sinton 1957). Soviet and other astronomers (Sinton 1959) claim to have discovered by spectrometric analysis that there is chlorophyll on Mars. The Martian chlorophyll gives a different diffraction picture from that usually found in green plants, but it shows marked resemblance to tundra vegetation. It is suggested, therefore, that lichens and similar cold-adapted plants grow in the arid climate and low density atmosphere of Mars.

This theory has not found universal acceptance and the nature of the green patches is still disputed.

Although Wallace rejected the idea of life on other planets, he was still taking an interest in spiritualism. He appeared in

London as a witness for spiritualism in an action between Archdeacon Colley and the conjuror Maskelyne. With Wallace's support, Colley won his case. "I found Maskelyne's performance to be a ludicrous parody of the actual materialisation. . . ." (1908 396).

There might be only one type of living material and only one world in the universe suitable for its existence, but the spirits were all pervading and directed the course of the universe.

Medals and Memorials

During the later years of Wallace's life many universities and scientific societies honoured him with offers of their degrees and medals. Never having been an academic biologist and never having considered himself in that light, he declined most of the academic honours but permitted the medals to pour in.

The University of Dublin had conferred on him an honorary doctorate and in 1889, after much persuasion, Wallace accepted an honorary D.C.L. from the University of Oxford.

The following year he was awarded the Darwin medal of the Royal Society for his "independent origination of the origin of species by natural selection".

The geographers were the next to recognize his contributions to their subject with the award in 1892 of the Founders' Medal of the Royal Geographical Society.

He was offered the Royal Medal of the Linnean Society. "A dreadful thing has happened! Just as I have had my medal-case made, 'regardless of expense', they are going to give me another medal! Hadn't I better decline it, with thanks? 'No room for more medals'!!" (M II 113).

Wallace in 1892 refused an invitation from the Fellows of the Royal Society to become one of their number, but his refusal was not accepted, and then in 1905 Wallace, then eighty-two, was persuaded to take his place beside his contemporaries with an autobiography. *My Life* was published in two thick volumes at the end of 1905.

To avoid the monotony and tedium he condemned in others, and to meet the criticisms of reviewers and friends, he condensed *My Life* into one volume and brought it up to date, when a new edition was called for in 1908.

In the same year, homage was paid to him for his part in

revolutionizing the biological philosophy of the nineteenth century. Wallace was elevated to the rank of a national monument when he received a medal struck in his own memory.

The occasion was the fiftieth anniversary of the meeting of the Linnean Society of London on 1st July 1858. To mark the occasion Darwin-Wallace medals were inaugurated, and Wallace became the first recipient.

"Today, in asking you to accept the first Darwin-Wallace Medal, we are offering you of your own, for it is you, equally with your great colleague, who created the occasion we celebrate" (M I 111).

Wallace thanked the Council of the Society for the honour, but disclaimed an equal part with Darwin in the discovery of the theory which had revolutionized biology. He declared: "The idea came to me as it had come to Darwin, in a sudden flash of insight; it was thought out in a few hours—was written down with such a sketch of its various applications and developments as occurred to me at the moment—then copied on thin letter paper and sent off to Darwin—all within a week. *I* was then (as often since) the 'young man in a hurry': *he,* the painstaking and patient student seeking ever the full demonstration of the truth he had discovered, rather than to achieve immediate personal fame" (M I 114).

Wallace outlined the main ideas and events that influenced him towards the recognition of natural selection, but disclaimed all honour for it. He would accept the first Darwin-Wallace medal for his work in showing the applications of the idea of natural selection. He said: "I have long since come to see that no one deserves either praise or blame for the *ideas* that come to him, but only for the actions resulting therefrom. Ideas and beliefs are certainly not voluntary acts. They come to us—we hardly know *how* or *whence,* and once they have got possession of us we cannot reject or change them at will. It is for the common good that the promulgation of ideas should be free—uninfluenced either by praise or blame, reward or punishment.

"But the *actions* which result from our ideas may properly be so treated, because it is only by patient thought and work that new ideas, if good and true, become adapted and utilised; while if untrue, or if not adequately presented to the world, they are rejected or forgotten.

"I therefore accept the crowning honour you have conferred

on me today, not for the happy chance through which I became an independent originator of the doctrine of 'survival of the fittest', but as a too liberal recognition by you of the moderate amount of time and work I have given to explain and elucidate the theory, to point out some novel applications of it, and (I hope I may add) for my attempts to extend those applications, even in directions which somewhat diverged from those accepted by my honoured friend and teacher Charles Darwin."

Sir Joseph Hooker, aged 91 and the only other surviving character of the 1858 drama, received the second Darwin-Wallace medal, and he gave an account of Darwin's reception of Wallace's letter and the arrangements made for "the most notable event in the annals of Biology that had followed the appearance in 1735 of the 'Systema Naturae' of Linnaeus" (M I 120).

Medals were awarded also to Professor Haeckel, Professor Weismann, neither of whom was present, to Professor Strasburger, who paid a special tribute to Wallace, to Sir Francis Galton and finally, seventh, to Ray Lankester, aged sixty-one, a young man.

In the same year the Royal Society presented their Copley Medal to Wallace, and shortly afterwards he received the Order of Merit in the birthday honours.

"Is it not awful—two more now! I should think very few men have had three such honours within six months! I have never felt myself worthy of the Copley Medal—and as to the Order of Merit—to be given to a red-hot Radical, Land Nationaliser, Socialist, Anti-Militarist, etc., etc., etc., is quite astounding and unintelligible" (M II 222).

On 22nd January, at the Royal Institute, two weeks after his eighty-sixth birthday, wearing his Order of Merit, Wallace gave his last lecture on Darwinism.

From then on Wallace, less and less inclined to make journeys to London, confined himself to his garden and the immediate surroundings. Physical weakness was no handicap, however, to his mental activities.

The lecture to the Royal Institute was published in the *Fortnightly Review*, but while preparing it for publication Wallace realized that there were many parts he wished to discuss at more length. So once again he was stimulated to expand into book form what had begun as a comparatively short statement.

The World of Life was published in 1910 and was his last

statement on any specifically biological problems. The interest of this work has been very much overshadowed by the underlying theme which runs through it and comes out at the end of almost every chapter. It is written with the aim of convincing that there is a purpose in the universe and an organizing mind behind it all. Wallace's belief in a pervading spiritual directiveness is consistent with his spiritualism and not, as some have suggested, the result of senility. As new biological phenomena unfolded it seemed to Wallace they left mysterious more than they explained: interpret heredity, and the cause is more baffling than the problem itself; describe embryological phenomena, but there is no answer to how. Something surely must guide the development of the organism. Surely something must initiate the process. There must be some organizing power. But Wallace had never read Bergson and did not approve of what he had heard of *élan vital* and *force créatrice*.

Not surprisingly the reiteration of the guiding principle of mind excited the critics. *Nature* accused Wallace of spoiling a good book by allowing his teleological speculations and his misguided political ideas to intrude.

But although the general thesis was uncongenial, *The World of Life* is interesting for two reasons. Firstly, it considers several aspects of the Darwinian theory which had not been expanded at length before; secondly, it is remarkable for having an outline of some of the new biological discoveries.

Distribution was discussed again, but expanded by the introduction of details of plant distribution and by a statistical treatment of certain problems. Wallace had become aware of the need for a mathematical basis for biological theory and, although he was not mathematician enough to provide this basis, he was constantly stressing numerical aspects of problems. He argued, for instance, that evolutionary advance only occurred when selection worked on large numbers of individuals and moreover, he accepted Galton's numerical theory of heredity.

Galton had shown that certain human features could be traced through their ancestry. He contended, therefore, that such features, intelligence and stature, were inherited in an orderly mathematically predictable way. Galton further deduced from his investigations the rule that one half of each individual's peculiarities is derived from its parents and the other half comes from its earlier ancestors.

"Now this simple law," Wallace wrote, "explains almost all the facts including the apparent failures of inheritance—all its irregularities in individual cases, together with its constancy and regularity when large numbers are examined" (103).

Wallace was not opposed therefore to theories of inheritance, as some have maintained; he was only opposed to theories which appeared to him to demand discontinuity. He could not accept discontinuity because it was contrary to his field experience. Wallace accepted Galton's theory of heredity; he even implicitly accepted non-blending inheritance, but what is perhaps more surprising is to find in *The World of Life* that he accepted the chromosome theory of inheritance as well.

In *The World of Life* there appears for the first time in any of his books a diagram of the chromosomes at cell-division, and an outline of Weismann's theory of inheritance which Wallace considered a satisfactory interpretation of the events.

Weismann believed that the chromosomes were the physical basis of heredity and that the chromosomes bore *ids,* and the *ids* were made up of determinants of heredity. These determinants were in their turn made up ultimately of numerous chemical molecules. In some respects, Weismann's interpretation differed little from that of Mendel, but it could be less determinative. Weismann believed there was germinal competition and selection between *ids* and that, therefore, the results of a mating could not be mathematically predicted.

Wallace preferred this less rigid theory to that of Mendel, although it could still be called a "mechanical explanation of heredity by means of the successive changes observed in the growing and dividing germ-cells" (344). There was selection amongst the *ids* and the *ids* represented only small variations. Weismann's theory did not necessitate the rejection of natural selection, did not purport to provide an alternative directive force for evolution as some of the followers of Mendel and de Vries maintained they had done.

So far Wallace was prepared to go: there was a physical basis for heredity, mathematical rules could explain how characteristics were inherited and natural selection was a mechanical force, operating on large variable populations.

Inheritance and selection were automatic and self-perpetuating, but they no longer satisfied Wallace completely. "Who or what *guides* or determines the atoms of the protoplasmic molecules into these new *combinations* chemically, and new *structures* mechanically?—combinations and structures which all the chemists and physicists of the world are powerless to produce even when they have the ready-formed protoplasm given them to start with? Then as the process goes on in an ever-increasing complexity which baffles the microscope of the observer to follow, never diverging at any one point from the precise mode of change which alone leads on to the completed living organism, we are asked to be satisfied with millions of 'gemmules', 'fundamental units', 'determinants', etc., which actually *do* build up the living body of each organism in a prescribed and unchangeable sequence of events. But this orderly process is quite unintelligible without some *directive organising* power constantly at work in or upon every chemical atom or physical molecule of the whole structure, as one after another they are brought to their places, and built in, as it were, to the structure of every tissue of every organ as it takes form and substance in the fabric of the living, moving, and, in the case of animals, sensitive Creation" (347).

Many had opposed the theory of natural selection because they saw in it nothing but cruelty and pain, and it was in answer to such critics that Wallace wrote a chapter on the painlessness of natural selection. He did not believe that the sensations of other animals were the same as those of man. In particular, he had realized long ago that, considering the differences in the structure of their eyes and brains, it was unlikely that insects saw things in the same way as man sees them. For the same reasons Wallace maintained that it was likely that events which man assumed painful, because they would be painful to him, were not painful to the animals involved. Pain itself, where it did occur, Wallace considered to be of adaptive value, and to have evolved under the influence of natural selection as a device to enable the animal to survive. Wallace had no patience with anthropomorphic interpretations of an animal's life.

Many thought *The World of Life* a "fine book", and the son of Alphonse de Candolle wrote a preface to the French edition. There is no doubt Wallace had succeeded again in pointing to problems that needed an answer, problems of gene behaviour and problems of embryological causation. But many thought it was a pity that, having exposed such problems, Wallace should then have felt compelled to solve them by the use of the all prevailing mind force.

Wallace was now ninety. "Although in his ninetieth year," wrote a visitor at this time, "he seemed to be in his prime. There was no sign of age but physical weakness, and you had to make an effort at times to remember even that. His eyes kindled as he spoke, and more than once he walked about and chuckled, like a schoolboy pleased" (M II 151).

Occasionally his gardener had to wheel him part of the way round his garden. He had virtually given up biological philosophy. But in other subjects he was mentally as active as ever.

In 1912 he was at work on two new books, as well as writing letters on the political events of the day. "The railway strike surpasses the Parliament Bill in excitement. On receipt of Friday's paper, I sat down and composed and sent off to Lloyd George a short but big letter, on large foolscap paper, urging him and Asquith, as the two strong men of the government, to take over at once the management of the railways of the entire country, by Royal Proclamation—on the ground of mismanagement for seventy years, and having brought the country to the verge of starvation and civil war. . . ." (M II 163).

The books, *Social Environment and Moral Progress* and *The Revolt of Democracy,* appeared in 1913, and they were Wallace's last publications.

In 1913 he made a contract to write a book on the social order. He was also helping James Marchant with the collection of material for a book to be called *Darwin and Wallace*. Nothing came of these projects.

By August 1913 Wallace felt compelled to admit in a letter: "The papers are wrong about me. I am not writing anything now; perhaps shall write no more. Too many letters and home business. Too much bothered with many slight ailments, which altogether keep me busy attending to them. I am like Job, who said 'the grasshopper was a burthen' to him! I suppose its creaking song."

But in the same letter Wallace energetically observed, "The Piltdown skull does not prove much, if anything!" (M II 101).

The occasions when Wallace could no longer walk round his garden became more frequent. He had some of his favourite plants brought to a piece of ground in front of the study windows where he could see them. In spite of increasing infirmity, he kept his thoughts on life: "I am glad to say I feel still able to jog on a few years longer in this *very good* world—for those who can make the best of it" (M II 136).

By October Wallace was past work, too weak to move about his room for books, liable to fall. On Sunday, 2nd November, he felt unwell and went to bed and then gradually became unconscious and died on Friday, 7th November two months before his ninety-first birthday.

Two years later his plaque, with those of Hooker and Lister, was unveiled in Westminster Abbey.

"Today there are uncovered to the public view, in the North Aisle of the Choir, three memorials to men who, I believe, will always be ranked among the most eminent scientists of the last century. . . . These are three men whose life work it was to utilise and promote scientific discovery for the preservation and betterment of the human race" (M II 255).

Amazon Journey

Year	Day	Month	Event
1848	26	May	Off the mouth of Amazon
			Residence in Belem (Pará)
	3	November	Journey to island of Mexiana
1849		March	To Belem
		July	Herbert Wallace arrives
		August	To Santarem
		November	To Obydos and Villa Nova
	31	December	Arrives Manaos (Barra)
1850		May	From Manaos to Manaquery
		July	Returns to Manaos
		August	Left Manaos for Rio Negro
	24	October	Arrives Guia
1851	27	January	Leaves Guia
	1	February	Into Venezuela
	14	February	Arrives Pimichín
	16	February	Arrives Javíta
	31	March	Leaves Javíta
		April	Arrives Guia
	3	June	Leaves for Rio dos Vaupes
	15	September	Arrives Manaos
		October	Leaves for Rio dos Vaupes again
			Stay at São Joaquim
1852	16	February	Leaves for Upper Vaupes
	12	March	Arrives Mucúra
	25	March	Leaves Mucúra
	17	May	Arrives Manaos
	10	June	Leaves Manaos
	2	July	Arrives Belem
	12	July	Leaves Belem
	1	October	Arrives Deal

Journeys in the Malay Archipelago

1854		March	Leaves England
	20	April	Arrives Singapore
	23	July	To Malacca
	28	September	Leaves Malacca
	16	October	Leaves Singapore
	1	November	Arrives Borneo Sarawak
1855	14	March	To Sadong River
	27	November	Leaves Sadong
1856	25	January	Leaves Borneo Sarawak
	31	January	Arrives Singapore
	24	May	Leaves Singapore by schooner
	13	June	Arrives Bali
	15	June	Leaves Bali
	17	June	Arrives Lombok
	30	August	Leaves Lombok
	2	September	Arrives Celebes Macassar
	15	December	Leaves Celebes by 70 ton prau
	31	December	Arrives Kei Islands
1857	6	January	Leaves Kei Islands
	8	January	Arrives Aru Islands
	5	February	To Wokan
	14	March	To N. mainland and middle islands and up river Wanumbai
	8	May	Leaves Wanumbai
	2	July	Leaves Aru Islands, Dobbo, by prau
	11	July	Arrives Celebes Macassar
	19	November	Leaves Celebes by steamer
	25	November	Arrives Timor Coupang
	26	November	Leaves Timor
	1	December	Arrives Banda
	3	December	Leaves Banda
	4	December	Arrives Amboyna
1858	4	January	Leaves Amboyna

	8 January	Arrives Ternate
	March	Halmahera (Gilolo)
	25 March	Leaves Ternate by schooner
	28 March	Arrives Halmahera, Gane
	29 March	Leaves Halmahera
	11 April	Arrives New Guinea, Dorey
	29 July	Leaves New Guinea, schooner
	15 August	Arrives Ternate
	September	To Halmahera
	October	Back to Ternate by boat
	9 October	Leaves Ternate in small native boat
	14 October	Arrives Kaioa Islands
	20 October	Leaves Kaioa Islands
	21 October	Arrives Batchian
1859	21 March	Kasserota and Langundi
	1 April	Back to main island
	13 April	Leaves Batchian by 4 ton Government open boat
	20 April	Arrives Ternate
	1 May	Leaves Ternate by Dutch mail steamer
	13 May	Arrives Timor Coupang
		To island of Senao
	27 May	Leaves Timor by mail steamer
	1 June	Arrives Banda
	3 June	Leaves Banda
		Touches Amboyna and Ternate
	10 June	Arrives Celebes Menado
	23 September	Leaves Celebes by mail steamer
	29 September	Arrives Amboyna
	29 October	Leaves Amboyna stopping along coast
	31 October	Arrives Ceram Hatosua
	20 November	To Awaiya for 3 weeks
	17 December	Inland
	24 December	Leaves Ceram
	25 December	Arrives Amboyna
1860	24 February	Leaves Amboyna
	26 February	Arrives Ceram, Amahay
	27 February to 8 March	Coasting
	March	In Kissa-laut

	4 April	Leaves Ceram for Kei Islands by 4 ton prau
	8 April	Arrives Manowolko
	11 April	Leaves Manowolko, touches Matabello and on to Teor. Journey abandoned, "miserable boat"
	18 April	Arrives Matabello Islands
	24 April	Leaves Matabello Islands
	25 April	Arrives Manowolko
	26 April	Leaves Manowolko
	26 April	Arrives Goram, Onda
	27 May	Leaves Goram in own 8 ton prau
	28 May	Arrives Kilwaru
	1 June	Leaves Kilwaru
	2 June	Arrives E. point Ceram, crew deserts
	10 June	Leaves Ceram East
	15 June	Arrives Ceram Wahai
	17 June	Leaves Ceram
	4 July	Arrives Waigiou
	29 September	Leaves Waigiou in own prau
	5 November	Arrives Ternate, few days on Halmahera
1861	1 January	Leaves Ternate by steamer
	12 January	Arrives Timor, Delli
	23 April	Leaves Timor, by Dutch mail steamer
	29 April	Arrives Banda
	1 May	Leaves Banda
	4 May	Arrives Bouru
	19 May	To Waypoti
	27 June	Leaves Bouru via Ternate, Menado, Macassar by steamer
	18 July	Arrives Java, Sourabaya
	15 September	Leaves Sourabaya
	18 September	Arrives Batavia
	1 November	Leaves Java, Batavia by steamer
	3 November	Arrives Banca
	7 November	Leaves Banca
	8 November	Arrives Sumatra, Palembang
1862	20 January	Leaves Sumatra by mail steamer
	20 January	Arrives Singapore
	20 February	Leaves Singapore
	1 April	Arrives London (BMNH)

Abbreviations

Used in the text for the works of A. R. Wallace

A	*Travels on the Amazon and Rio Negro.*
D	*Darwinism.*
GD I and II	*Geographical Distribution of Animals,* vols I and II.
IL	*Island Life.*
LN	*Land Nationalisation.*
MA I and II	*Malay Archipelago,* vols I and II.
MPU	*Man's Place in the Universe.*
MS	*Miracles and Modern Spiritualism.*
NS	*Contributions to the Theory of Natural Selection.*
SEMP	*Social Environment and Moral Progress.*
SSS I and II	*Studies, Scientific and Social,* vols I and II.
TN	*Tropical Nature.*
WC	*The Wonderful Century.*
WL	*The World of Life.*
I and II	*My Life,* vols I and II.
M I and II	Marchant, *Alfred Russel Wallace Letters and Reminiscences,* vols I and II.
BM	Unpublished works in British Museum.
BMNH	Unpublished works in British Museum (Natural History).
Linn. Soc.	Unpublished works in the Linnean Society London.

References

ACOSTA, J. d' 1589. *Historia natural y moral de las Indias.* Leon.

ADAMS, H. 1865. Descriptions of the new species of land-shells collected by Mr A. R. Wallace in the Malayan Archipelago. *Proc. Zool. Soc. Lond.* 414.

AGASSIZ, E. C. (ed.) 1885. *Louis Agassiz.* London.

AGASSIZ, L. 1850. Geographical distribution of animals. *Christian Examiner* 48:181.

ALLEN, A. A. 1934. Sex rhythm in the ruffed grouse (*Bonasa umbellus* Linn.) and other birds. *Auk* 51:180.

ALLEN, J. A. 1871. On the mammals and winter birds of east Florida. *Bull. Mus. Comp. Zool.* 2:161.

AMHERST, LORD AND THOMSON, B. 1901. The discovery of the Solomon Islands by Alvaro de Mendaña in 1568. *Hakluyt Soc. 2nd Series* 7 & 8.

ANONYMOUS, 1878. *Nature, Lond.* 19:16.

ANONYMOUS, 1913. Dr Alfred Russel Wallace O.M. F.R.S. *Nature, Lond.* 92:322.

ARISTOTLE, 1911. *De partibus animalium.* Oxford.

ARNOLD, J. R. & LIBBY, W. F. 1951. Radiocarbon dates. *Science* 113:111.

BAER, C. E. v 1828-37. *Über Entwicklungsgeschichte der Thiere, Beobachtung und Reflexion.* Königsberg.

BARBER, H. N., DADSWELL, H. E. & INGLE, H. D. 1959. Transport of driftwood from South America to Tasmania and Macquarie Island. *Nature, Lond.* 184:203.

BARLOW, N. (ed.) 1945. *Charles Darwin and the Voyage of the Beagle.* London.

BARTHOLOMEW, J. G., CLARKE, W. E. & GRIMSHAW, P. H. 1911. *Atlas of Zoogeography.* Edinburgh.

BATES, H. W. 1863. Contributions to an insect fauna of the Amazon valley. *Trans. Linn. Soc. Lond.* 23:495.

BATES, H. W. 1863. *The Naturalist on the River Amazons.* London.

BATESON, W. 1894. *Materials for the study of Variation.* London.

BATESON, W. 1909. *Experiments in Plant Hybridisation by G. Mendel.* Cambridge.

BEAUFORT, L. F. DE 1951. *Zoogeography of the Land and Inland Waters.* London.

BEDDARD, F. E. 1892. *Animal Coloration.* Cambridge.

BEDDARD, F. E. 1895. *A Text-book of Zoogeography.* Cambridge.

BEER, G. R. DE (ed.) 1938. *Evolution.* Oxford.

BEER, G. R. DE 1940. *Embryos and Ancestors.* Oxford.

BEIRNE, B. P. 1952. *The Origin and History of the British Fauna.* London.

BELL, T. 1859. Presidential Address *Proc. Linn. Soc. Lond.* 1858-9: viii.

BENNETT, A. W. 1870. The theory of selection from a mathematical point of view. *Nature, Lond.* 3:30.

BERGSON, H. L. 1907. *L'Evolution Créatrice.* Paris.

BERNAL, J. D. 1951. *The Physical Basis of Life.* London.

BERNAL, J. D. 1953. *Science and Industry in the Nineteenth Century.* London.

BERRILL, N. J. 1955. *The Origin of Vertebrates.* Oxford.

BLACKETT, P. M. S., CLEGG, J. A. & STUBBS, P. H. S. 1960. An analysis of rock magnetic data. *Proc. Roy. Soc.* A, 256:291

BLAIR, W. F. 1955. Mating call and stage of speciation in the *Microhyla olivacea—M. Carolinensis* complex. *Evolution* 9:469.

BLEST, A. D. 1957. The functions of eyespot patterns in the Lepidoptera. *Behaviour* 11:209.

BLYTH, E. 1871. A suggested new division of the earth into zoological regions. *Nature, Lond.* 3:427.

BOISDUVAL, J. A. 1832. *Faune Entomologique de l'Océan Pacifique.* Paris.

BONAPARTE, C. L. J. L. 1850. *Conspectus Generum Avium.* Leyden.

BROOM, R. 1932. *The Mammal-Like Reptiles of South Africa and the Origin of Mammals.* London.

BROOM, R. & SCHEPERS, G. W. H. 1946. The South African fossil ape-men, the Australopithecinae. *Transv. Mus. Mem.* 2:1.

BROWER, J. VAN Z. 1957. Experimental studies of mimicry in some North American butterflies. *Nature, Lond.* 180:444.

BROWER, J. VAN Z. 1960. Experimental studies of mimicry. *Amer. Nat.* 44:271.

BROWER, L. P. 1959. Speciation in butterflies of the *Papilio glaucus* group. *Evolution* 13:212.

BROWNE, SIR T. 1643. *Religio Medici.* London.

BRY, T. DE 1590-1634. *America.* Frankfurt am Main.

BUFFON, G. L. L. COMTE DE 1749-89. *Histoire Naturelle.* Paris.

BURTON, R. 1652. *Anatomy of Melancholy.* 6th ed. Oxford.

BUTLER, A. G. 1869. Remarks upon certain caterpillars. *Trans. R. Ent. Soc. Lond:* 27.

BUXTON, P. A. 1938. The formation of species among insects in Samoa and other oceanic islands. *Proc. Linn. Soc. Lond.* 150th Session: 264.

CAIN, A. J. & SHEPPARD, P. M. 1950. Selection in the polymorphic land snail *Cepaea nemoralis. Heredity* 4:275.

CARTER, G. S. 1951. *Animal Evolution.* London.

CASTER, K. E. 1952. Stratigraphic and paleontological data relevant to the problem of Afro-American ligation during the Paleozoic and Mesozoic. *Bull. Amer. Mus. Nat. Hist.* 99:105.

Chambers, R. 1844. *Vestiges of the Natural History of Creation*. London.

Chaney, R. W. 1940. Tertiary forests and continental history. *Bull. Geol. Soc. Amer.* 51a:469.

Clark, W. E. le Gros 1955. *Fossil Evidence for Human Evolution*. Chicago.

Clodd, E. 1892. *Bates' River Amazons*. London.

Clodd, E. 1897. *Pioneers of Evolution*. London.

Cope, E. D. 1887. *The Origin of the Fittest*. New York.

Cortesão, A. 1944. Suma Oriental of Tomé Pires 1512-1515. The Book of Francisco Roderiques a. 1515. *Hakluyt Soc.* 2nd series 89 & 90.

Cott, H. B. 1940. *Adaptive Coloration in Animals*. London.

Cott, H. B. 1947. The edibility of birds. *Proc. Zool. Soc. Lond.* 116:371.

Couper, R. A. 1960. Southern hemisphere Mesozoic and Tertiary Podocarpaceae and Fagaceae and their paleogeographic significance. *Proc. Roy. Soc.* B, 152:491.

Cragg, J. B. 1959. Biological studies in the antarctic regions. *New Biol.* 29:102.

Croizat, L. 1958. *Panbiogeography*. Caracas.

Croll, J. 1875. *Climate and Time in their Geological Relations*. London.

Cunningham, J. T. 1892. Darwin and after Darwin. *Nat. Sci.* 1:541.

Cuvier, G. 1812. *Recherches sur les Ossemens Fossiles de Quadrupèdes*. Paris.

Cuvier, G. 1817. *Discours sur les Revolutions de la Surface du Globe*. Paris.

Cuvier, G. & Brongniart, A. 1808. *Essai sur la géographie minéralogique des environs de Paris*. Paris.

Dana, E. S. 1918. *A Century of Science in America*. New Haven.

Dana, J. D. 1857. Thoughts on Species. *Ann. Mag. Nat. Hist.* 20:485.

Darlington, P. J. 1938. Experiments on mimicry in Cuba. *Trans R. Ent. Soc. Lond.* 87:681.

Darlington, P. J. 1957. *Zoogeography: the Geographical Distribution of Animals*. New York & London.

Darlington, P. J. 1959. Area, climate and evolution. *Evolution* 13:488.

Darwin, C. 1859. *On the Origin of Species by Means of Natural Selection*. London.

Darwin, C. 1868. *The Variation of Animals and Plants under Domestication*. London.

Darwin, C. 1871. *The Descent of Man*. London. 2nd. ed. 1874.

Darwin, C. 1880. The sexual colours of certain butterflies. *Nature, Lond.* 21:237.

Darwin, C. 1881. *The Formation of Vegetable Mould, through the Action of Worms, with Observations on their Habits*. London.

Darwin, C. & Wallace, A. R. 1858. On the tendency to form varieties; and on the perpetuation of varieties and species by natural means of selection. *Proc. Linn. Soc. Lond.* 3:45.

Darwin, E. 1788-91. *The Botanic Garden*. London.

Darwin, E. 1803. *The Temple of Nature*. London.

Darwin, F. 1887. *Life and Letters of Charles Darwin*. London.

DARWIN, F. 1903. *More Letters of Charles Darwin.* London.

DELACOUR, J. 1947. *Birds of Malaysia.* New York.

DICKERSON, R. E. & OTHERS, 1928. Distribution of life in the Philippines. *Philippine Bureau Sci. Monogr.* 21.

DIETZ, R. S. 1961. Continent and ocean basin evolution by spreading of the sea floor. *Nature, Lond.* 190:854.

DIVER, C. 1940. The problem of closely related species living in the same area. *New Systematics* ed. Huxley. Oxford.

DOBZHANSKY, T. & PAVLOVSKY, A. 1957. An experimental study of interaction between genetic drift and natural selection. *Evolution* 11:311.

DUFF, M. E. GRANT 1892. Presidential Address. *Proc. Roy. Geogr. Soc.* 14:485.

EHRLICH, P. R. 1958. The comparative morphology, phylogeny and higher classification of the butterflies (Lepidoptera: Papilionidae). *Univ. Kansas. Sci. Bull.* 39:305.

EISELEY, L. 1959. *Darwin's Century.* London.

EKMAN, S. 1953. *Zoogeography of the Sea.* London.

ELLERMAN, J. R. & MORRISON-SCOTT, T. C. S. 1951. *Check List of Palearctic and Indian Mammals.* London.

ELLERMAN, J. R., MORRISON-SCOTT, T. C. S. & HAYMAN, R. W. 1951. *Southern African Mammals 1758 to 1951.* London.

FABRICIUS, J. C. 1778. *Philosophia Entomologica.* Hamburg.

FARADAY, M. 1853. Experimental investigation of table-moving. *Athenaeum J.*: 801.

FISHER, R. A. 1930. *The Genetical Theory of Natural Selection.* Oxford.

FISHER, R. A. & FORD, E. B. 1947. The spread of a gene in natural conditions in a colony of the moth *Panaxia dominula L. Heredity* 1:143.

FORBES, E. 1846. On the connection between the distribution of the existing fauna and flora of the British Isles with the geological changes which have affected this area. *Geol. Mem. N.Z.*1.

FORBES, H. O. 1916. *Alfred Russel Wallace Letters and Reminiscences by* J. Marchant. London.

FORD, E. B. 1938. The genetic basis of adaptation in *Evolution* ed. de Beer. Oxford.

FORD, E. B. 1945. Polymorphism. *Biol. Rev.* 20:73.

FURON, R. 1958. *Causes de la répartition des êtres vivants.* Paris.

GARSTANG, W. 1928. The morphology of the tunicata, and its bearing on the phylogeny of the chordata. *Quart. J. Micr. Sci.* 72:51.

GEDDES, P. 1886. On the nature and causes of variation in plants. *Trans. Edinb. Bot. Soc.*

GEGENBAUER, C. 1861. Über den Bau und die Entwicklung der Wirbelthiereier mit partieller Dottertheilung. *Arch. Anat. Physiol. u Wiss. Med.*

GEGENBAUER, C. 1912. *Gesammelte Abhandlungen.* Leipzig.

GEORGE, H. 1879. *Progress and Poverty*. New York.

GEORGE, W. 1962. *Animal Geography*. London.

GILLISPIE, C. C. 1951. *Genesis and Geology*. Harvard.

GLASS, B., TEMKIN, O. & STRAUS, W. L. (ed.) 1959. *Forerunners of Darwin 1745-1859*. Baltimore.

GOLDSCHMIDT, R. 1940. *The Material Basis of Evolution*. New Haven.

GOLDSMITH, O. 1776. *An History of the Earth and Animated Nature*. Dublin.

GOODWIN, D. 1951. Some aspects of the behaviour of the jay *Garrulus garrulus*. *Ibis* 93:414, 602.

GOULD, J. 1858. Remarks on a series of birds collected by Mr A. R. Wallace in the Aru Islands. *Proc. Zool. Soc. Lond:* 95.

GRAY, G. R. 1858. A list of the birds with description of new species obtained by Mr Alfred R. Wallace in the Aru and Ké Islands. *Proc. Zool. Soc. Lond:* 169.

GRAY, G. R. 1859a. List of birds lately sent by Mr A. R. Wallace from Dorey or Dorery, New Guinea. *Proc. Zool. Soc. Lond:* 153.

GRAY, G. R. 1859b. Notes on the new Bird of Paradise discovered by Mr Wallace. *Proc. Zool. Soc. Lond:* 130.

GRAY, G. R. 1860. List of birds collected by Mr Wallace at the Moluccas Islands. *Proc. Zool. Soc. Lond:* 341.

GRAY, G. R. 1861. Remarks on and descriptions of new species of birds lately sent by Mr A. R. Wallace from Waigiou, Mysol and Gagie Islands. *Proc. Zool. Soc. Lond:* 427.

GRAY, J. 1858. List of species of mammalia sent from the Aru Islands by Mr A. R. Wallace to the British Museum. *Proc. Zool. Soc. Lond:* 106.

GRAY, J. 1860. Description of a new species of cuscus (*C. ornatus*) from the island of Batchian. *Proc. Zool. Soc Lond:* 1.

GÜNTHER, A. 1858. On the geographical distribution of reptiles. *Proc. Zool. Soc. Lond:* 373.

GURNEY, R. 1942. *Larvae of Decapod Crustacea*. London.

HAKLUYT, R. 1903-5. *The Principal Navigations Voyages Traffiques and Discoveries of the English Nation*. Glasgow.

HALDANE, J. B. S. 1932. *The Inequality of Man*. London.

HAMILTON, T. H. 1961. On the functions and causes of sexual dimorphism in breeding plumage and characters of North American species of warblers and orioles. *Amer. Nat.* 95:121.

HASKINS, C. P. & HASKINS, E. F. 1949. The role of sexual selection as an isolating mechanism in three species of Poeciliid fishes. *Evolution* 3:160.

HAUGHTON, S. 1863. On the bee's cell and the origin of species. *Ann. Mag. Nat. Hist:* 415.

HEILPRIN, A. 1883. On the value of the "Nearctic" as one of the primary zoological regions. *Proc. Acad. Nat. Sci. Philad*: 266.

HEILPRIN, A. 1887. *The geographical and geological distribution of animals*. New York.

HEMPRICH, W. 1820. *Grundriss der Naturgeschichte für höhere Lehranstalten*. Berlin & Vienna.

Hertwig, O. 1884-85. Das Problem der Befruchtung und der Isotropie des Eies, eine Theorie der Vererbung. *Z. Med. u. Naturw. Jena*

Hewitson, W. C. 1858-61. Descriptions of some butterflies from the collection of Mr Wallace. *Proc. Zool. Soc. Lond.*

Heyerdahl, T. 1952. *American Indians in the Pacific.* London.

Hill, W. C. O. 1960. *Primates IV. Cebidae.* Edinburgh.

Himmelfarb, G. 1959. *Darwin and The Darwinian Revolution.* London.

Holmes, A. 1960. A revised geological time-scale. *Trans. Edinb. Geol. Soc.* 17:183.

Holmes, O. W. 1858. *The Autocrat of the Breakfast-Table.* Boston.

Hooker, J. D. 1867. On insular faunas. *J. Bot. Lond.* 5:23.

Hooker, J. D. 1881. On geographical distribution. *Brit. Ass. Trans.*

Howard, H. Eliot, 1907-14. *A History of the British Warblers.* London.

Huene, F. v, & Matley, C. A. 1933. The Cretaceous saurischia and ornithischia of the central provinces of India. *Paleont. Indica* new ser. 21.

Humboldt, A. v, & Bonpland, A. 1851. *A Personal Narrative of Travels.* London & New York.

Hutton, F. W. 1873. On the geographical relations of the New Zealand fauna. *Trans. N. Z. Inst.* 5:229.

Hutton, J. 1795. *Theory of The Earth.* Edinburgh.

Huxley, J. S. 1922-24. Courtship activities in the red-throated diver (*Colymbus stellatus*). *J. Linn. Soc. Lond.* 35:253.

Huxley, J. S. 1938. The present standing of the theory of sexual selection. *Evolution* ed. de Beer. Oxford.

Huxley, J. S. & Montague, F. A. 1925. Studies on the courtship and sexual life of birds. *Ibis:* 868.

Huxley, L. (ed.) 1903. *Life and Letters of T. H. Huxley.* 2nd. ed. London.

Huxley, L. (ed.) 1918. *Life and Letters of Sir J. D. Hooker.* London.

Huxley, T. H. 1863. *Evidence as to Man's Place in Nature.* London.

Huxley, T. H. 1868. On the classification and distribution of the Alectoromorphae and Heteromorphae. *Proc. Zool. Soc. Lond:* 294.

Ihering, H. v, 1907. *Archhelenis und Archimotis.* Leipzig.

Iredale, T. 1950. *Birds of Paradise and Bower Birds.* Melbourne.

Irvine, W. 1955. *Apes, Angels and Victorians.* London.

Irving, E. 1957. Directions of magnetization in the carboniferous glacial varves of Australia. *Nature, Lond.* 180:280.

Jeannel, R. 1942. *La Genèse des Faunes Terrestres.* Paris.

Jóhannesson, A. 1950. The gestural origin of language. *Nature, Lond.* 166:60.

Joleaud, L. 1939. *Atlas de Paléobiogéographie.* Paris.

Kant, I. 1755. *Allgemeine Naturgeschichte und Theorie des Himmels.* new ed. 1797. Frankfurt.

KEAST, A., CROCKER, R. L. & CHRISTIAN, C. S. (eds.) 1959. *Biogeography and Ecology in Australia*. Den Haag.

KERMACK, K. A. & MUSSETT, F. 1959. The first mammals. *Discovery* 20: 144.

KETTLEWELL, H. B. D. 1955. Selection experiments on industrial melanism in the Lepidoptera. *Heredity* 9:323.

KETTLEWELL, H. B. D. 1956. Further selection experiments on industrial melanism in the Lepidoptera. *Heredity* 10:287.

KEW, H. W. 1893. *The Dispersal of Shells*. London.

KIDD, J. 1833. On the adaptations of external nature to the physical condition of man. *Bridgewater Treatise* II.

KUENEN, P. H. 1935. Geological interpretation of the bathymetrical results. *Snellius Exped. in the Eastern part of Netherlands E. Indies 1929-30*. 5:1.

KÜHNE, W. G. 1950. A symmetrodon tooth from the Rhaeto-Lias. *Nature, Lond.* 166:696.

KÜHNE, W. G. 1956. The liassic therapsid *Oligokyphus*. *Brit. Mus. Cat.*

KUIPER, G. P. 1949. *The Atmospheres of the Earth and Planets*. Chicago and Cambridge.

KUSCHEL, G. 1960. Terrestrial zoology in southern Chile. *Proc. Roy. Soc.* B, 152:540.

LACK, D. 1946. *The Life of the Robin*. London.

LACK, D. 1954. *The Natural Regulation of Animal Numbers*. Oxford.

LAMARCK, J. B. P. A. DE M. DE, 1800. *Système des Animaux sans Vertèbres*. Paris.

LAMARCK, J. B. P. A. DE M. DE, 1802. *Recherches sur l'organisation des corps vivants*. Paris.

LAMARCK, J. B. P. A. DE M. DE, 1802. Hydrogéologie. Paris.

LAMARCK, J. B. P. A. DE M. DE, 1809 *Philosophie Zoologique*. Paris.

LANKESTER, E. R. 1887. The transmission of acquired characters. *Brit. Ass. Trans.*

LANKESTER, E. R. 1889. Darwinism. *Nature, Lond* 40:566.

LANKESTER, E. R. 1908. *Alfred Russel Wallace Letters and Reminiscences* by J. Marchant. London.

LATREILLE, P. A. 1819. Mémoires sur divers sujets de l'histoire naturelle des insectes, de géographie ancienne et de chronologie. *Mem. Mus. Hist. Nat. Paris*. 3.

LAURIE, E. M. O. & HILL, J. E. 1954. *List of Land-Mammals of New Guinea, Celebes and Adjacent Islands*. London.

LEAKEY, L. S. B. 1959. A new fossil skull from Olduvai. *Nature* 184:491.

LINDAHL, P. E. & OBERG, K. E. 1960. Mechanism of the physiological action of rotenone. *Nature, Lond.* 187:784.

LINNAEUS, C. 1735. *Systema Naturae*. 10th ed. 1758. Stockholm.

LINNAEUS, C. 1743. *Oratio de Telluris Habitabilis Incremento*. Upsala.

LORENZ, K. Z. 1931. Beitrage zu Ethologie sozialer Corviden *J. Orn. Lpz.* 79:67.

LORENZ, K. Z. 1937. The companion in the bird's world. *Auk* 54:245.

LOVEJOY, A. O. 1936. *The Great Chain of Being*. Cambridge, Mass.

LOWELL, P. 1906. *Mars and its Canals*. New York and London.

LYDEKKER, R. 1896. *A Geographical History of Mammals*. Cambridge.

LYELL, C. 1830-33. *Principles of Geology*. 10th ed. 1866. London.

LYELL, C. 1863. *The Antiquity of Man*. London.

MALTHUS, T. R. 1798. *An Essay on the Principle of Population*. London.

MARCHANT, J. 1916. *Alfred Russel Wallace Letters and Reminiscences*. London.

MATTHEW, W. D. 1915. Climate and evolution. *Ann. N.Y. Acad. Sci.* 24:171.

MATTHEWS, L. H. 1952. *British Mammals*. London.

MATTHEWS, L. H. 1958. Darwin, Wallace and pre-adaptation. *J. Linn. Soc. Lond.* 44:93.

MAYR, E. 1934. Notes on the genus *Petroica*. *Amer. Mus. Novit.* 714:1.

MAYR, E. 1940. Speciation phenomena in birds. *Amer. Nat.* 74:249.

MAYR, E. 1942. *Systematics and the Origin of Species*. New York.

MAYR, E. 1944a. The birds of Timor and Sumba. *Bull. Amer. Mus. Nat. Hist.* 83:125.

MAYR, E. 1944b. Wallace's line in the light of recent zoogeographic studies. *Quart. Rev. Biol.* 19:1.

MAYR, E. 1946. History of the North American bird fauna. *Wilson Bull.* 58:3.

MAYR, E. 1952. The problem of land connexions across the South Atlantic with special reference to the Mesozoic. *Bull. Amer. Mus. Nat. Hist.* 99:85.

MAYR, E. & AMADON, D. 1951. A classification of recent birds. *Amer. Mus. Novit.* 1496.

MILL, J. S. 1859-61. *Utilitarianism, Liberty and Representative Government*. Reprint 1910. London.

MILL, J. S. 1873. *Autobiography*. London.

MONGREDIEN, A. 1878. *Brit. Mus. MS.*

MOORE, J. A. 1955. Abnormal combinations of nuclear and cytoplasmic systems in frogs and toads. *Advanc. in Genet.* 7:139.

MOREAU, R. E. 1952. Africa since the Mesozoic. *Proc. Zool. Soc. Lond.* 121:869.

MOSELEY, H. N. 1885. The continuity of the germ-plasma considered as the basis of a theory of heredity. *Nature, Lond.* 33:154.

MOURANT, A. E. 1954. *The Distribution of the Human Blood Groups*. Oxford.

MOVIUS, H. L. 1942. *The Irish Stone Age*. Cambridge.

MURRAY, A. 1866. *The Geographical Distribution of Mammals*. London.

NAIRN, A. E. M. 1956. Relevance of paleomagnetic studies of Jurassic rocks to continental drift. *Nature, Lond.* 178:935.

NEAVERSON, E. 1955. *Stratigraphical Palaeontology*. 2nd. ed. Oxford.

NOBLE, G. K. 1936. Courtship and sexual selection of the flicker, *Colaptes auratus luteus*. *Auk* 53:269.

NORMAN, J. R. 1942. Discussion on the biogeographic division of the Indo-Australian Archipelago. *Proc. Linn. Soc. Lond.* 154:163.

OPARIN, A. I. 1957. *The Origin of Life on the Earth.* Edinburgh.
OPARIN, A. I. (ed.) 1959. *Origin of Life on the Earth.* London.
ORWIN, C. S. & PEEL, W. R. 1926. *The Tenure of Agricultural Land.* Cambridge.
OSBORN, H. F. 1910. *The Age of Mammals in Europe, Asia and North America.* New York.
OSBORN, H. F. 1912. Scientific worthies, Dr Alfred Russel Wallace D.C.L. O.M. F.R.S. *Nature, Lond.* 89:367.
OWEN, RICHARD, 1877. *Researches on the Fossil Remains of the Extinct Mammals of Australia.* London.
OWEN, ROBERT 1857. *The Life of Robert Owen.* London.

PAGET, R. A. S. 1951. The origin of language. *Sci. News* 20:82.
PARRINGTON, F. R. 1941. On two mammalian teeth from the lower Rhaetic of Somerset. *Ann. Mag. Nat. Hist.* 8:140.
PELSENEER, P. 1904. La "Ligne de Weber" limite zoologique de l'Asie et de l'Australie. *Bull. Acad. R. Belg. Cl. Sci.* 1001.
PENNANT, T. 1791. *Indian Zoology.* London.
PÉRON, F. 1807. *Voyage de Découvertes aux Terres Australes.* Paris.
PETERS, J. L. 1931-51. *Check-List of Birds of the World.* Harvard.
POLUNIN, N. 1951. Arctic aerobiology. *Nature, Lond.* 168-718.
PORCACCHI, T. 1576. *L'Isole piu Famose del Mondo.* Venice.
POULTON, E. B. 1888. Notes, *Trans. R. Ent. Soc. Lond:* 515.
POULTON, E. B. 1890. *The Colours of Animals.* London.
POULTON, E. B. 1913. Alfred Russel Wallace. *Nature, Lond.* 92:347.
POULTON, E. B. 1929. British insectivorous bats and their prey. *Proc. Zool. Soc Lond:* 277
PRICHARD, J. C. 1813-47. *Researches into the Physical History of Mankind.* 3rd ed. London.

RÁDL, E. 1930. *The History of Biological Theories.* Oxford & London.
RAND, A. L. 1936. The distribution and habits of the Madagascar birds. *Bull. Amer. Mus. Nat. Hist.* 72:142.
RAVEN, H. C. 1935. Wallace's line and the distribution of Indo-Australian mammals. *Bull. Amer. Mus. Nat. Hist.* 68:179.
RAVENSTEIN, E. G. 1898. A journal of the first voyage of Vasco da Gama 1497-1499. *Hakluyt Soc.* 99.
RENSCH, B. 1933. Zoologische Systematik und Artbildungsproblem. *Verh. Dtsch Zool. Ges:* 19.
RENSCH, B. 1936. *Die Geschichte des Sundabogens.* Berlin.
RHINE, J. B. 1938. *New Frontiers of the Mind.* London.
RICE, H. 1914. Further explorations in the north-west Amazon basin. *Geogr. J.* 44:137.
RICE, H. 1918. Notes on the Rio Negro. *Geogr. J.* 52:205.
RICE, H. 1921. The Rio Negro, the Casiquiare canal, and the Upper Orinoco. *Geogr. J.* 58:321. Rick, E. F. 1959 in *Biogeography and Ecology in Australia.* ed. Keast, Crocker & Christian. Den Haag.

Romanes, G. J. 1892-97. *Darwin and After Darwin.* London.

Romer, A. S. 1945. *Vertebrate Paleontology.* Chicago.

Romer, A. S. 1956. *Osteology of Reptiles.* Chicago.

Ross, W. D. (ed.) 1911. *The Works of Aristotle.* Oxford.

Scharff, R. F. 1907. *European Animals.* London.

Scharff, R. F. 1911. *Distribution and Origin of Life in America.* London.

Schleiden, M. J. 1838. Beiträge zur Phytogenesis. *Arch. Anat. Physiol. u. Wiss. Med.*

Schwann, T. 1839. *Mikroskopische Untersuchungen über die Übereinstimmung in der Struktur und dem Wachstum der Thiere und Pflanzen.* Berlin.

Sclater, P. L. 1858. On the general distribution of the members of the class Aves. *J. Linn. Soc. Lond.* 2:130.

Sclater, P. L. 1874. *The Geographical Distribution of Mammals.* Manchester.

Sclater, P. L. 1875. Residential Address. *Brit. Ass. Trans:* 85.

Sclater, P. L. 1878. Evolution and the Distribution of Animals. *Nineteenth Century.*

Sclater, W. L. & Sclater, P. L. 1899. *The Geography of Mammals.* London.

Scott, W. B. 1937. *A History of Land Mammals in the Western Hemisphere.* New York.

Scrivenor, J. B; Burkill, T. H.; Smith, M. A.; Corbet, A. St.; Airy Shaw, H. K.; Richards, P. W.; & Zeuner, F. E. 1942. A discussion of the biogeographic division of the Indo-Australian Archipelago. *Proc. Linn. Soc. Lond.* 154:120.

Seitz, A. 1860-1938. *The Macrolepidoptera of the World.* Stuttgart.

Shaw, G. B. (ed.) 1889. *Fabian Essays in Socialism.* London.

Sheppard, P. M. 1958. *Natural Selection and Heredity.* London.

Sheppard, P. M. 1959. The evolution of mimicry. *Cold Spr. Harb. Symp. Quant. Biol.* 24:131.

Simpson, G. G. 1928. *A Catalogue of the Mesozoic Mammalia.* London.

Simpson, G. G. 1929. *American Mesozoic Mammalia.* London.

Simpson, G. G. 1940. Antarctica as a faunal migration route. *Proc. 6th. Pacif. Sci. Congr.* 2:755.

Simpson, G. G. 1943a. Mammals and the nature of continents. *Amer. J. Sci.* 241:1.

Simpson, G. G. 1943b. Turtles and the origin of the fauna of Latin America. *Amer. J. Sci.* 241:413.

Simpson, G. G. 1945. The principles of classification and a classification of mammals. *Bull. Amer. Mus. Nat. Hist.* 85:1.

Simpson, G. G. 1947a. Evolution, interchange, and resemblance of the North American and Eurasian Cenozoic mammalian faunas. *Evolution* 1:218.

Simpson, G. G. 1947b. Holarctic faunas. *Bull. Geol. Soc. Amer.* 58:613.

Simpson, G. G. 1951a. *Horses.* New York.

Simpson, G. G. 1951b. History of the fauna of Latin America. *Sci. in Progr.* 7th series ch. XI.

SIMPSON, G. G. 1952. Probabilities of dispersal in geologic time. *Bull. Amer. Mus. Nat. Hist.* 99:163.

SIMPSON, G. G. 1953. *Evolution and Geography.* Eugene.

SINTON, W. M. 1957. Spectroscopic evidence for vegetation on Mars. *Astrophys. J.* 126:231.

SINTON, W. M. 1959. Vegetation on Mars. *Nature, Lond.* 184:1612.

SKUTCH, A. F. 1957. The incubation patterns of birds. *Ibis* 99:69.

SMART, W. M. 1951. *The Origin of the Earth.* London.

SMITH, J. M. 1956. Fertility, mating behaviour and sexual selection in *Drosophila subobscura. J. Genet.* 54:261.

SOMERVELL, D. C. 1929. *English Thought in the Nineteenth Century.* London.

SPENCE, T. 1775. *The Nationalization of the Land.* Newcastle-on-Tyne.

SPENCER, H. 1851. *Social Statics.* London.

SPENCER, H. 1852. The Development Hypothesis. *Leader:* March.

SPENCER, H. 1876-82. *The Principles of Sociology.* London.

SPENCER-BROWN, G. 1953. Statistical significance in psychical research. *Nature, Lond.* 172:154.

SPRUCE, R. 1908. *Notes of a Botanist on the Amazon and Andes.* London.

STEVENS, H. N. & BARWICK, G. F. 1930. New light on the discovery of Australia as revealed by the journal of Captain Don Diego de Prado y Tovar. *Hakluyt. Soc.* 2nd. ser. 64.

STEVENS, S. 1857. A box of Lepidoptera taken at Sarawak by Mr Wallace. *Trans. R. Ent. Soc. Lond:* 38.

STEVENS, S. 1859. Exhibition of two beautiful new butterflies collected by Mr Wallace in the island of Batchian. *Proc. Zool. Soc. Lond:* 351.

STEVENS, S. 1860. Exhibition of a series of birds and lepidopterous insects contained in Mr Wallace's recent collections from the island of Batchian. *Proc. Zool. Soc. Lond:* 1.

STEVENS, S. 1861. Exhibition of birds forwarded by Mr Wallace from Mysol and Waigiou. *Proc. Zool. Soc. Lond:* 306.

STONOR, C. R. 1938. Some features of the variation of the birds of paradise. *Proc. Zool. Soc. Lond.* 108:417.

STONOR, C. R. 1940. *Courtship and Display among Birds.* London.

STRESEMANN, E. 1927-34. *Handbuch der Zoologie.* Berlin & Leipzig.

STRESEMANN, E. 1939. Die Vögel von Celebes. *J. f. Ornith. Lpz.* 87:312.

SWAINSON, W. 1835. *Treatise on the Geography and Classification of Animals.* London.

TAWNEY, R. H. 1931. *Equality.* London.

TAYLOR, L. R. 1960. Mortality and viability of insect migrants high in the air. *Nature, Lond.* 186:410.

TERCAFS, R. R. 1961. Research report. *Nature, Lond.* 191:125.

TERMIER, H. & TERMIER, G. 1960. *Atlas de Palégéographie.* Paris.

THAYER, A. H. 1903. Protective coloration in its relation to mimicry, common warning colours, and sexual selection. *Trans. R. Ent. Soc. Lond:* 553.

THOMSON, D. 1950. *England in the Nineteenth Century.* London.

TINBERGEN, N. 1948. Social releasers and the experimental method required for their study. *Wilson Bull.* 601:6.

TOIT, A. L. DU, 1937. *Our Wandering Continents.* Edinburgh.

TUCKER, B. W. 1949. Species and subspecies. *Brit. Birds.* 42:193.

TURRILL, W. B. 1948. On the flora of St Helena. *Kew Bull:* 358.

TYLOR, A. 1886. *Coloration in Animals and Plants.* London.

TYLOR, E. B. 1881. *Anthropology.* London.

UMBGROVE, J. H. F. 1947. *The Pulse of the Earth.* The Hague.

UMBGROVE, J. H. F. 1949. *Structural History of the East Indies.* Cambridge.

URVILLE, J. D. D', 1832. *Voyage de Découverts de l'Astrolabe.* Paris.

VAURIE, C. 1959. *The Birds of the Palearctic Fauna.* London.

VIRCHOW, R. 1855. Cellular-Pathologie. *Virchows Arch.* 8:1.

VOLTAIRE, 1746. Dissertation sur les changements arrivés dans notre globe. *Oeuvres complètes de Voltaire.* ed. Kehl. Paris.

VRIES, H. DE, 1901. *Der Mutationstheorie.* Leipzig.

A complete list of the published works of A. R. Wallace can be found in Marchant, J. 1916. *Alfred Russel Wallace Letters and Reminiscences.*

WALLACE, A. R. 1850-51. Drawings of fishes of the Amazon. MS. *Brit. Mus.* (*Nat. Hist.*).

WALLACE, A. R. 1852. On the monkeys of the Amazon. *Proc. Zool. Soc. Lond:* 107.

WALLACE, A. R. 1852-53. On the habits of the butterflies of the Amazon valley. *Trans. R. Ent. Soc. Lond.* 2:253.

WALLACE, A. R. 1853a. *Palm Trees of the Amazon.* London.

WALLACE, A. R. 1853b. *A Narrative of Travels on the Amazon and Rio Negro.* 2nd ed. 1889. London.

WALLACE, A. R. 1853c. On some fishes allied to Gymnotus. *Proc. Zool. Soc. Lond.* 21:75.

WALLACE, A. R. 1853d. Some remarks on the habit of the Hesperidae. *Zoologist* 11:3884.

WALLACE A. R. 1854-56. Notebooks. MS. *Linn. Soc. Lond.*

WALLACE, A. R. 1855a. On the law which has regulated the introduction of new species. *Ann. Mag. Nat. Hist.* 16:84.

WALLACE, A. R. 1855b. The entomology of Malacca. *Zoologist* 13:4636.

WALLACE, A. R. 1855-61. Notebooks. MS. *Brit. Mus.* (Nat. Hist.).

WALLACE, A. R 1856a. Attempts at a natural arrangement of birds. *Ann. Mag. Nat. Hist.* 18:193.

WALLACE, A. R. 1856b. Observations on the zoology of Borneo.. *Zoologist* 14:5 ii 3.

WALLACE, A. R. 1856c. On the orang-utan or mias of Borneo. *Ann. Mag. Nat. Hist.* 17:471.

WALLACE, A. R. 1857. On the natural history of the Aru Islands. *Ann. Mag. Nat. Hist.* 20:473.

WALLACE, A. R. 1858a. Note on the theory of permanent and geographical varieties. *Zoologist* 16:5887.

WALLACE, A. R. 1858b. A disputed case of priority in nomenclature. *Zoologist* 16:6117.

WALLACE, A. R. 1859a. Remarks on enlarged coloured figures of insects. *Zoologist* 17:6617.

WALLACE, A. R. 1859b. Letter from Mr Wallace concerning the geographical distribution of birds. *Ibis* 1:449.

WALLACE, A. R. 1859c. Correction of an important error affecting the classification of the Psittacidae. *Ann. Mag. Nat. Hist.* 3:147.

WALLACE, A. R. 1860. On the zoological geography of the Malay Archipelago. *J. Linn. Soc. Lond.* 4:172.

WALLACE, A. R. 1862a. Descriptions of three new species of *Pitta* from the Moluccas. *Proc. Zool. Soc. Lond:* 187.

WALLACE, A. R. 1862b. List of birds from the Sula Islands. *Proc. Zool. Soc. Lond:* 333.

WALLACE, A. R. 1863a. Remarks on Rev. S. Haughton's paper on the bee's cell, and on the origin of species. *Ann. Mag. Nat. Hist.* 12:303.

WALLACE, A. R. 1863b. A list of the birds inhabiting the islands of Timor, Flores and Lombok, with descriptions of the new species. *Proc. Zool. Soc. Lond:* 480.

WALLACE, A. R. 1863c. List of birds collected in the island of Bouru (one of the Moluccas). *Proc. Zool. Soc. Lond:* 18.

WALLACE, A. R. 1863d. On the physical geography of the Malay Archipelago. *J. Geogr. Soc.* 33:217.

WALLACE, A. R. 1863-76. Contributions to the problem of geographical distribution. *Brit. Ass. Trans.*

WALLACE, A. R. 1864a. Remarks on the habits, distribution, and affinities of the genus *Pitta. Ibis* 6:100.

WALLACE, A. R. 1864b. Origin of human races and the antiquity of man deduced from natural selection. *Anthrop. Rev.* 2:clviii.

WALLACE, A. R. 1864c. On the parrots of the Malayan region, with remarks on their habits, distribution, and affinities, and the descriptions of two new species. *Proc. Zool. Soc. Lond:* 272.

WALLACE, A. R. 1864d. Remarks on the value of osteological characters in the classification of birds. *Ibis* 6:36.

WALLACE, A. R. 1865a. Man in the Malay Archipelago. *Trans. Ethnol. Soc.* 3:196.

WALLACE, A. R. 1865b. On the pigeons of the Malay Archipelago. *Ibis* new ser. 1:365.

WALLACE, A. R. 1865c. List of the land shells collected by Mr Wallace in the Malay Archipelago. *Proc. Zool. Soc. Lond:* 405.

WALLACE, A. R. 1865d. Descriptions of new birds from the Malay Archipelago. *Proc. Zool. Soc. Lond:* 474.

WALLACE, A. R. 1865e. On the phenomena of variation and geographical distribution, as illustrated by the Papilionidae of the Malayan region. *Trans. Linn. Soc. Lond.* 25:1.

WALLACE, A. R. 1866a. *The Scientific Aspect of the Supernatural.* London.

Wallace, A. R. 1866b. On reversed sexual characters in a butterfly. *Brit. Ass. Trans:* 79.

Wallace, A. R. 1866c. Letter from A. R. Wallace to F. P. Pascoe. *Proc. R. Ent. Soc. Lond.* A 14:77 (1939).

Wallace, A. R. 1867a. Mimicry and other protective resemblances among animals. *Westminster Rev.* July.

Wallace, A. R. 1867b. On birds' nests and their plumage. *Brit. Ass. Trans:* 97.

Wallace, A. R. 1868a. A theory of birds' nests. *J. Travel & Nat. Hist.* 1:73.

Wallace, A. R. 1868b. On the raptorial birds of the Malay Archipelago. *Ibis* 4:1.

Wallace, A. R. 1869a. *The Malay Archipelago.* 10th. ed. 1890 London.

Wallace, A. R. 1869b. Geological climates and origin of species. *Quart. Rev:* 126.

Wallace, A. R. 1870a. *Contributions to the Theory of Natural Selection.* London.

Wallace, A. R. 1870b. Government aid to science. *Nature, Lond.* 1:288.

Wallace, A. R. 1870c. Mimicry versus hybridity. *Nature, Lond.* 3:165.

Wallace, A. R. 1874a. *Miracles and Modern Spiritualism.* 2nd. ed. 1896. London.

Wallace, A. R. 1874b. On the arrangement of the families constituting the order Passeres. *Ibis* 4:406.

Wallace, A. R. 1876a. *The Geographical Distribution of Animals.* London.

Wallace, A. R. 1876b. Presidential address. *Brit. Ass. Trans:* 100.

Wallace, A. R. 1878a. *Tropical Nature.* London.

Wallace, A. R. 1878b. Remarkable local colour-variation in lizards. *Nature* 19:4.

Wallace, A. R. 1879a. *Australasia.* London.

Wallace, A. R. 1879b. Animals and their native countries. *Nineteenth Century* Feb.

Wallace, A. R. 1880a. *Island Life.* 2nd. ed. 1895. London.

Wallace, A. R. 1880b. The origin of species and genera. *Nineteenth Century* Jan.

Wallace, A. R. 1881a. Tylor's "Anthropology". *Nature, Lond.* 24:242.

Wallace, A. R. 1881b. Monkeys: their affinities and distribution *Contemp. Rev.* Dec.

Wallace, A. R. 1882a. *Land Nationalisation.* London.

Wallace, A. R. 1882b. Müller's "difficult cases of mimicry". *Nature, Lond.* 26:86.

Wallace, A. R. 1885. *Bad Times.* London.

Wallace, A. R. 1889a. *Darwinism.* 3rd. ed. 1901. London.

Wallace, A. R. 1889b. Lamarck versus Weismann. *Nature, Lond.* 40:619.

Wallace, A. R. 1890. The colours of animals. *Nature, Lond.* 42:289.

Wallace, A. R. 1892a. Note on sexual selection. *Nat. Sci.* 1:749.

Wallace, A. R. 1892b. Glacial theory of alpine lakes. *Nature, Lond.* 47:437.

Wallace, A. R. 1893a. Supposed glaciation of Brazil. *Nature, Lond.* 48:589.

Wallace, A. R. 1893b. On malformation from pre-natal influence on the mother. *Brit. Ass. Trans:* 798.

Wallace, A. R. 1894a. The influence of previous fertilization of the female on her subsequent offspring. *Brit. Ass. Trans:* 346.

Wallace, A. R. 1894b. What are zoological regions? *Nature, Lond.* 49:610.

Wallace, A. R. 1896. Cause of an Ice Age. *Nature, Lond.* 53:220.

Wallace, A. R. 1898. *The Wonderful Century.* 2nd. ed. 1903. London & New York.

Wallace, A. R. 1900. *Studies, Scientific and Social.* London.

Wallace, A. R. 1901a. *The Wonderful Century Reader.* London.

Wallace, A. R. 1901b. *Vaccination a Delusion.* London.

Wallace, A. R. 1903. *Man's Place in the Universe.* 3rd. ed. 1912. London.

Wallace, A. R. 1905. *My Life.* 2nd. ed. 1908. London.

Wallace, A. R. 1907. *Is Mars Habitable?* London.

Wallace, A. R. 1908. Present position of Darwinism. *Contemp. Rev.* Aug.

Wallace, A. R. 1910. *The World of Life.* London.

Wallace, A. R. 1913a. *Social Environment and Moral Progress.* London.

Wallace, A. R. 1913b. *The Revolt of Democracy.* London.

Watson, D. M. S. 1921. The bases of classification of the Theriodontia. *Proc. Zool. Soc. Lond:* 35.

Watson, J. A. Scott & Hobbs, M. E. 1951. *Great Farmers.* London.

Webb, M. B. 1926. *My Apprenticeship.* London.

Weber, M. 1894. *Zoologische Ergebnisse einer Reise in Niederländisch Ost-Indien.* Bd. III. Leiden.

Weber, M. 1902. *Der Indo-Australische Archipel und die Geschichte seiner Tierwelt.* Jena.

Weber, M. 1904. *Die Säugetiere. Einführung in die Anatomie und Systematik der Recenten und Fossilen Mammalia.* Jena.

Wegener, A. 1924. *The Origin of Contents and Oceans.* London.

Weir, J. J. 1869. On insects and insectivorous birds. *Trans. R. Ent. Soc. Lond:* 21.

Weismann, F. L. A. 1885. *Die Continuität des Keimplasmas als Grundlage einer Theorie der Vererbung.* Jena.

Weismann, F. L. A. 1886. *Die Bedeutung der Sexuellen Fortpflanzung für die Selektions Theorie* Jena.

Weismann, F. L. A. 1889. *Essays upon Heredity and Kindred Biological Problems.* Oxford.

Weismann, F. L. A. 1891. *Amphimixis, oder die Vermischung der Individuen.* Jena.

Wells, H. G.; Huxley, J. S. & Wells, G. P. 1931. *The Science of Life.* London.

Westwood, J. O. 1855. Descriptions of some new species of Cleridae (Coleoptera) collected at Singapore by Mr Wallace. *Proc. Zool. Soc. Lond:* 19.

Wills, L. J. 1951. *Paleogeographical Atlas.* London & Glasgow.

Wilson, J. T. 1957. Origin of the earth's crust. *Nature, Lond.* 179:228.

Wollaston, T. V. 1854. *Insecta Maderensia.* London.

Wollaston, T. V. 1877. *Coleoptera Sanctae-Helenae.* London.

WOLLASTON, T. V. 1878. *Testacea Atlantica.* London.

WOOD, A. E. 1950. Porcupines, paleogeography and parallelism. *Evolution* 4:87.

WRIGHT, S. 1931. Evolution in Mendelian populations. *Genet.* 16:97.

WRIGHT, S. 1943. Isolation by distance. *Genet.* 28:14.

WRIGHT, S. 1949. Population structure in evolution. *Proc. Amer. Phil. Soc.* 93:471.

WRIGHT, S. 1955. Classification of the factors of evolution. *Cold Spr. Harb. Symp. Quant. Biol.* 20:16.

ZEUNER, F. E. 1942. The divisions as indicated by the distribution of insects in relation to geology. *Proc. Linn. Soc. Lond.* 154:157.

ZEUNER, F. E. 1945. *The Pleistocene Period.* London.

ZEUNER, F. E. 1950. *Dating the Past.* London.

Index

MADE AND PRINTED IN GREAT BRITAIN BY
CHARLES BIRCHALL & SONS LTD.
LONDON AND LIVERPOOL